350089q

Tii

Oxford Applied Mathemat
and Computing Science S

STEPHEN BARNETT
University of Bradford

Introduction to mathematical control theory

CLARENDON PRESS · OXFORD
1975

Oxford University Press, Ely House, London W. 1

GLASGOW NEW YORK TORONTO MELBOURNE WELLINGTON
CAPE TOWN IBADAN NAIROBI DAR ES SALAAM LUSAKA ADDIS ABABA
DELHI BOMBAY CALCUTTA MADRAS KARACHI LAHORE DACCA
KUALA LUMPUR SINGAPORE HONG KONG TOKYO

ISBN 0 19 859619 7

Text set in 10/12 pt. IBM Press Roman, printed by
photolithography and bound in Great Britain at
The Pitman Press, Bath

Preface

Control theory has developed rapidly over the past two decades, and is now established as an important area of contemporary applied mathematics. Some justification for this latter claim is provided in Chapter 1, which begins with a general discussion on the scope and relevance of control theory. The aim of this book is to present a concise, readable account of some basic mathematical aspects of control. The origins of the book lie in courses of lectures which I have given for a number of years to final honours mathematics students and to postgraduate control engineers at the University of Bradford. My approach concentrates on so-called state space methods, and emphasises points of mathematical interest, but I have avoided undue abstraction and the contents should be accessible to anyone with a basic background in calculus and matrix theory. To help achieve this objective a summary is given in Chapter 2 of some appropriate topics in linear algebra. The book should therefore also be useful to qualified engineers seeking an introduction to contemporary control theory literature, some of which tends to be expressed with rather forbidding mathematical formulation.

I have provided problems to be attempted at the end of each section. Most of these have been class-tested, and so should be within the reader's grasp; all answers are given. In an introductory work it is essential to supply references for further study, and except in a few cases I have quoted text books rather than journal papers which are usually more suitable for specialists. It is of interest that most of the references listed have appeared within the last ten years, giving some measure of the publishing 'explosion' in the control field in recent times.

In any compact treatment many points of detail, refinements and extensions are inevitably omitted; in particular I regret that it has not been possible to include any material on statistical concepts which arise in control. Despite the many texts now available on control theory it is my hope that this book fills a niche in the literature by its combination of conciseness and range of topics. I hope also that it will help to promote interest in this exciting field, thus providing at least a small counterbalance to the deadweight of British classical applied mathematics.

I have done my best to eliminate errors, although in an entertaining article P. J. Davis (*Amr. Math. Mon.,* 1972, **79**, 252) suggests that such attempts are doomed to failure! Thanks however are due to P. A. Cook, A. T. Fuller, J. B. Helliwell, G. T. Joyce, A. G. J. MacFarlane, D. D. Siljak, C. Storey, and H. K. Wimmer who have made useful comments on various parts of the manuscript. I should also like to thank Dr. Hedley Martin for encouraging me to write this book and for his helpful assistance through-out the project, and the Clarendon Press for their efficient co-operation. Finally, as on many previous occasions, I am grateful to Mrs. Margaret Balmforth for her skilful preparation of the typescript.

Bradford   S.B.
July 1974

Contents

† May be omitted on a first reading.

† May be omitted on a first reading.

1 Introduction to control theory

1.1. General remarks and examples

In most branches of applied mathematics, the aim is to *analyse* a given situation. To take a very simple example, if a mass is suspended by a string from a fixed point then the assumptions might be that air resistance, the mass of the string and the dimensions of the body could all be neglected, and that gravitational attraction is constant. A familiar mathematical problem would then be to determine the nature of small motions about the equilibrium position. Thus in order to be able to obtain a mathematical description, or *model*, of the real-life situation it is necessary to make certain simplifying assumptions so that established laws from science, engineering, economic theory, etc., can be used. Mathematical methods can then be applied to investigate the properties of the model, and the conclusions reached will reflect reality only insofar as the accuracy of the model permits. Of course the more realistic the model, the more difficult in general will it be to solve the resultant mathematical equations. The 'classical' areas of applied mathematics such as mechanics (of particles, solids, fluids), electromagnetic theory, thermodynamics, etc., have been extensively developed during the last two hundred years and generally reflect this emphasis on analysis. However, many problems of great importance in the contemporary world require a quite different approach, the aim being to compel or *control* a system to behave in some desired fashion. Here 'system' is used to mean a collection of objects which are related by interactions and produce various outputs in response to different inputs. This statement is deliberately very vague so as to embrace a very wide range of situations. These can include for example industrial complexes such as chemical plants or steelworks; electro-mechanical machines such as motor cars, aircraft, or spaceships; biological systems such as the human body; and economic structures of countries or regions. Control problems associated with these systems might be production of some chemical or steel product as efficiently as possible; automatic landing of aircraft, soft landings on the moon, or rendezvous with an artificial satellite; regulation of body functions such as heartbeat, blood pressure, temperature, and the ever-present problem of control of economic inflation. The complexity of many systems in the present-day world is such that it is often desirable for control to be carried out *automatically* without direct human intervention. To take a simple example, the room thermostat in a domestic central heating system turns the boiler on and off so as to maintain room temperature at a predetermined level. Nature provides many other examples of remarkable self-regulation, such as the way in which body temperature is kept constant despite large variations in external conditions, or the manner in which it is possible to fix the eyes on some object whilst engaged in strenuous physical activity.

The main features of a control system can be represented as in Fig. 1.1

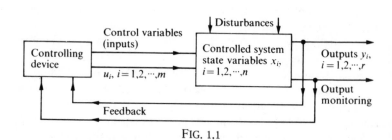

FIG. 1.1

The *state variables* x_i describe the condition or state of the system, and provide the information which (together with a knowledge of the equations describing the system) enables us to calculate the future behaviour from a knowledge of the inputs; the *n*-dimensional space containing the x_is is the *state space* — hence the widespread use of terms like 'state space approach'. In practice it is often not possible to determine the values of the state variables directly, perhaps for reasons of expense or inaccessibility. Instead only a set of *output variables* y_i, which depend in some way on the x_i, is measured and almost invariably $r \leqslant n$. For example, the state of the economy of a country is described by a great many variables, but it is only practicable to measure a few of these, such as the volume of production, the number in employment, the value of gold reserves, and so on. In general the object is to make a system perform in some required way by suitably manipulating the *control variables* u_i, this being done by some controlling device, or 'controller'. Systems are often subject to external disturbances of an unpredictable nature, for example wind gusts during aircraft landing, or variations in the cost of raw materials for a manufacturing process. Such factors require a statistical treatment and will not be dealt with in this book. We shall assume that all our system models have the property that, given an initial state and any input then the resulting state and output at some specified later time are *uniquely* determined. Such models are often termed *dynamical systems*, although of course they need have nothing to do with Newtonian mechanics, and can be defined in rigorous formal terms (e.g. Desoer 1970).

If the controller operates according to some pre-set pattern without taking account of the output or state, the system is called *open loop*, because the 'loop' in Fig. 1.1 is not completed. If however there is *feedback* of information concerning the outputs to the controller, which then appropriately modifies its course of action, the system is *closed loop*. Simple illustrations of open and closed loop systems are provided by traffic lights which change at fixed intervals of time, and those which are controlled by some device which measures traffic flow and reacts accordingly.

Another familiar example is provided by the closed loop feedback system which controls the water level in the cistern of the domestic toilet. After flushing is completed the water outlet valve closes, and water flows into the cistern. A ball float measures the water level, and closes the supply valve when the water reaches a pre-set level. Thus a knowledge of the actual water level is 'fed back' via the float to obtain a measured level which is compared with the desired level; when this difference, or 'error' e, exceeds a predetermined value the supply valve is open, and when e is less than this value the valve is closed. This is represented diagrammatically in Fig. 1.2.

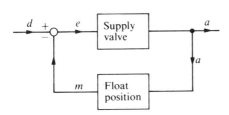

FIG. 1.2 a = actual water level; d = desired water level; m = measured water level; $e = d - m$.

Both Figs 1.1 and 1.2 are examples of *block diagrams*, which are widely used in control engineering as a convenient method of representing the relationships within a system in a pictorial form. The convention used is that flows are added with their indicated signs where the junction is shown as a circle, otherwise signals proceed along branching paths without alteration. The rectangles represent operators of some sort.

In the plumbing system it is clear that the control of water level will
be satisfactory even if there are wide variations in the pressure of the in-
flowing water. Similarly, in the central heating system mentioned earlier,
the performance may well be acceptable even if the heat output of the
boiler varies or if outside weather conditions change suddenly. These
examples illustrate a very important property of feedback systems: their
ability to operate satisfactorily even when parameters in various parts of
a system may vary considerably. This insensitivity will be discussed in a
little more detail in Section 1.2. Feedback is thus a crucial concept in
control engineering, and indeed a water level control of the type described
above was known to the Greeks in the first century A.D. Although feedback has a long history (see Mayr 1970), it is only in the last forty years
or so that extensive efforts have been given to the study of feedback
theory. The so-called 'classical' control engineering methods rely heavily
on transform methods for solving linear differential or difference equations, and received great impetus from military applications during the
Second World War. Before going into further details in the next section,
we first discuss some aspects of 'modern' control theory, which has been
developed mainly over the last twenty years using the state variable
approach, and on which this book concentrates most attention. The
examples presented below will be referred to again in subsequent chapters, and all illustrate the important feature of control theory, mentioned
earlier, namely to *synthesize* a control strategy which satisfies requirements.

Example 1.1. Suppose a car is to be driven along a straight, level road,
and let its distance from an initial point 0 be $s(t)$ at time t. For simplicity
assume that the car is controlled only by the throttle, producing an accelerating force of $u_1(t)$ per unit mass, and by the brake which produces
a retarding force of $u_2(t)$ per unit mass. Suppose that the only factors of
interest are the car's position $x_1(t) = s(t)$ and velocity $x_2(t) = \dot{s}(t)$, where
$(\cdot) \equiv d/dt$. Ignoring other forces such as road friction, wind resistance,
etc., the equations which describe the state of the car at time t are

$$\left. \begin{array}{l} \dot{x}_1 = x_2 \\ \dot{x}_2 = u_1 - u_2 \end{array} \right\}$$

or in matrix notation

$$\dot{x} = Ax + Bu \tag{1.1}$$

where

$$x = \begin{bmatrix} x_1 \\ x_2 \end{bmatrix}, \quad u = \begin{bmatrix} u_1 \\ u_2 \end{bmatrix}, \quad A = \begin{bmatrix} 0 & 1 \\ 0 & 0 \end{bmatrix}, \quad B = \begin{bmatrix} 0 & 0 \\ 1 & -1 \end{bmatrix}.$$

In practice there will be limits on the values of u_1 and u_2, for obvious reasons, and it will also be necessary to impose restrictions on the magnitudes of velocity and acceleration to ensure passenger comfort, safety, etc.

It may then be required to start from rest at 0 and reach some fixed point in the least possible time, or perhaps with minimum consumption of fuel. The mathematical problems are firstly to determine whether such objectives are achievable with the selected control variables, and if so, to find appropriate expressions for u_1 and u_2 as functions of time and/or x_1 and x_2.

The complexity of the model could be increased so as to take into account factors such as engine speed and temperature, vehicle interior temperature, and so on. A further aspect of realism could be added by imagining the car to be travelling in one lane of a motorway, in which case the objective might be to maintain the distance from the vehicle in front within certain limits.

Example 1.2. The interior temperature of an electrically heated oven is to be controlled by varying the heat input u to the jacket, as shown in Fig. 1.3.

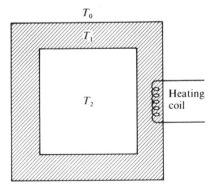

FIG. 1.3

Let the heat capacities of the oven interior and of the jacket be c_1 and c_2 respectively; let the interior and exterior jacket surface areas be a_1 and a_2; and let the radiation coefficients of the interior and exterior jacket surfaces be r_1 and r_2. Assume that there is uniform and instantaneous distribution of temperature throughout, and that rate of loss of heat is proportional to area and the excess of temperature over that of the surroundings. Ignoring other effects, if the external temperature is T_0, the jacket temperature is T_1 and the oven interior temperature is T_2, then we have:

For the jacket:

$$c_1 \dot{T}_1 = -a_2 r_2 (T_1 - T_0) - a_1 r_1 (T_1 - T_2) + u. \tag{1.2}$$

For the oven interior:

$$c_2 \dot{T}_2 = a_1 r_1 (T_1 - T_2). \tag{1.3}$$

Let the state variables be the excesses of temperature over the exterior, i.e. $x_1 = T_1 - T_0, x_2 = T_2 - T_0$. It is easy to verify that (1.2) and (1.3) can be written in the form (1.1) with

$$A = \begin{bmatrix} -(a_2 r_2 + a_1 r_1)/c_1 & a_1 r_1/c_1 \\ a_1 r_1/c_2 & -a_1 r_1/c_2 \end{bmatrix}, \quad B = \begin{bmatrix} 1/c_1 \\ 0 \end{bmatrix}. \tag{1.4}$$

This problem will be studied again in Examples 2.5 and 3.7, and Exercise 3.16. Two further aspects which will be discussed in Chapter 4 (Examples 4.3, 4.5) are firstly whether it is possible to maintain the temperature of the oven interior at any desired level merely by altering u; and secondly, to determine whether the value of T_2 can be determined even if it is not possible to measure it directly. If the desired objective is attainable then there may well be many different suitable control schemes, and considerations of economy, practicability of application, and so on will then determine how control is actually applied.

The preceding two examples involve linear differential equations. Generally, a system is *linear* if, when the response to some input $u(t)$ is $y(t) = L(u)$ then the response to $c_1 u_1 + c_2 u_2$ is $c_1 L(u_1) + c_2 L(u_2)$. Here L is some operator — differential, integral, probabilistic, etc., the c_i are constants; and the u_i in general will be vectors. The system is called *time invariant* (or *constant*) if the response to $u(t-\tau)$ is $y(t-\tau)$, i.e. $L[u(t-\tau)] = y(t-\tau)$ for any fixed τ. Because linear mathematics is very well developed, linear time invariant sets of state equations are the easiest to manage analytically and numerically, and the first model of a situation is often constructed to be linear for this reason. Furthermore, the technique of linearization of nonlinear systems is an important one, and relies on the fact that if the perturbation $z(t)$ from some desired state $x(t)$ is small then a set of linear equations in z can be formed by neglecting all but the first terms in a Taylor series expansion in z. Chapters 3 and 4 are devoted to the study of basic properties of linear systems. Of course in many cases linear descriptions may be inapplicable, as the following example illustrates.

Example 1.3. Consider a simplified space rendezvous problem, in which a spacecraft S_1 wishes to join up with a second non-manoeuvering mothership S_2. Suppose that the only control variable is the thrust direction u, the thrust itself being assumed to provide a constant acceleration c. Take S_2 as the origin of the coordinate system, as shown in Fig. 1.4.

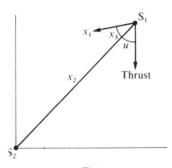

FIG. 1.4

The state variables are the velocity x_1 of S_1 relative to S_2, the distance x_2 between S_1 and S_2 and the angle x_3. Ignoring any external gravitational forces, the state equations are

$$\dot{x}_1 = c \cos (u + x_3)$$

$$\dot{x}_2 = - x_1 \cos x_3$$

$$\dot{x}_3 = (x_1/x_2) \sin x_3 - (c/x_1) \sin (u + x_3).$$

The problem might then be to find a function u, if possible, which takes S_1 to S_2 in minimum time T or with minimum consumption of fuel. A numerical solution to the former problem, with $x_1(T) = 0$, can be found in Bryson and Ho (1969, p. 143).

Example 1.4. In contrast to the simple pendulum referred to at the beginning of this section, consider the 'inverted pendulum' represented in Fig. 1.5.

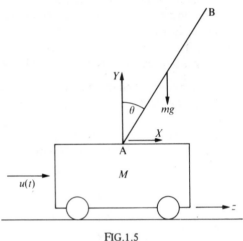

FIG.1.5

A uniform rod AB, mass m, length 2ℓ is smoothly hinged to the centre of a platform of mass M which runs on smooth straight rails. When the rod is vertical ($\theta = 0$) it is in equilibrium, but clearly this is an unstable condition since any small perturbation will cause the rod to fall. The aim is to apply a control force u to the platform so as to keep the rod upright. Standard theory of mechanics gives the equations of motion as

$$
\left.
\begin{array}{c}
\frac{1}{3} m\ell^2 \ddot{\theta} = (Y \sin\theta - X \cos\theta)\ell \\[2mm]
X = m \dfrac{\mathrm{d}^2}{\mathrm{d}t^2} (z + \ell \sin\theta) \\[2mm]
Y - mg = m \dfrac{\mathrm{d}^2}{\mathrm{d}t^2} (\ell \cos\theta) \\[2mm]
u - X = M \dfrac{\mathrm{d}^2 z}{\mathrm{d}t^2},
\end{array}
\right\} \qquad (1.5)
$$

where X and Y are the horizontal and vertical components of the force exerted by the hinge on the rod, and z is the displacement of the centre of mass of the platform from some fixed point. Again, an initial problem is to determine whether the desired objective can be achieved.

The problem described above is sometimes referred to as that of 'broom balancing', by analogy with the idea of keeping a broom balanced vertically on the end of one finger by moving the finger in a horizontal plane. Two interesting applications of the inverted pendulum model are to a one-dimensional version of a rocket on take-off, the vehicle being balanced by the engine thrust; and to biped locomotion systems relating to prosthetic limbs for the physically disabled. The theory of stability of systems is a fundamental one and will be developed in Chapter 5, and stability aspects of the inverted pendulum are studied in Exercises 5.42 and 5.49.

Applications of control theory to economic problems are becoming of increasing importance, and we present a very simple example.

Example 1.5. Suppose that the sales $S(t)$ of a product are affected by the amount of advertising $A(t)$ in such a way that the rate of change of sales decreases by an amount proportional to sales, but increases by an amount proportional to the advertising applied to the share of the market not already purchasing the product. If the total extent of the market is M, the state equation is therefore

$$\dot{S} = -aS + bA(t)(1 - S/M)$$

subject to $S(0) = S_0$, a and b being positive constants. In practice the amount of advertising will be limited, i.e. $0 \leqslant A(t) \leqslant K$, where K is a constant, and the aim would be to find the advertising schedule (i.e. the function $A(t)$) which maximizes the sales over some given period of time. Further details of this and other applications in economics can be found in Intriligator (1971).

In both this example and in Example 1.3 the objective was to find a control strategy which was the best possible, according to some criterion. Such problems of 'optimal' control are dealt with in Chapter 6.

Exercise 1.1.
In Example 1.1, list as many factors as you can think of which are present in reality and can affect the motion of a car being driven along a road.

Exercise 1.2.
Consider the system composed of two masses lying on a smooth horizontal table and connected by two springs to a fixed support, as shown below.

The springs are assumed to obey Hooke's law (force = $k \times$ extension). A force $u(t)$ is applied to the right hand mass. Obtain the system equations in the form (1.1) taking the displacements x_1, x_2 of the masses from equilibrium and velocities $\dot{x}_1 = x_3, \dot{x}_2 = x_4$ as state variables.

This problem will be returned to in Example 2.6 and Exercises 2.19, 4.4 and 4.14.

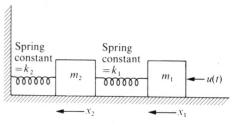

FIG. 1.6

Exercise 1.3.

In the inverted pendulum problem in Example 1.4 take as state variables $x_1 = \theta, x_2 = \dot{\theta}, x_3 = z, x_4 = \dot{z}$, and set $u = 0$. By eliminating X and Y in eqns (1.5), obtain the system equations in state space form $\dot{x} = f(x, \dot{x})$.

Exercise 1.4.

Consider a controlled environment consisting of rabbits and foxes, the numbers of each at time t being $x_1(t)$ and $x_2(t)$ respectively. Suppose that without the presence of foxes the number of rabbits would grow exponentially, but that the rate of growth of rabbit population is reduced by an amount proportional to the number of foxes. Furthermore suppose that, without rabbits to eat, the fox population would decrease exponentially, but that the rate of growth in the number of foxes is increased by an amount proportional to the number of rabbits present. Show that under these assumptions the system equations can be written

$$\dot{x}_1 = a_1 x_1 - a_2 x_2, \dot{x}_2 = a_3 x_1 - a_4 x_2 \qquad (1.6)$$

where the a_i are positive constants.

This system will be studied again in Exercises 1.7, 4.15, and 4.33, and Example 5.2.

1.2. Classical control and transform theory

Classical control theory deals with a *linear* time invariant systems having
scalar input $u(t)$ and scalar output $z(t)$. The analysis problem is to study
the behaviour of a given system in specified circumstances. The aim of
design is to ensure that the performance of the system satisfies required
specifications. If $z(t)$ is required to be as close as possible (in some sense)
to a given reference signal $r(t)$ the control system is called a *servomechanism,* and if r is constant, a *regulator.* For example, the inverted pendulum
discussed in Example 1.4 is a regulator, since it is required to keep the
angle to the vertical θ as near to zero as possible. Similarly, a central-
heating system is designed to keep room temperature close to a predetermined value.

1.2.1. Continuous-time systems: Laplace transform

If u and z are continuous functions of time then the model of classical
linear control theory is the n-th order differential equation

$$z^{(n)} + k_1 z^{(n-1)} + \cdots + k_{n-1} z^{(1)} + k_n z = \beta_0 u^{(m)} + \beta_1 u^{(m-1)}$$
$$+ \cdots + \beta_m u \quad (1.7)$$

where superscript (j) denotes jth derivative with respect to time t and the
k_i and β_i are constants. It can be assumed that $m < n$. In fact it is easy to
convert (1.7) into the matrix-vector form (1.1) and this is dealt with in
Section 3.7. However, the standard techniques of Laplace transforms can
be applied to (1.7) using the result

$$\mathcal{L}\{z^{(j)}(t)\} = s^j \bar{z} - s^{j-1} z(0) - s^{j-2} z^{(1)}(0) - \cdots - s z^{(j-2)}(0) - z^{(j-1)}(0)$$
$$(1.8)$$

where $\bar{z}(s)$ is the Laplace transform of $z(t)$ defined by

$$\bar{z}(s) = \mathcal{L}\{z(t)\} = \int_0^\infty z(t) e^{-st} \, dt. \quad (1.9)$$

It is assumed that the reader has a working knowledge of the use of Laplace transforms for solving ordinary differential equations.
    Assuming that all the $z^{(i)}(0)$ and $u^{(i)}(0)$ are zero, application of (1.8)
to (1.7) gives

$$k(s)\,\bar{z}(s) = \beta(s)\,\bar{u}(s) \quad (1.10)$$

where

$$k(s) = s^n + k_1 s^{n-1} + \cdots + k_{n-1} s + k_n, \qquad (1.11)$$

$$\beta(s) = \beta_0 s^m + \beta_1 s^{m-1} + \cdots + \beta_{m-1} s + \beta_m. \qquad (1.12)$$

Eqn (1.10) can be written

$$\bar{z}(s) = g(s)\, \bar{u}(s) \qquad (1.13)$$

where $$g(s) = \beta(s)/k(s) \qquad (1.14)$$

is the *transfer function,* which is the ratio of the Laplace transform of the output to that of the input. The zeros of the *characteristic polynomial* $k(s)$ are called the *poles* of the transfer function, and the zeros of $\beta(s)$ are the *zeros* of $g(s)$. In block diagram form eqn (1.13) can be represented as in Fig. 1.7.

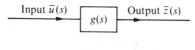

FIG. 1.7

If $u(t)$ (and hence $\bar{u}(s)$) is known then solution for $z(t)$ requires expansion of the right hand side of eqn (1.13) into partial fractions. If the poles of $g(s)$ are denoted by $\lambda_1, \lambda_2, \ldots, \lambda_n$ (these of course may be real or complex numbers) then this expansion will involve terms of the form $c_i/(s - \lambda_i)$, the c_i being constants. These correspond to terms $c_i \exp(\lambda_i t)$ in $z(t)$. Solution of linear systems is dealt with systematically in Chapter 3 using matrix methods, which are generally preferable unless n is small. It is worth noting that if the system is *unforced* (i.e. $u \equiv 0$) and is subject to given initial conditions at $t = 0$, then the solution for $z(t)$ (i.e. the complementary function for (1.7)) tends to a steady state as $t \to \infty$ only if all the λ_i have non-positive real parts. Constant terms in the steady state solution correspond to zero λs, and sinusoidal terms to purely imaginary λs. The question of stability of linear systems is gone into in detail in Chapter 5.

Classical control theory is based on the study of transfer functions, and a number of powerful methods have been evolved. However, with one exception (see Section 5.3) these will be dealt with only very briefly in this book. This is not to deny the enormous practical utility of the techniques, but reflects the fact that for the mathematician, at least, greater interest lies in the more recent approaches to the study of control systems, especially those involving vector inputs (*multivariable* control systems). Moreover, transform methods are applicable only to constant linear systems and are of no help with time varying or nonlinear systems.

Consider a closed loop system represented in the block diagram below Fig. 1.8, where $g(s)$ is the open loop transfer function and $h(s)$ is the feedback transfer function.

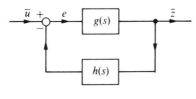

FIG. 1.8

Since $e = \bar{u} - h(s)\bar{z}$ and $\bar{z} = g(s)e$ it follows by eliminating e that

$$\bar{z}(s) = g_{\mathrm{c}}(s)\bar{u}(s),$$

where the *closed loop transfer function* is

$$g_{\mathrm{c}}(s) = \frac{g(s)}{1 + g(s)h(s)}. \tag{1.15}$$

Suppose that the input is a *unit step* function, i.e.

$$\left. \begin{array}{l} u(t) = 1, t \geqslant 0 \\ \quad\ \ = 0, t < 0 \end{array} \right\} \tag{1.16}$$

and that

$$g_{\mathrm{c}}(s) = \frac{\displaystyle\prod_{i=1}^{n} (-\mu_i) \prod_{i=1}^{m} (s - z_i)}{\displaystyle\prod_{i=1}^{m} (-z_i) \prod_{i=1}^{n} (s - \mu_i)} \tag{1.17}$$

where all the poles $\mu_1, \ldots, \mu_n$ of the closed loop system transfer function are assumed distinct. Then it is easy to show using $\bar{u}(s) = 1/s$ that the system response to the step input is

$$z(t) = 1 + \sum_{i=1}^{n} A_i \exp(\mu_i t), \qquad (1.18)$$

where

$$A_j = \left[\frac{(s - \mu_j)g_c(s)}{\mu_j} \right]_{s = \mu_j} \qquad (1.19)$$

so that the response is entirely determined by the poles and zeros of $g_c(s)$.

If the system input is harmonic, say $u = u_0 \cos\omega t$, then if all the μ_i have negative real parts this leads to a steady state response which is also harmonic with the same frequency ω. After elementary manipulations this steady state response can be expressed as

$$z(t) = u_0 \, |g_c(i\omega)| \cos [\omega t + \arg\{g_c(i\omega)\}] \qquad (1.20)$$

$[i = \sqrt{(-1)}]$ showing that the amplitude is $|g_c(i\omega)|$ times that of the input, and that the phase is increased by $\arg\{g_c(i\omega)\}$. The function $g_c(i\omega)$ is called the *frequency transfer function,* and because of the multiplicative effect on the amplitude of the output, $|g_c(i\omega)|$ is called the *gain.* Information about the behaviour of a system is thus provided by a knowledge of the modulus and argument of the frequency transfer function. For example, a hi-fi amplifier can be regarded as a control system whose purpose is to magnify the input with as little distortion as possible over frequencies ranging from 50 Hz to 15 kHz. A large range of values of ω such as this is common in applications, so it is convenient to draw graphs of $\log_{10} |g_c(i\omega)|$ and $\arg\{g_c(i\omega)\}$ against $\log_{10}\omega$ when studying system performance. Such diagrams are called *Bode plots* (after their originator), and methods for drawing them are straightforward, the actual mathematical details not being of great interest. It is possible in some cases to apply the procedure in reverse, so that if the gain is measured experimentally a corresponding transfer function can be deduced. Because of the way ω is used as a variable the method is often referred to as one in the 'frequency domain'. A second such technique, due to Nyquist, will be dealt with in some detail in Chapter 5.

We have seen that system response depends on the poles and zeros of $g_c(s)$. Suppose that the open loop transfer function $g(s)$ is multiplied by a gain parameter K so that (1.15) becomes

$$g_c(s) = Kg(s)/[1 + Kg(s)h(s)]. \tag{1.21}$$

The *root locus* method has been devised for investigating how the poles of $g_c(s)$ in (1.21) vary with K. These poles are the roots of

$$1 + Kg(s)h(s) = 0 \tag{1.22}$$

and sets of rules have been drawn up for determining the loci of these roots graphically as K varies from 0 to ∞. Again, the mathematical detail is rather tedious.

There are very many textbooks available on control engineering and the reader should consult these for comprehensive accounts of the above and other classical methods. In particular the books by Elgerd (1967), Eveleigh (1972) and Takahashi, Rabins, and Auslander (1970) can be recommended for treatments which combine the classical and modern approaches, and the account by Truxal (1972) is clear and interesting.

It is instructive to return in more detail to the question of sensitivity of feedback systems, briefly mentioned in Section 1.1. For a transfer function $t(s)$ the *sensitivity* with respect to small variations in some parameter θ is defined by

$$S_\theta(t) = \frac{\mathrm{d}t/t}{\mathrm{d}\theta/\theta} = \frac{\mathrm{d}t}{\mathrm{d}\theta} \cdot \frac{\theta}{t}. \tag{1.23}$$

Consider the systems represented in Fig. 1.9, and

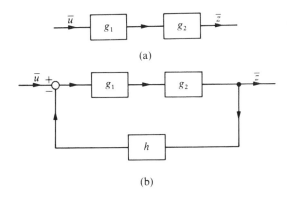

(a)

(b)

FIG. 1.9

suppose for simplicity that g_1, g_2, and h are constants. For the open loop system in Fig. 1.9(a) the transfer function is just $t_1 = g_1 g_2$ so $S_{g_2}(t_1) = 1$. Thus a small percentage change in g_2 causes the same percentage change in t_1. For the closed loop system in Fig. 1.9(b) eqn (1.15) gives

$$t_2 = g_1 g_2 / (1 + g_1 g_2 h), \tag{1.24}$$

and differentiation with respect to g_2 and use of (1.23) leads to

$$S_{g_2}(t_2) = 1/(1 + g_1 g_2 h). \tag{1.25}$$

Clearly in this case for a given g_2, the values of g_1 and h can be chosen so as to make the sensitivity to small changes in g_2 as small as we please. Such sensitivity considerations carry over in a fairly general way to more complicated systems, and thus provide a very important practical justification for the use of feedback. In a similar way it can be demonstrated that feedback can reduce the effect of external disturbances on a system output. As is illustrated by (1.25), the denominator of the transfer function plays an important role in these discussions. More generally, the denominator $1 + g(s)h(s)$ in the transfer function (1.15) is termed the *return difference* for the following reason. Suppose that in the corresponding block diagram (Fig. 1.8) $\bar{u} = 0$, but that an input $e = 1$ is inserted. The returning signal will be $-g(s)h(s)$, so the difference between them is just $1 + gh$.

We shall encounter the ideas of transfer functions in our subsequent work on linear systems, especially the extension (for multi-input multi-output systems) to matrices whose elements are transfer functions.

1.2.2. Discrete-time systems: z-transform

We now turn to situations where the variables are measured (or 'sampled') only at discrete intervals of time instead of continuously, producing what are referred to as *sampled-data*, or *discrete-time* systems. Such circumstances are common in real life: for example, the interest on savings accounts is calculated daily or monthly; the temperature of a hospital patient is recorded at perhaps hourly intervals; a driver of a car glances at the instruments, rear mirror, etc., only intermittently — the reader can easily add many instances of his own (see Cadzow 1973, ch. 2).

We shall suppose that our variables are defined at fixed intervals of time $0, T, 2T, 3T, \ldots$ where T is a constant, and use $X(k), u(k)$ to denote the values of the output $X(kT)$, and the input $u(kT)$ respectively ($k = 0$,

1, 2, 3, ...). For linear systems the differential eqn (1.7) is replaced by the *difference equation*

$$X(k + n) + k_1 X(k + n - 1) + \cdots + k_{n-1}X(k + 1) + k_n X(k)$$

$$= \beta_0 u(k + m) + \beta_1 u(k + m - 1) + \cdots + \beta_m u(k). \qquad (1.26)$$

The technique corresponding to Laplace transforms is to define the *z-transform* of a scalar (or indeed a vector) function $X(k)$, $k = 0, 1, 2, 3, \ldots$ by

$$\tilde{X}(z) = Z\{X(k)\} = \sum_{k=0}^{\infty} X(k) z^{-k} \qquad (1.27)$$

$$= X(0) + \frac{X(1)}{z} + \frac{X(2)}{z^2} + \cdots \qquad (1.28)$$

The reader may not have encountered z-transforms previously so it will be useful to go into a little detail here.

Example 1.6. Obtain the z-transforms of the following functions, defined for $k = 0, 1, 2, \ldots$: (a) $X(k) = 1$; (b) $X(k) = a^k$, where a is a constant.

(*a*)   From the definition (1.27)

$$Z\{1\} = 1 + \frac{1}{z} + \frac{1}{z^2} + \cdots$$

$$= (1 - \frac{1}{z})^{-1}, \text{ by the binomial theorem}$$

$$= z/(z - 1).$$

(*b*)   Similarly

$$Z\{a^k\} = 1 + \frac{a}{z} + \frac{a^2}{z^2} + \cdots$$

$$= (1 - \frac{a}{z})^{-1}$$

$$= z/(z - a). \qquad (1.29)$$

The result corresponding to $\mathcal{L}\{dz(t)/dt\}$ obtained by taking $j = 1$ in (1.8) is

$$Z\{X(k+1)\} = \sum_{k=0}^{\infty} X(k+1)z^{-k}, \text{ by } (1.27)$$

$$= X(1) + \frac{X(2)}{z} + \frac{X(3)}{z^2} + \cdots$$

$$= z\left[\frac{X(1)}{z} + \frac{X(2)}{z^2} + \frac{X(3)}{z^3} + \cdots\right]$$

$$= z\,[\bar{X}(z) - X(0)] \text{ by } (1.27) \tag{1.30}$$

A repetition of this argument produces

$$Z\{X(k+j)\} = z^j\bar{X}(z) - z^j X(0) - z^{j-1}X(1) - z^{j-2}X(2)\cdots - z^2 X(j-2) -$$

$$zX(j-1) \tag{1.31}$$

which is the analogue of the result for the Laplace transform of the jth derivative of $z(t)$ given in (1.8). Application of (1.31) to the difference equation (1.26) then transforms this into an algebraic equation for $\bar{X}(z)$. The resulting expression is expanded into partial fractions as for Laplace transforms.

Example 1.7. Solve the difference equation

$$X(k+2) + 5X(k+1) + 6X(k) = 0$$

subject to $X(0) = X_0$, $X(1) = X_1$.

Take z-transforms of both sides of the equation and use (1.30) and (1.31) with $j = 2$ to obtain

$$z^2\bar{X} - z^2 X_0 - zX_1 + 5z(\bar{X} - X_0) + 6\bar{X} = 0$$

Thus

$$\bar{X}(z) = \frac{z(zX_0 + X_1 + 5X_0)}{z^2 + 5z + 6}$$

$$= z\left[\frac{-(2X_0 + X_1)}{z+3} + \frac{(3X_0 + X_1)}{z+2}\right]$$

Hence using (1.29) the solution of the equation is

$$X(k) = -(2X_0 + X_1)(-3)^k + (3X_0 + X_1)(-2)^k.$$

As the example illustrates, if all the roots λ_i of $k(z)$ defined in (1.11) are distinct, the general solution of (1.26) involves terms of the form $c_i(\lambda_i)^k$, where c_i is a constant, so for unforced systems there is a steady state solution only if all the λ_i have modulus not greater than unity. In particular, constant terms in the solution correspond to λs equal to unity Solution and stability of linear discrete-time systems are dealt with in detail in Chapters 3 and 5, along with their continuous-time equivalents. Clearly there are close parallels between Laplace and z-transform methods, and in fact a formal relationship between the two techniques can be established. For details of this, together with standard theorems and lists of transform pairs, reference texts such as that by Jury (1965) should be consulted.

Application of z-transforms to (1.26) gives

$$\tilde{X}(z) = g(z)\bar{u}(z)$$

where g is defined by (1.14). Some of the continuous-time frequency domain methods have been extended to deal with sampled-data transfer functions (see for example Saucedo and Schiring 1968).

Exercise 1.5.
Show that the system represented in Fig. 1.8. is equivalent to that shown in Fig. 1.10.

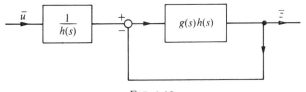

FIG. 1.10

Since the feedback is simply equal to the output, it is called *unity feedback*.

Exercise 1.6.
Find the transfer function for the system represented by the block diagram in Fig. 1.11.

Exercise 1.7.
Consider the rabbit-fox environment described in Exercise 1.4. If the experiment begins with initial population sizes $x_1(0)$ and $x_2(0)$ and if

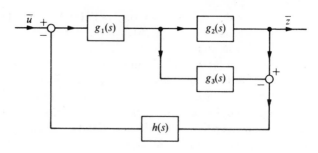

FIG. 1.11

in eqns (1.6) $a_1/a_3 = a_2/a_4$, use Laplace transforms to solve for $x_1(t)$. Hence show that for arbitrary initial conditions the populations will attain a steady state as $t \to \infty$ only if $a_1 - a_4 < 0$, and give an expression for the ultimate size of the rabbit population in this case. Finally, deduce that if the environment is to reach a steady state in which both rabbits and foxes are present then $x_1(0) > (a_1/a_3)x_2(0)$.

What happens if $x_1(0) = (a_2/a_1)x_2(0)$?

Exercise 1.8.
Deduce by considering eqn (1.22) that the root loci start (i.e. $K = 0$) and terminate (i.e. $K = \infty$) at the poles and zeros respectively of the function $g(s)h(s)$.

Exercise 1.9.
For the transfer function obtained in Exercise 1.6. derive an expression for the sensitivity with respect to g_2. How can this be made equal to zero?

Exercise 1.10.
Obtain the z-transforms of the following functions, defined for $k = 0, 1, 2, \ldots$ (a) $X(k) = kT$ (b) $X(k) = e^{ak}$, where a is a constant.

By replacing a by ia in (b) and considering imaginary parts, deduce that

$$Z\{\sin ak\} = \frac{z \sin a}{z^2 - 2z \cos a + 1}.$$

Exercise 1.11.
Prove that

$$Z\{e^{bk}X(k)\} = \tilde{X}(ze^{-b})$$

where $Z\{X(k)\} = \tilde{X}(z)$ and b is a constant. Hence show, using the result of the preceding exercise, that

$$Z\{e^{bk} \sin ak\} = \frac{ze^b \sin a}{z^2 - 2ze^b \cos a + e^{2b}} \tag{1.32}$$

Exercise 1.12.
A very simple model of a national economy can be constructed by assuming that at year k the national income I_k is given by

$$I_k = C_k + P_k + G_k, k = 0, 1, 2, \therefore.$$

where C_k is consumer expenditure, P_k is private investment and G_k is government expenditure. Assuming that consumer spending is proportional to national income in the previous year, i.e.

$$C_k = \alpha I_{k-1}, 0 < \alpha < 1,$$

and that private investment is proportional to the change in consumer spending over the previous year, i.e.

$$P_k = \beta (C_k - C_{k-1}), 0 < \beta \leqslant 1,$$

show that

$$I_{k+2} - \alpha (1 + \beta)I_{k+1} + \alpha \beta I_k = G_{k+2}.$$

If $\alpha = \frac{1}{2}$, $\beta = 1$, government spending is at a constant level $G_k = G$ (all k) and $I_0 = 2G, I_1 = 3G$, show by using z-transforms that

$$I_k = 2\{1 + (1/\sqrt{2})^k \sin \frac{1}{4} k \pi\}G$$

(the result in (1.32) is needed).

The assumptions of the model therefore lead to a national income which is oscillatory, and as $k \to \infty$ national income tends to twice government expenditure.

Exercise 1.13.
The following simplified model for the buffalo population in the American West in 1830 has been suggested by Truxal (1972). Let F_k, M_k be the numbers of female and male buffalo at the start of year k ($k = 0$ corresponding to 1830). Five per cent of adults die each year. Buffalo reach maturity at age two years, and the number of new adult females alive at the beginning of year $k + 2$, taking into account infant mortality, is

22

12 per cent of F_k; more male calves than female are born, and the corresponding figure is 14 per cent of F_k. Thus

$$F_{k+2} = 0.95F_{k+1} + 0.12F_k \qquad (1.33)$$

$$M_{k+2} = 0.95M_{k+1} + 0.14F_k \qquad (1.34)$$

Use z-transforms to find expressions for F_k and M_k, and deduce that as $k \to \infty$ the population increases by 6.3 per cent per year.

This model will be studied further in Exercise 4.53 and Example 5.11.

2 Preliminary matrix theory

A brief review is now given of some mathematical material necessary for the main part of the book. It has been assumed that the reader possesses a basic knowledge of matrices and related topics. The aims of this chapter are twofold: firstly, to supplement this knowledge with some less familiar results; and secondly to establish notation and techniques so as to provide a convenient source of reference for the remainder of the book. A generally non-rigorous presentation is used and most results are given without proof. Further details can be found in the many standard textbooks available — see, for example, Cullen (1972) and Gantmacher (1959) for mathematical treatment of linear algebra, and Director and Rohrer (1972) for a systems theory approach.

If desired, this chapter can be omitted on a first reading without loss of continuity, and any unfamiliar points which occur later can then be referred to here.

2.1. Definitions

A useful compact way of writing a *matrix* is

$$A = [a_{ij}], i = 1, 2, \ldots, m, \quad j = 1, 2, \ldots, n \qquad (2.1)$$

where a_{ij} is the *element* in the ith row and jth column, and A thus has m rows and n columns. The *transpose* A^T is obtained by interchanging the rows and columns of A, so $A^T = [a_{ji}]$ and is $n \times m$; the *conjugate transpose* is $A^* = [\bar{a}_{ji}]$, where the overbar denotes complex conjugate. If either m or n is equal to 1, the matrix is termed a *row n-vector* or *column m-vector* respectively. When $m = n$ A is said to be *square* of *order n*. We shall write

$$I_n = \begin{bmatrix} 1 & 0 & . & . & . \\ 0 & 1 & & & \\ . & . & . & & \\ & & & . & \\ . & . & & & 1 \end{bmatrix} \qquad (2.2)$$

for the *unit matrix* of order n which has the property that $AI_n = I_nA$ for any $n \times n$ matrix A. The matrix in (2.2) has all its elements zero except those on the *principal diagonal,* and any square matrix of this form is called a *diagonal* matrix, written diag $[a_{11}, a_{22}, \ldots, a_{nn}]$. It is assumed that the reader is familiar with the usual rules of addition, subtraction, multiplication, inversion, etc. for matrices. If the elements in any $k(\leqslant m)$ rows and $\ell(\leqslant n)$ columns of A are selected they form a $k \times \ell$ *submatrix* of A. In particular A can be *partitioned* into submatrices (or *blocks*) α_{ij} of orders $m_i \times n_j$, as follows:

$$
A = \begin{array}{cccccc}
n_1 & n_2 & \cdot & \cdot & n_s & \\
\left[\begin{array}{ccccc}
\alpha_{11} & \alpha_{12} & \cdot & \cdot & \alpha_{1s} \\
\alpha_{21} & \alpha_{22} & \cdot & \cdot & \alpha_{2s} \\
\cdot & \cdot & \cdot & \cdot & \cdot \\
\alpha_{r1} & \alpha_{r2} & \cdot & \cdot & \alpha_{rs}
\end{array}\right] & & & & & \begin{array}{c} m_1 \\ m_2 \\ \cdot \\ m_r \end{array}
\end{array}
$$

where $\Sigma m_i = m$, $\Sigma n_j = n$. When A is square, a *block diagonal* matrix is defined by

$$
\text{diag } [\alpha_{11}, \alpha_{22}, \ldots, \alpha_{rr}] = \begin{array}{cccccc}
m_1 & m_2 & \cdot & \cdot & m_r & \\
\left[\begin{array}{ccccc}
\alpha_{11} & 0 & \cdot & \cdot & 0 \\
0 & \alpha_{22} & \cdot & \cdot & 0 \\
\cdot & \cdot & \cdot & \cdot & \cdot \\
0 & 0 & \cdot & \cdot & \alpha_{rr}
\end{array}\right] & & & & & \begin{array}{c} m_1 \\ m_2 \\ \cdot \\ m_r \end{array}
\end{array} \qquad (2.3)
$$

A useful form of partitioned matrix is obtained by defining the *Kronecker product* of two matrices $A(m \times n)$ and $B(p \times q)$ by

$$
A \otimes B = \begin{bmatrix}
a_{11}B & a_{12}B & \cdot & \cdot & \cdot & a_{1n}B \\
a_{21}B & a_{22}B & \cdot & \cdot & \cdot & a_{2n}B \\
\cdot & \cdot & \cdot & \cdot & \cdot & \cdot \\
a_{m1}B & a_{m2}B & \cdot & \cdot & \cdot & a_{mn}B
\end{bmatrix} \qquad (2.4)
$$

where A is given by (2.1). Thus $A \otimes B$ is an $mp \times nq$ matrix and is partitioned into the mn blocks shown in (2.4). It is easy to verify using the definition that

$$(A \otimes B)(C \otimes D) = AC \otimes BD \tag{2.5}$$

$$(A \otimes B)^* = A^* \otimes B^*. \tag{2.6}$$

If A is $n \times n$ and X is $n \times m$ then the matrix equation $AX = C$ can be written in the form

$$(A \otimes I_m)x = c, \tag{2.7}$$

where

$$x = [x_{11}, x_{12}, \ldots, x_{1m}, x_{21}, \ldots, x_{2m}, \ldots, x_{nm}]^T \tag{2.8}$$

is the column mn-vector formed from the rows of X taken in order, and c is formed in an identical fashion from C. Similarly, $XB = C$ can be written

$$(I_n \otimes B^T)x = c. \tag{2.9}$$

Thus linear equations involving matrices can easily be rewritten in the more usual matrix–vector form (see (2.18) and (2.19)).

The *determinant* det A or $|A|$ is a scalar function of a square matrix, and a knowledge of the basic properties of determinants is also assumed. For example,

$$\det A^T = \det A, \quad \det A^* \equiv \overline{\det A},$$

$$\det (AB) = \det A \det B \tag{2.10}$$

for any two $n \times n$ matrices A and B, and

$$\det A = a_{11} a_{22} \ldots a_{nn} \tag{2.11}$$

if A is diagonal or *triangular*, i.e. all the elements above (or below) the principal diagonal are zero, so that $a_{ij} = 0$ if $j > i$ (or $j < i$). If det $A = 0$, A is *singular*, otherwise *nonsingular*; in the latter case the *inverse* of A is

$$A^{-1} = \text{Adj } A/\det A$$

where Adj $A = [A_{ji}]$, the *adjoint* of A, is defined by

$$A_{ij} = (-1)^{i+j}M_{ij}$$

and M_{ij} is the determinant of the submatrix formed by deleting row i and column j of A. In general the determinant of any submatrix is termed a *minor* of A.

The following result due to Schur on evaluation of partitioned determinants is often useful. If W, X, Y, and Z are matrices having dimensions $n \times n$, $n \times m$, $m \times n$ and $m \times m$ respectively, with W nonsingular, then

$$\det \begin{bmatrix} W & X \\ Y & Z \end{bmatrix} = \det W \det (Z - YW^{-1} X) \qquad (2.12)$$

A similar result holds if Z is nonsingular (see Exercise 2.3).

Exercise 2.1.
What is the condition on the dimensions of A and B for the product AB to exist? What does this imply for the matrices in eqn (2.5)?

Exercise 2.2.
If A and B are nonsingular matrices, use (2.5) to show that $(A \otimes B)^{-1} = A^{-1} \otimes B^{-1}$. What is the corresponding expression for $(AB)^{-1}$?

Exercise 2.3.
By considering the product

$$\begin{bmatrix} W^{-1} & 0 \\ -YW^{-1} & I_m \end{bmatrix} \begin{bmatrix} W & X \\ Y & Z \end{bmatrix}$$

and using (2.10), verify Schur's formula (2.12). Similarly, if Z is nonsingular show that

$$\det \begin{bmatrix} W & X \\ Y & Z \end{bmatrix} = \det Z \det (W - XZ^{-1} Y).$$

Hence deduce that

$$\det (I_n - XY) = \det (I_m - YX).$$

Exercise 2.4.
Show that the matrix equation

$$AX + XB = C$$

Preliminary matrix theory

where A is $n \times n$, B is $m \times m$, and C is $n \times m$, can be written in the form

$$(A \otimes I_m + I_n \otimes B^{\mathrm{T}}) x = c$$

where x is defined in (2.8) and c is formed similarly from C.

2.2. Linear dependence and rank

An important concept which we will find essential in linear control theory is now introduced. Consider a set of n column m-vectors

$$a_1 = \begin{bmatrix} a_{11} \\ a_{21} \\ \vdots \\ a_{m1} \end{bmatrix}, \quad a_2 = \begin{bmatrix} a_{12} \\ a_{22} \\ \vdots \\ a_{m2} \end{bmatrix}, \quad \ldots, \quad a_n = \begin{bmatrix} a_{1n} \\ a_{2n} \\ \vdots \\ a_{mn} \end{bmatrix} \quad (2.13)$$

with the a_{ij} allowed to be complex in general. The set of *all* such vectors is called an *m-space*, denoted by C^m (or R^m if the a_{ij} are restricted to be real). Both R^m and C^m are examples of a *vector-space*, and development of the theory of vector spaces can be found in standard texts on linear algebra. Notice that the vectors in (2.13) could equally well be written in row form.

If $x_1, x_2, \ldots, x_n$ are scalars then the vector

$$x_1 a_1 + x_2 a_2 + \ldots + x_n a_n = \begin{bmatrix} a_{11} x_1 + a_{12} x_2 + \ldots + a_{1n} x_n \\ \vdots \\ a_{m1} x_1 + a_{m2} x_2 + \ldots + a_{mn} x_n \end{bmatrix} \quad (2.14)$$

is called a *linear combination* of $a_1, \ldots, a_n$. If a set of the xs, with not all of them zero, can be found so that all the elements of the vector on the right hand side of (2.14) are zero, then the vectors $a_1, a_2, \ldots, a_m$ are said to be *linearly dependent*; otherwise they are *linearly independent*.

Example 2.1. If

$$a_1 = \begin{bmatrix} 1 \\ 2 \\ 3 \end{bmatrix}, \quad a_2 = \begin{bmatrix} -6 \\ 0 \\ 2 \end{bmatrix}, \quad a_3 = \begin{bmatrix} -1 \\ 1 \\ 2 \end{bmatrix} \quad (2.15)$$

then $2a_1 + a_2 - 4a_3 = 0$, so we can write

$$a_1 = -\frac{1}{2} a_2 + 2a_3$$

or

$$a_2 = -2a_1 + 4a_3$$

or

$$a_3 = \frac{1}{2} a_1 + \frac{1}{4} a_2.$$

Thus each vector can be expressed as a linear combination of the other two, so a_1, a_2, a_3 are linearly dependent, whereas any two a_i, a_j are linearly independent.

Given a particular set of n column m-vectors in (2.13), then the set of all linear combinations (2.14) forms a *subspace* of C^m. This subspace is said to be *spanned* by $a_1, \ldots, a_n$. If *every* column m-vector can be expressed as a linear combination of the a_i then (2.13) is termed a *spanning set* for C^m.

Example 2.2. When $m = 3$ consider the vectors

$$a_1 = \begin{bmatrix} 1 \\ 0 \\ 0 \end{bmatrix}, \quad a_2 = \begin{bmatrix} 0 \\ 1 \\ 0 \end{bmatrix}, \quad a_3 = \begin{bmatrix} 0 \\ 0 \\ 1 \end{bmatrix}, \quad a_4 = \begin{bmatrix} 1 \\ 1 \\ 1 \end{bmatrix} \qquad (2.16)$$

The subspace spanned by a_1 and a_2 consists of all vectors of the form

$$\begin{bmatrix} x_1 \\ x_2 \\ 0 \end{bmatrix}, x_1, x_2 \text{ arbitrary.}$$

The vectors a_1, a_2, a_3, a_4 form a spanning set for C^3, and for example

$$\begin{bmatrix} 1 \\ 0 \\ 2 \end{bmatrix} = 2a_1 + a_2 + 3a_3 - a_4.$$

In general there will not be a unique spanning set for C^m. However, if the members of a spanning set are linearly independent then the set is called a *basis*, and it can be shown that any basis for C^m contains exactly m vectors, so that C^m is said to have *dimension m*.

Example 2.3. For the vectors in (2.16) $a_4 = a_1 + a_2 + a_3$ but

$$x_1 a_1 + x_2 a_2 + x_3 a_3 = \begin{bmatrix} x_1 \\ x_2 \\ x_3 \end{bmatrix}$$

$\neq 0$ unless $x_1 = x_2 = x_3 = 0$.

so a_1, a_2, a_3 are linearly independent and form a basis for C^3.

In general for any finite value of m the set of *unit m-vectors*

$$\begin{bmatrix} 1 \\ 0 \\ 0 \\ \cdot \\ \cdot \\ 0 \end{bmatrix}, \begin{bmatrix} 0 \\ 1 \\ 0 \\ \cdot \\ \cdot \\ 0 \end{bmatrix}, \begin{bmatrix} 0 \\ 0 \\ 1 \\ \cdot \\ \cdot \\ 0 \end{bmatrix}, \dots, \begin{bmatrix} 0 \\ 0 \\ \cdot \\ \cdot \\ \cdot \\ 1 \end{bmatrix} \qquad (2.17)$$

forms a basis for C^m or R^m.

Closely related to the idea of dependence is that of the *rank r* of an $m \times n$ matrix $A = [a_{ij}]$, defined as the maximum number of linearly independent rows (or columns) of A. Clearly r cannot exceed $p = \min(m,n)$, and $p - r$ is called the *rank defect* of A.

Example 2.4. Suppose a matrix is formed by using the three vectors in (2.15) as columns, i.e.

$$A = \begin{bmatrix} 1 & -6 & -1 \\ 2 & 0 & 1 \\ 3 & 2 & 2 \end{bmatrix}$$

As was seen in Example 2.1, any two of the columns are linearly independent, so rank $A = 2$. Similarly, any two rows of A are independent.

The rank of A can be shown to be equal to the order of the largest nonsingular submatrix of A. In particular, if A is square then it is nonsingular if and only if its rows (columns) are linearly independent.

Suppose now that the a_{ij} are the coefficients in a set of m linear algebraic equations in n unknowns

$$\sum_{j=1}^{n} a_{ij}x_j = b_i, \quad i = 1, 2, \dots, m. \qquad (2.18)$$

These equations can be written in matrix-vector form as

$$Ax = b \qquad (2.19)$$

where

$$x = [x_1, x_2, \ldots, x_n]^\mathrm{T}, \quad b = [b_1, b_2, \ldots, b_m]^\mathrm{T} \tag{2.20}$$

Notice that the elements of Ax in (2.19) are precisely the same as those on the right hand side of (2.14). Thus the problem of solving (2.19) for the x_i is equivalent to finding the coefficients in the expression of b as a linear combination of the columns a_i of A, if possible. It then follows that (2.19) possesses a solution if and only if

$$\text{Rank } A \equiv \text{Rank } [A,b] \tag{2.21}$$

where $[A,b]$ is the $m \times (n+1)$ matrix obtained by appending b to A as an extra column. Two particular cases should be mentioned: when A is square the equations (2.19) have a unique solution if and only if A is nonsingular, and when the equations are *homogeneous* (i.e. all $b_i = 0$) then the necessary and sufficient condition for a nonzero solution to exist is Rank $A < n$. Similar remarks apply to the set of equations.

$$yA = b, \quad y = [y_1, y_2, \ldots, y_m] \ .$$

Exercise 2.5.
If a given m-vector v is expressed in terms of a given basis, i.e. $v = x_1 a_1 + \cdots + x_m a_m$, show that the coefficients x_i are unique.

Exercise 2.6.
Let A be an $n \times n$ matrix and b a nonzero column n-vector such that $A^r b \neq 0, A^{r+1} b = 0$ for some positive integer r less than n. By considering the equation

$$c_0 b + c_1 Ab + c_2 A^2 b + \cdots + c_r A^r b = 0$$

where the c_i are scalars, deduce that the vectors $b, Ab, A^2 b, \ldots, A^r b$ are linearly independent.

2.3. Polynomials

A *polynomial a* (λ) of *degree* $\delta a = n$ is an expression of the form

$$a(\lambda) = a_0 \lambda^n + a_1 \lambda^{n-1} + \cdots + a_{n-1} \lambda + a_n, \tag{2.22}$$

where the *leading coefficient* a_0 is nonzero. When $a_0 = 1$ the polynomial is called *monic*, and in this book the a_i will be real or complex numbers. We have seen in Section 1.2 that polynomials arise in linear system theory

when Laplace or z-transforms are applied to linear differential or difference equations respectively, and this led us to define a transfer function
in (1.14) as a *rational* function, namely the ratio of two polynomials. In
this section we record some basic properties of polynomials which are
often required.

If $b(\lambda)$ is a second polynomial with $\delta b \leqslant n$ then $a(\lambda)$ can be divided
by $b(\lambda)$ to give

$$a(\lambda) = b(\lambda)q(\lambda) + r(\lambda), \tag{2.23}$$

where the remainder $r(\lambda)$ has $\delta r < \delta b$; if $r \equiv 0$ then $a(\lambda)$ is *divisible without remainder* by $b(\lambda)$. Any polynomial $d(\lambda)$ which divides both a and b
without remainder is a *common divisor* of a and b. The *greatest common
divisor* (g.c.d.) is the unique monic common divisor having greatest
possible degree, and is divisible by all other common divisors. The polynomials a and b are *relatively prime* if their g.c.d. is equal to unity. A
resultant of a and b is a scalar function of the coefficients of a and b
which is nonzero if and only if a and b are relatively prime. These definitions carry over in an obvious way to any number of polynomials. For
example, a set of m polynomials $p_1(\lambda), p_2(\lambda), \ldots, p_m(\lambda)$ is a relatively
prime if there is no polynomial $d(\lambda)$ with $\delta d > 0$ which divides each of
the $p_i(\lambda)$ without remainder.

If the number c is such that $a(c) = 0$ then c is a *root* or *zero* of $a(\lambda)$.
This implies that $a(\lambda)$ is divisible by $\lambda - c$ without remainder, and in
general every nth degree polynomial can be written in the form

$$a(\lambda) = (\lambda - \lambda_1)^{t_1} (\lambda - \lambda_2)^{t_2} \cdots (\lambda - \lambda_p)^{t_p} \tag{2.24}$$

where the λ_i are complex numbers, all different from each other, and the
t_i are positive integers. The root λ_i has *multiplicity* t_i, and $t_1 + t_2 + \cdots
+ t_p = n$. Any root having unit multiplicity is called *simple,* and if $t_i = 1$,
$i = 1,2, \ldots, n$, the polynomial is said to have n *distinct* roots.

Exercise 2.7.
Deduce that if there exist polynomials $x(\lambda)$ and $y(\lambda)$ such that

$$a(\lambda)x(\lambda) + b(\lambda)y(\lambda) = 1$$

than $a(\lambda)$ and $b(\lambda)$ are relatively prime.
The converse of this result also holds.

Exercise 2.8.
If the coefficients a_i in (2.22) are all real numbers, show that if c is a
root of $a(\lambda)$ so is its complex conjugate $\bar{c}$.

2.4. Characteristic roots

Polynomials also arise in a fundamental way when matrix methods are applied to differential equations in the state space form

$$\dot{x}(t) = Ax(t). \tag{2.25}$$

Eqn (2.25) is the unforced version of (1.1), but now $x(t)$ is an n-dimensional state vector and A is a constant $n \times n$ matrix. We remarked in Section 1.2.1 that the solution of linear systems consists of exponential terms. Substituting $x(t) = w \exp(\lambda t)$ into (2.25), where w is a column n-vector and λ a scalar, gives

$$\lambda w \exp(\lambda t) = Aw \exp(\lambda t)$$

which implies $Aw = \lambda w$, or

$$(\lambda I_n - A)w = 0. \tag{2.26}$$

It follows from the discussion at the end of Section 2.2 that for the solution w of the homogeneous linear equations (2.26) to be nonzero we must have

$$\det(\lambda I_n - A) = 0. \tag{2.27}$$

When expanded eqn (2.27) represents an nth degree polynomial equation

$$k(\lambda) \equiv \lambda^n + k_1 \lambda^{n-1} + \cdots + k_{n-1}\lambda + k_n = 0. \tag{2.28}$$

called the *characteristic equation* of A. The n roots $\lambda_1, \lambda_2, \ldots, \lambda_n$ of the *characteristic polynomial* $k(\lambda)$ are the *characteristic roots* of A (often called the *eigenvalues*, an Anglo–German hybrid term), and may be written as $\lambda_i(A)$.

Since by virtue of (2.24) we can write

$$k(\lambda) \equiv \det(\lambda I_n - A)$$
$$= (\lambda - \lambda_1)(\lambda - \lambda_2) \cdots (\lambda - \lambda_n)$$

where some of the λ_i may be repeated, it follows by comparing terms in λ^0 and λ^{n-1} that

$$\left.\begin{array}{c} (-1)^n k_n = \det A = \lambda_1 \lambda_2 \cdots \lambda_n \\[2ex] -k_1 = \operatorname{tr} A = \displaystyle\sum_{i=1}^{n} \lambda_i \end{array}\right\} \tag{2.29}$$

where $\operatorname{tr} A = a_{11} + a_{22} + \cdots + a_{nn}$, the *trace* of A.

For each value of λ there is a corresponding solution w_i of (2.26), and these vectors are called the *characteristic vectors* (or *eigenvectors*) of A, and thus satisfy

$$Aw_i = \lambda_i w_i, \quad i = 1, 2, \ldots, n. \tag{2.30}$$

The solution of (2.25) is therefore a sum of terms $w_i \exp(\lambda_i t)$ and this will be developed formally in Section 3.1. The w_i are sometimes called *right* characteristic vectors of A, the left vectors which are rows being defined by

$$v_i A = \lambda_i v_i.$$

If the λ_i are all different from one another it can be shown that the w_i are linearly independent so the matrix

$$W = [w_1, w_2, \ldots, w_n]$$

is nonsingular. In this case we have

$$W^{-1} A W = W^{-1} [Aw_1, Aw_2, \ldots, Aw_n]$$
$$= W^{-1} [\lambda_1 w_1, \lambda_2 w_2, \ldots, \lambda_n w_n]$$
$$= \text{diag}[\lambda_1, \lambda_2, \ldots, \lambda_n] \equiv \Lambda \tag{2.31}$$

Generally, two matrices A and B are said to be *similar* if there exists a nonsingular matrix T such that $T^{-1} A T = B$. Thus (2.31) shows that when all the characteristic roots of A are distinct it is similar to the diagonal matrix Λ of its characteristic roots. This is not a necessary condition: A may have some repeated roots but will still be similar to Λ if it has n linearly independent characteristic vectors. The case when A has repeated roots will be dealt with in detail in Section 2.6. The matrix Λ is an example of a *canonical form*, this being a standard form to which a class of matrices can be reduced by specified operations.

The matrix

$$C = \begin{bmatrix} 0 & 1 & 0 & \cdot & \cdot & 0 \\ 0 & 0 & 1 & \cdot & \cdot & \cdot \\ \cdot & \cdot & \cdot & \cdot & \cdot & \cdot \\ \cdot & \cdot & \cdot & \cdot & \cdot & \cdot \\ -k_n & -k_{n-1} & -k_{n-2} & \cdot & \cdot & -k_1 \end{bmatrix} \tag{2.32}$$

is the *companion form* matrix associated with $k(\lambda)$ in (2.28), since it is easy to show that

$$\det (\lambda I_n - C) = k(\lambda). \qquad (2.33)$$

Other companion form matrices can be written down with the k_i in the first or last column, or first row. The companion matrix is useful because it possesses the same characteristic roots as A but has the relatively simple form displayed in (2.32). We shall see that C plays an important role in the study of linear control systems. Unfortunately however a practical disadvantage of eqn (2.32) is that it is generally very difficult to calculate the k_i accurately for a given matrix A. A formula which is useful, but mainly for theoretical rather than computational purposes, is *Leverrier's algorithm*, which states that the inverse of the characteristic matrix is

$$(\lambda I_n - A)^{-1} = [\lambda^{n-1} I_n + \lambda^{n-2} B_1 + \lambda^{n-3} B_2 + \cdots + B_{n-1}] / k(\lambda)$$
$$(2.34)$$

where the k_i and B_i are determined successively by

$$\left. \begin{array}{ll} B_1 = A + k_1 I_n, & B_i = AB_{i-1} + p_i I_n, \quad i = 2, 3, \ldots, n-1 \\[2mm] k_1 = -\text{tr } A, & k_i = -\dfrac{1}{i} \text{tr}(AB_{i-1}), \quad i = 2, 3, \ldots, n \end{array} \right\} \quad (2.35)$$

Another very useful result is the *Cayley–Hamilton* theorem, which states that every square matrix satisfies its own characteristic equation, i.e.

$$A^n + k_1 A^{n-1} + k_2 A^{n-2} + \cdots + k_{n-1} A + k_n I_n = 0. \quad (2.36)$$

The expression in (2.36) is a polynomial in the matrix A and is written $k(A)$. It is not to be confused with (2.28), which is a polynomial equation in the scalar λ, and is satisfied by the n values $\lambda_1, \ldots, \lambda_n$.

If B is an $m \times m$ matrix having characteristic roots and vectors μ_i, y_j respectively then by (2.5) and (2.30)

$$(A \otimes B)(w_i \otimes y_j) = Aw_i \otimes By_j$$

$$= \lambda_i w_i \otimes \mu_j y_j$$

$$= \lambda_i \mu_j (w_i \otimes y_j)$$

so the characteristic roots of $A \otimes B$ are $\lambda_i \mu_j$, $i = 1, 2 \ldots, n, j = 1, 2, \ldots, m$. We can use this result to study the matrix equation

$$AX + XB = C \qquad (2.37)$$

where X and C are $n \times m$. Using (2.7) and (2.9) this can be written in the form (see Exercise 2.4)

$$Dx = c \tag{2.38}$$

which is a set of nm equations in the familiar forms (2.18). The solution of (2.38) is unique if and only if the $mn \times mn$ matrix

$$D = A \otimes I_m + I_n \otimes B^T$$

is nonsingular. To find the condition for this to hold, consider

$$(I_n + \epsilon A) \otimes (I_m + \epsilon B^T) = I_n \otimes I_m + \epsilon D + \epsilon^2 A \otimes B^T$$

which has characteristic roots (see Exercise 2.9 (c))

$$(1 + \epsilon \lambda_i)(1 + \epsilon \mu_j) = 1 + \epsilon(\lambda_i + \mu_j) + \epsilon^2 \lambda_i \mu_j .$$

It follows by comparing terms in ϵ that D has characteristic roots $\lambda_i + \mu_j$, $i = 1, 2, \ldots, n, j = 1, 2, \ldots, m$. Hence by (2.29) D is nonsingular if and only if there are no characteristic roots of A and B such that $\lambda_i + \mu_j = 0$, and this is the condition for the solution X of the matrix equation (2.37) to be unique.

We shall find in Chapter 5 that a particular form of eqn (2.37) enters into the study of stability of the linear system (2.25) using Liapunov theory. (See also Exercise 2.17.)

Exercise 2.9.
Prove the following

(a) $\lambda_i(A^T) = \lambda_i(A)$ (b) $\lambda_i(A^*) = \overline{\lambda_i(A)}$

(c) $\lambda_i(I_n + A) = 1 + \lambda_i(A)$ (d) $\lambda_i(A^{-1}) = 1/\lambda_i(A)$, provided A is nonsingular.

Exercise 2.10.
A square matrix U is said to be *unitary* if $UU^* = I$. Use the preceding exercise to show that $|\lambda_i(U)| = 1$.

The result still holds when U is real, in which case it is called *orthogonal.*

Exercise 2.11.
By considering eqn (2.30) show that if m is a positive integer the characteristic roots and vectors of A^m are A_i^m and w_i. Hence deduce that if

$$\beta(\lambda) = \beta_0 \lambda^m + \beta_1 \lambda^{m-1} + \cdots + \beta_m$$

then the characteristic roots and vectors of $\beta(A)$ are $\beta(\lambda_i)$ and w_i.

Exercise 2.12.
Using the result of the preceding exercise, show that the matrix $\beta(C)$, where C is defined in (2.32), is nonsingular if and only if $\beta(\lambda)$ and $k(\lambda)$ defined in (2.28) are relatively prime.

This shows that $\det \beta(C)$ is a resultant for the polynomials $\beta(\lambda)$ and $k(\lambda)$.

Exercise 2.13.
If in the preceding two exercises $m < n$, show that the first row of $\beta(C)$ is

$$r = [\beta_m, \beta_{m-1}, \ldots, \beta_1, \beta_0, 0, \ldots, 0].$$

Show also that the subsequent rows are $rC, rC^2, \ldots, rC^{n-1}$. (Hint: if e_i denotes the ith row of I_n, first show that $e_i = e_{i-1} C$, $i = 2, 3, \ldots, n$, and then consider $e_i \beta(C)$).

Exercise 2.14.
Show that if $k_n \neq 0$ then the inverse of C in (2.32) is also a companion form matrix with first row

$$[-k_{n-1}/k_n, -k_{n-2}/k_n, \cdots, -k_1/k_n, -1/k_n]$$

and deduce that the characteristic polynomial of C^{-1} is $(\lambda^n/k_n) k (1/\lambda)$.

Using an argument like that in Exercise 2.13, show that if $\beta(\lambda)$ is the polynomial in Exercise 2.11 with $m < n$, then the rows of $\beta(C^{-1})$ are $sC^{-n+1}, sC^{-n+2}, \ldots, sC^{-1}, s$, where $s = [0, \ldots, 0, \beta_0, \beta_1, \ldots, \beta_m]$.

Exercise 2.15.
If the characteristic roots of C in (2.32) are $\lambda_1, \lambda_2, \ldots, \lambda_n$, assumed distinct, show that corresponding characteristic vectors are

$$m_i = [1, \lambda_i, \lambda_i^2, \ldots, \lambda_i^{n-1}]^T, i = 1, 2, \ldots, n.$$

The matrix $M = [m_1, m_2, \ldots, m_n]$ is called the *Vandermonde* matrix. Prove by induction on n, or otherwise, that $\det M = \prod_{j > i} (\lambda_j - \lambda_i)$.

Exercise 2.16.
The linear discrete-time system corresponding to (2.25) takes the form

$$x(k+1) = Ax(k); k = 0, 1, 2 \ldots.$$

Show that a solution of the form $x(k) = w\lambda^k$ leads to the same characteristic root and vector equation (2.26).

Exercise 2.17.
Show that the matrix equation

$$AXB - X = C,$$

where A is $n \times n$ and B is $m \times m$ has a unique solution if and only if there are no characteristic roots λ_i, μ_j of A, B respectively such that $\lambda_i \mu_j = 1$, $i = 1,2, \ldots, n, j = 1,2, \ldots, m$.

A particular version of this equation occurs in Chapter 5 involving stability of discrete-time linear systems.

Exercise 2.18.
By a suitable choice of W and Z in Exercise 2.3, show that for any matrices $X(n \times m)$ and $Y(m \times n)$

$$\det (\mu I_n - XY) = \mu^{n-m} \det (\mu I_m - YX).$$

This shows that, assuming $m < n$, the characteristic roots of XY are those of YX together with $n - m$ zero roots.

2.5. Polynomial matrices

We saw in Section 1.2 how systems described by a single linear differential or difference equation lead to scalar transfer functions. Consider now an nth order linear system with multiple inputs and outputs described by the vector–matrix equation (1.1), namely

$$\dot{x} (t) = Ax(t) + Bu(t). \qquad (2.39)$$

where A is $n \times n$, B is $n \times m$, $x(t)$ is the column n-vector of state variables and $u(t)$ is the column m-vector of input or control variables. Suppose that there are r output variables, each a linear combination of the x_i, so that

$$y(t) = Cx(t) \qquad (2.40)$$

where C is a constant $r \times n$ matrix. Taking Laplace transforms of (2.39) and assuming zero initial conditions gives

$$s\bar{x} (s) = A\bar{x} (s) + B\bar{u} (s)$$

and after rearrangement

$$\bar{x}(s) = (sI_n - A)^{-1} B\bar{u}(s) \qquad (2.41)$$

Since from (2.40) the Laplace transform of the output is

$$\bar{y}(s) = C\bar{x}(s) \qquad (2.42)$$

clearly

$$\bar{y}(s) = C(sI - A)^{-1} B \bar{u}(s)$$

$$= G(s)\bar{u}(s) \qquad (2.43)$$

where the $r \times m$ matrix

$$G(s) = C(sI - A)^{-1} B \qquad (2.44)$$

is called the *transfer function matrix* by analogy with the scalar case
(1.13), since it relates the Laplace transform of the output vector to that
of the input vector. A block diagram representation of the form shown in
Fig. 1.8 can still be drawn, with input and output now vectors, and the
operator is the matrix $G(s)$ which of course reduces to $g(s)$ when $r = m = 1$.
Using eqn (2.34), the expression (2.44) becomes

$$G(s) = (s^{n-1} G_0 + s^{n-2} G_1 + \cdots + G_{n-1})/k(s)$$

$$= H(s)/k(s), \qquad (2.45)$$

where $k(s)$ is the characteristic polynomial of A and the $G_k = \left[g\,_{ij}^{(k)} \right]$ are
constant $r \times m$ matrices. The $r \times m$ matrix $H(s)$ is called a *polynomial
matrix*, since each of its elements is itself a polynomial, i.e.

$$h_{ij} = s^{n-1} g\,_{ij}^{(0)} + s^{n-2} g\,_{ij}^{(1)} + \cdots + g\,_{ij}^{(n-1)}$$

Example 2.5. Consider the electrically-heated oven described in
Example 1.2, and suppose that the values of the constants in (1.4) are such
that the state equations are

$$\dot{x} = \begin{bmatrix} -2 & 2 \\ 1 & -1 \end{bmatrix} x + \begin{bmatrix} 1 \\ 0 \end{bmatrix} u. \qquad (2.46)$$

Suppose that the output is provided by a thermocouple in the jacket
measuring the jacket (excess) temperature, i.e.

$$y = \begin{bmatrix} 1 & 0 \end{bmatrix} x.$$

The expression (2.44) gives

$$G(s) = \begin{bmatrix} 1 & 0 \end{bmatrix} \begin{bmatrix} s+2 & -2 \\ -1 & s+1 \end{bmatrix}^{-1} \begin{bmatrix} 1 \\ 0 \end{bmatrix}$$

$$= \frac{s+1}{s^2 + 3s},$$

using $(sI - A)^{-1} = \text{Adj}\,(sI - A)/k\,(s)$.

In practice it may well happen that the differential equations describing a linear system may not all be first order, as they are in (2.39). Suppose that there are ℓ state variables ξ_i and m control variables u_i. After Laplace transformation the equation corresponding to (2.41) is

$$T(s)\,\bar{\xi}\,(s) = U(s)\,\bar{u}\,(s), \tag{2.47}$$

again assuming zero initial conditions. The matrix–vector equation (2.47) is obtained using the expression for the Laplace transform of a derivative in (1.8), so each of $T(s)$, $U(s)$ will be a polynomial matrix. If the output is now a linear combination of ξ and its derivatives then (2.42) is replaced by

$$\bar{y}\,(s) = V(s)\,\bar{\xi}\,(s) \tag{2.48}$$

where $V(s)$ is also a polynomial matrix. Combining (2.47) and (2.48) we again have eqn (2.43) but now the transfer function matrix is

$$G(s) = V(s)\,T^{-1}\,(s)\,U(s). \tag{2.49}$$

This of course reduces to (2.44) when $T(s) = sI_n - A$, $V(s) = C$, $U(s) = B$. We have said that the system (2.39) has nth order since there are n first order differential equations; more generally the *order* of the system described by (2.47) is defined to be the degree of det $T(s)$, which is the characteristic polynomial of the system.

Example 2.6. Consider the problem of two masses joined by springs described in Exercise 1.2. Using the notation of Fig. 1.6, Newton's equations of motion are

$$m_1 \frac{d^2 x_1}{dt^2} = -k_1\,(x_1 - x_2) + u$$

$$m_2 \frac{d^2 x_2}{dt^2} = k_1\,(x_1 - x_2) - k_2 x_2.$$

Hence

$$\overline{\xi}\,(s) = \begin{bmatrix} \overline{x}_1 \\ \overline{x}_2 \end{bmatrix}, \quad T(s) = \begin{bmatrix} m_1 s^2 + k_1 & -k_1 \\ -k_1 & m_2 s^2 + k_1 + k_2 \end{bmatrix}$$

$$U(s) = \begin{bmatrix} 1 \\ 0 \end{bmatrix}$$

Assume that the output is $y = x_2$, so that $V(s) = [0, 1]$. Hence from (2.49)

$$G(s) = V(\text{Adj } T)\, U/\det T(s)$$
$$= k_1/[m_1 m_2 s^4 + (k_1 m_1 + k_1 m_2 + k_2 m_1)s^2 + k_1 k_2]$$

and the order of the system is 4.

An extensive theory of multivariable linear control systems using polynomial matrices has been developed by Rosenbrock (1970) and others. The following properties of polynomial matrices are however developed mainly for the limited objective of studying matrices with repeated characteristic roots.

Let $P(\lambda)$ be an arbitrary $n \times n$ polynomial matrix having *rank r*, which is the order of the largest minor of P not identically zero. The following *elementary* operations on P leave its rank unaltered:

(*i*)   interchange any two lines
(*ii*) multiply any line by a nonzero constant
(*iii*) add to any line any other line multiplied by an arbitrary polynomial ('line' stands for *either* row *or* column).

Two matrices $P_1(\lambda)$ and $P_2(\lambda)$ having the same dimensions are said to be *equivalent* if and only if it is possible to pass from one to the other by a sequence of elementary operations. This turns out to be the same as stating that

$$P_1(\lambda) = L(\lambda)P_2(\lambda)M(\lambda) \tag{2.50}$$

where $L(\lambda)$ and $M(\lambda)$ are both polynomial matrices having determinants which are nonzero constants (i.e. independent of λ). It can be shown that every square polynomial matrix† can be put into diagonal form by appropriate elementary operations: specifically $P(\lambda)$ is equivalent to the *Smith canonical form*

$$S(\lambda) = \text{diag}[i_1(\lambda), i_2(\lambda), \ldots, i_r(\lambda), 0, \ldots, 0]. \qquad (2.51)$$

where the elements in (2.51) are polynomials such that $i_k(\lambda)$ divides $i_{k+1}(\lambda)$, $k = 1, 2, \ldots, r-1$. It can also be shown that the $i_k(\lambda)$ satisfy

$$i_k(\lambda) = d_k(\lambda)/d_{k-1}(\lambda), \qquad k = 1, 2, \ldots, r. \qquad (2.52)$$

where $d_k(\lambda)$ is the g.c.d. of all minors of $P(\lambda)$ of order k (these minors are of course polynomials) and d_k is called the kth *determinantal divisor* of $P(\lambda)$ (taking $d_0 = 1$). Notice that it easily follows from (2.52) that if $r = n$ then

$$i_1 i_2 \cdots i_n = d_n$$

$$= \det P(\lambda). \qquad (2.53)$$

Since the application of elementary operations to $P(\lambda)$ does not alter its Smith form, the $i_k(\lambda)$ in (2.52) are called the *invariant factors* of $P(\lambda)$. As in (2.24), each $i_k(\lambda)$ can be written

$$i_k(\lambda) = (\lambda - \alpha_1)^{\beta_{k1}} (\lambda - \alpha_2)^{\beta_{k2}} \cdots (\lambda - \alpha_s)^{\beta_{ks}}, k = 1, \ldots, r \qquad (2.54)$$

where the α_i are in general complex numbers, and the notation is chosen so that $\alpha_1, \alpha_2, \ldots, \alpha_s$ are the distinct roots of $i_r(\lambda)$, which implies that $\beta_{r1}, \beta_{r2}, \ldots, \beta_{rs}$ are all positive integers. In view of the divisibility property of the i_k, it therefore follows that all the remaining $\beta_{k\ell}$ will be nonnegative integers. The factors $(\lambda - \alpha_j)^{\beta_{k\ell}}$ occurring in (2.54) for all values of j, k, ℓ such that $\beta_{k\ell} \neq 0$ are called the *elementary divisors* of $P(\lambda)$. It can be shown that $P_1(\lambda)$ and $P_2(\lambda)$ are equivalent if and only if they have the same rank and their respective sets of elementary divisors are identical.

Example 2.7. If a matrix has Smith form

$$S = \begin{bmatrix} \lambda^3 & 0 & 0 \\ 0 & \lambda^4(\lambda+1)^2 & 0 \\ 0 & 0 & \lambda^5(\lambda+1)^4(\lambda+2) \end{bmatrix}$$

†Extension to rectangular matrices is straightforward.

then it is very easy, by considering minors of orders 1, 2, and 3, to obtain the determinantal divisors

$$d_1 = \lambda^3, d_2 = \lambda^7(\lambda + 1)^2, d_3 = \lambda^{12}(\lambda + 1)^6 (\lambda + 2).$$

The invariant factors are the diagonal elements of S, so the elementary divisors are

$$\lambda^3, \lambda^4, \lambda^5, (\lambda + 1)^2, (\lambda + 1)^4, (\lambda + 2).$$

Our main interest in this book is in the special case when $P(\lambda)$ is the characteristic matrix $\lambda I_n - A$. In this case the invariant factors are often called the *similarity invariants* of A, because it can be shown that two $n \times n$ matrices are similar if and only if their similarity invariants are identical. This result enables us to determine when a given matrix A with characteristic polynomial $k(\lambda)$ is similar to the associated companion form matrix C defined in (2.32). The argument requires some further definitions. Firstly, the Cayley–Hamilton theorem states in (2.36) that $k(A) \equiv 0$, but it can happen that there are other polynomials for which this holds. Suppose that the monic polynomial $m(\lambda)$ is such that

$$m(A) = A^p + m_1 A^{p-1} + \cdots + m_p I_n \equiv 0. \tag{2.55}$$

If there are no polynomials which have degree less than p and satisfy (2.55), then $m(\lambda)$ is called the *minimum polynomial* of A.

Example 2.8. If

$$A = \begin{bmatrix} 0 & 1 & 0 \\ 0 & 0 & 0 \\ 0 & 0 & 0 \end{bmatrix}$$

it is trivial to verify that $k(\lambda) = \lambda^3$ and that $A^2 = 0$, but $A + m_1 I \neq 0$ for any value of m_1, so the minimum polynomial is $m(\lambda) = \lambda^2$.

When $m(\lambda)$ is identical to $k(\lambda)$ then A is termed *nonderogatory*, otherwise *derogatory* (much of the nomenclature in matrix theory was coined in the Victorian era – the implication is clear that a derogatory matrix has undesirable properties!). The next step in determining similarity of A and C is to note that it can be shown that $m(\lambda)$ is equal to the similarity invari-

ant of A having highest degree. As we have seen in (2.53) these similarity
invariants $s_i(\lambda)$ satisfy

$$s_1 s_2 \cdots s_n = \det(\lambda I_n - A)$$
$$= k(\lambda), \qquad (2.56)$$

and also s_i divides s_{i+1}. It therefore follows that if A is nonderogatory
then $s_n(\lambda) = k(\lambda)$, so its similarity invariants are $1, 1, \ldots, 1, k(\lambda)$. By
definition the similarity invariants of C are the invariant factors of $\lambda I_n - C$,
and using the form of C in (2.32) it is immediately obvious that the first
$n - 1$ determinantal divisors of $\lambda I - C$ are equal to unity. Thus by (2.52)
and (2.53) it follows that the similarity invariants of C are $1, 1, \ldots,$
$1, \det(\lambda I - C) = k(\lambda)$. We have therefore established that A and C have
the same similarity invariants, and so are similar, if and only if A is nonderogatory. This result is of course independent of whichever of the four
companion forms is used.

Example 2.9. By considering minors of $\lambda I_3 - A$ of orders 1, 2, and 3
it can be verified that when

$$A = \begin{bmatrix} 1 & 1 & 0 \\ 0 & 1 & 0 \\ 0 & 0 & 1 \end{bmatrix}, \qquad (2.57)$$

the determinantal divisors are $d_1 = 1, d_2 = (\lambda - 1), d_3 = (\lambda - 1)^3$. Thus
eqn (2.52) gives

$$i_1 = 1, i_2 = (\lambda - 1), i_3 = (\lambda - 1)^2,$$

and $m(\lambda) = i_3$. Clearly $k(\lambda) = (\lambda - 1)^3$ so A is derogatory, and there is no
nonsingular matrix T such that

$$TAT^{-1} = \begin{bmatrix} 0 & 1 & 0 \\ 0 & 0 & 1 \\ 1 & -3 & 3 \end{bmatrix}.$$

It should be noted that if all the characteristic roots of A are distinct
then it has the same similarity invariants as the diagonal matrix A in

(2.31). Because of the assumption on the λ_i these invariants are easily calculated to be

$$1, 1, \ldots, 1, (\lambda - \lambda_1)(\lambda - \lambda_2) \cdots (\lambda - \lambda_n) = \det(\lambda I - A).$$

It therefore follows by the preceding discussion that in this case A is nonderogatory; in other words, only a matrix with repeated roots can be derogatory.

Exercise 2.19.
Derive the transfer function in Example 2.6 using the first order linear state equations obtained in Exercise 1.2.

Exercise 2.20.
Suppose a harmonic input $u = u_0 \cos \omega t$, where u_0 is a constant vector, is applied to (2.39). Assume that $x(t)$ has the form $a \cos \omega t + b \sin \omega t$, and determine the constant vectors a and b (assume A has no purely imaginary characteristic roots). Hence show that the output (2.40) is

$$y = \mathcal{R}e\{G(i\omega)\}u_0 \cos \omega t - \text{Im}\{G(i\omega)\}u_0 \sin \omega t$$

where $G(s)$ is defined in (2.44).

This provides an interpretation for the frequency transfer function matrix $G(i\omega)$, and when G is a scalar the expression for y reduces to precisely that given in eqn (1.20).

Exercise 2.21.
Show that the minimum polynomial of any square matrix A is a factor of its characteristic polynomial. (Hint: assume that division of $k(\lambda)$ by $m(\lambda)$ produces a remainder term, and obtain a contradiction).

Exercise 2.22.
Given an $n \times n$ matrix A, if a column n-vector b can be found such that

$$\text{rank } [b, Ab, A^2 b, \ldots, A^{n-1} b] = n \qquad (2.58)$$

deduce that A is nonderogatory. (Hint: show that in (2.55) $p = n$, and apply the result of Exercise 2.21).

The condition in (2.58) will be encountered again in a control context in Sections 3.7 and 4.1.

2.6. Jordan canonical form

We can now return to the problem mentioned in Section 2.4 of determining a canonical form for A when its characteristic roots are not all distinct. A general result states that any square matrix is similar to the *Jordan form*.

$$\text{diag} \, [J_{m_1}(\lambda_1), J_{m_2}(\lambda_1), \ldots, J_{m_s}(\lambda_1), J_{n_1}(\lambda_2), \ldots, J_{t_v}(\lambda_q)] \,, \quad (2.59)$$

using the notation of (2.3), where $J_k(\lambda)$ is the $k \times k$ *Jordan block*

$$J_k(\lambda) = \begin{bmatrix} \lambda & 1 & 0 & \cdot & 0 & 0 \\ 0 & \lambda & 1 & \cdot & 0 & 0 \\ \cdot & \cdot & \cdot & \cdot & \cdot & \cdot \\ \cdot & 0 & 0 & \cdot & \lambda & 1 \\ 0 & 0 & \cdot & \cdot & 0 & \lambda \end{bmatrix} \quad (2.60)$$

(an alternative form has the 1s below the principal diagonal). The distinct characteristic roots of A are $\lambda_1, \lambda_2, \ldots, \lambda_q$ and the multiplicity of λ_1 is $m_1 + m_2 + \cdots + m_s$, and so on. The Jordan form of a matrix is unique up to the ordering of the blocks in (2.59), and can be written down once the elementary divisors of $\lambda I - A$ are known (see Exercise 2.24). If none of the characteristic roots of A is repeated, so that $q = n$, eqn (2.59) reduces to the diagonal matrix (2.31). In this case each Jordan block is simply $J_1(\lambda_i) = \lambda_i$.

It should also be noted that the Jordan form of A can be a diagonal matrix even if some of the characteristic roots of A are repeated. There is just one linearly independent characteristic vector of A associated with each Jordan block, so the total number of such vectors is equal to the number of blocks in the Jordan form (2.59). In other words, A is similar to a diagonal matrix if and only if it has n linearly independent characteristic vectors. An important special case of this is that every real *symmetric* matrix (i.e. $A^T = A$) has a diagonal Jordan form; in addition a transforming matrix can be found which is orthogonal.

Example 2.10. The matrix in Example 2.9 is clearly in the Jordan form (2.59), and (2.57) can be written as

$$A = \text{diag} \, [J_2(1), J_1(1)] \,.$$

In the above example A is derogatory and has two Jordan blocks associated with the root 1. This illustrates a general result: A is nonderogatory if and only if there is only *one* Jordan block associated with each

$\lambda_i (i = 1, 2, \ldots, q)$. Furthermore if α_i is the order of the largest Jordan block associated with λ_i in (2.59) then the minimum polynomial of A is

$$m(\lambda) = (\lambda - \lambda_1)^{\alpha_1} (\lambda - \lambda_2)^{\alpha_2} \cdots (\lambda - \lambda_q)^{\alpha_q}, \qquad (2.61)$$

and of course coincides with $k(\lambda)$ when $q = n$, each α_i then being equal to unity. Since $J_k(\lambda)$ in (2.60) is triangular its rank is clearly k if $\lambda \neq 0$ and zero if $\lambda = 0$. The matrix A is similar to (2.59) and so has the same rank, which because of the triangular form of (2.59) is the sum of the ranks of each Jordan block. In other words, the rank of A is equal to the number of its nonzero characteristic roots, including repetitions.

Although A cannot be transformed into companion form when it is derogatory we can rearrange its Jordan form (2.59) into

$$\text{diag } [D_1, D_2, \ldots]$$

where

$$D_1 = \text{diag } [J_{m_1} (\lambda_1), J_{n_1} (\lambda_2), \ldots, J_{t_1} (\lambda_q)],$$
$$D_2 = \text{diag } [J_{m_2} (\lambda_1), J_{n_2} (\lambda_2), \ldots, J_{t_2} (\lambda_q)],$$

etc. Each D_i is nonderogatory and so *can* be put into companion form, so A is similar to

$$\text{diag } [C_1, C_2, \ldots]$$

where the C_i are companion form matrices.

It should be noted that although the Jordan form is of fundamental theoretical importance it is of little use in practical calculations, being generally very difficult to compute.

Exercise 2.23.

It will be shown later (Section 2.8) that if A is a real symmetric matrix then all its characteristic roots are real. If none of these roots is negative deduce that there exists a nonsingular matrix T such that

$$TAT^{\mathrm{T}} = \text{diag } [I_p, 0_{n-p}]$$

where $p = \text{rank } A$ and 0_q denotes a $q \times q$ matrix of zeros.

Exercise 2.24.

Show that $\lambda I_k - J_k(\lambda_i)$ has the single elementary divisor $(\lambda - \lambda_i)^k$.

It can be shown that the elementary divisors of $\lambda I - A$ are

$$(\lambda - \lambda_1)^{m_1}, (\lambda - \lambda_1)^{m_2}, \ldots, (\lambda - \lambda_1)^{m_s}, (\lambda - \lambda_2)^{n_1}, \ldots, (\lambda - \lambda_q)^{t_v}.$$

Exercise 2.25.

Prove by induction on r that

$$
[J_3(\lambda)]^r = \begin{bmatrix} \lambda^r & \binom{r}{1}\lambda^{r-1} & \binom{r}{2}\lambda^{r-2} \\ 0 & \lambda^r & \binom{r}{1}\lambda^{r-1} \\ 0 & 0 & \lambda^r \end{bmatrix}, \quad r = 2, 3, \ldots.
$$

A similar result holds in general:

$$
[J_k(\lambda)]^r = \begin{bmatrix} \lambda^r & \binom{r}{1}\lambda^{r-1} & \cdot & \cdot & \binom{r}{k-1}\lambda^{r-k+1} \\ 0 & \lambda^r & \cdot & \cdot & \binom{r}{k-2}\lambda^{r-k+2} \\ \cdot & \cdot & \cdot & \cdot & \cdot \\ 0 & 0 & \cdot & \cdot & \lambda^r \end{bmatrix}.
$$

$$
\left[\binom{r}{i} \text{ denotes the binomial coefficient } r!/i!(r-i)! \right].
$$

2.7. Functions of a matrix

We now extend some ideas of scalar functions to matrices. These results will be used to solve linear system equations in Chapter 3.

To discuss convergence of infinite sequences and series involving matrices and vectors it is first necessary to define the *euclidean norm* of an $m \times n$ matrix A:

$$
\| A \|_e = \left[\sum_{i=1}^{m} \sum_{j=1}^{n} |a_{ij}|^2 \right]^{\frac{1}{2}} \tag{2.62}
$$

where $|a_{ij}|$ denotes modulus of a_{ij}. For a vector x (2.62) gives

$$
\| x \|_e = \left[\sum_{i=1}^{n} |x_i|^2 \right]^{\frac{1}{2}} \tag{2.63}
$$

$$
= (x^*x)^{\frac{1}{2}},
$$

which can be thought of as the 'length' of the vector x. Other norms can also be defined, for example $\sum\sum |a_{ij}|$ or $\sum_{i=1}^{n} |x_i|$. All norms for both matrices and vectors with complex elements satisfy the conditions

$$\| K \| > 0 \text{ unless } K = 0, \tag{2.64}$$

$$\| kK \| = | k | \, \| K \| \text{ for any scalar } k, \tag{2.65}$$

$$\| K + L \| \leqslant \| K \| + \| L \|. \tag{2.66}$$

If K and L are matrices then

$$\| KL \| \leqslant \| K \| \, \| L \|, \tag{2.67}$$

and if ℓ is a vector

$$\| K\ell \|_e \leqslant \| K \|_e \, \| \ell \|_e. \tag{2.68}$$

A *sequence* $\{A_r\}$, $r = 0, 1, 2, \ldots$ of matrices is said to *converge* to the limit A if each element of A_r tends to the corresponding element of A as $r \to \infty$. A necessary and sufficient condition for convergence is that

$$\lim_{r \to \infty} \| A_r - A \| = 0$$

for any norm. It is easy to show that if P and Q are constant matrices then $PA_rQ \to PAQ$ as $r \to \infty$. In particular a square matrix A can be written as $A = TJT^{-1}$ where J is the Jordan form in (2.59). Thus $A^r = TJ^r T^{-1}$ and since the elements of J^r depend upon powers of the characteristic roots λ_i of A (see Exercise 2.25) it follows that $\lim_{r \to \infty} A^r = 0$ if and only if all the characteristic roots of A have modulus less than unity.

The infinite matrix *series* $\sum_{k=0}^{\infty} A_k$ *converges* provided the sequence of partial sums $X_r = \sum_{k=0}^{r} A_k$, $r = 0, 1, 2, \ldots$, converges to a finite limit as $r \to \infty$. The series is *absolutely convergent* if the scalar series $\sum_{k=0}^{\infty} \| A_k \|$ is convergent, and absolute convergence implies convergence.

We consider scalar functions which can be defined by the power series

$$f(\lambda) = \sum_{k=0}^{\infty} c_k \lambda^k \tag{2.69}$$

which is assumed to converge for $|\lambda| < R$. The associated *function of an $n \times n$ matrix A* is defined by

$$f(A) = c_0 I_n + c_1 A + c_2 A^2 + \dots . \tag{2.70}$$

A powerful general result states that the matrix power series in (2.70) is convergent if all the characteristic roots λ_i of A satisfy $|\lambda_i| < R$.

Example 2.11. The series

$$\ell n \, (1 + \lambda) = \lambda - \tfrac{1}{2} \lambda^2 + \tfrac{1}{3} \lambda^3 - \dots$$

converges for $|\lambda| < 1$. Hence the matrix series

$$\ell n \, (I_n + A) = A - \tfrac{1}{2} A^2 + \tfrac{1}{3} A^3 - \dots$$

converges provided A is such that all its characteristic roots have modulus less than unity.

It can be shown that when all the λ_i are distinct, then assuming convergence,

$$f(A) = \sum_{k=1}^{n} Z_k f(\lambda_k) \tag{2.71}$$

where

$$Z_k = \frac{(A - \lambda_1 I)(A - \lambda_2 I) \cdots (A - \lambda_{k-1} I)(A - \lambda_{k+1} I) \cdots (A - \lambda_n I)}{(\lambda_k - \lambda_1)(\lambda_k - \lambda_2) \cdots (\lambda_k - \lambda_{k-1})(\lambda_k - \lambda_{k+1}) \cdots (\lambda_k - \lambda_n)}$$

$$= \prod_{\substack{j=1 \\ j \neq k}}^{n} [(A - \lambda_j I_n)/(\lambda_k - \lambda_j)] . \tag{2.72}$$

The expression (2.71) with the Z_k defined in (2.72) is known as *Sylvester's formula*. The reader with some knowledge of numerical analysis may recognize the resemblance between (2.72) and the Lagrange interpolation polynomial (see Exercise 2.28). It is important to realize that the Z_k are independent of f, and that only the n values $f(\lambda_k)$ occur in (2.71), so any two scalar functions (2.69) for which these values coincide will lead to the *same* matrix function. Note also that (2.71) still holds if $f(\lambda)$ is a *finite* series.

An alternative way of evaluating $f(A)$ when all the λ_i are distinct is as follows. As in (2.23) we can write

$$f(\lambda) = q(\lambda)\, k(\lambda) + r(\lambda), \qquad (2.73)$$

where $k(\lambda)$ is the characteristic polynomial of A in (2.28), and $\delta r < n$. The expression in (2.73) is an identity, so we have

$$f(A) \equiv q(A)\, k(A) + r(A)$$

which by the Cayley–Hamilton theorem (2.36) reduces to

$$f(A) \equiv r(A), \qquad (2.74)$$

showing that $f(A)$ can be represented by a finite sum of powers of A of degree not exceeding $n - 1$. To determine

$$r(\lambda) = r_1 \lambda^{n-1} + r_2 \lambda^{n-2} + \cdots + r_n$$

substitution of $k(\lambda_i) = 0$ into (2.73) gives

$$f(\lambda_i) = r(\lambda_i),\ i = 1, 2, \ldots, n \qquad (2.75)$$

which are n linear equations for the n unknown coefficients r_i. Examples using both approaches to evaluation of $f(A)$ are given in Chapter 3.

When A has repeated characteristic roots the general expression for $f(A)$ is

$$f(A) = \sum_{k=1}^{q} [f(\lambda_k) Z_{k1} + f^{(1)}(\lambda_k) Z_{k2} + \cdots + f^{(\alpha_k - 1)}(\lambda_k) Z_{k\alpha_k}] \qquad (2.76)$$

where the α_i are the indices in the expression for the minimum polynomial in (2.61). In (2.76) $f^{(r)}(\lambda_k)$ denotes the rth derivative of f with respect to λ, (*not t*) evaluated at $\lambda = \lambda_k$. The matrices Z_{kj} are constant and again are determined entirely by A, not the function f. Although an explicit formula can be given for these matrices, they are best determined by taking simple choices for f, and again this is illustrated by means of examples in Chapter 3. When all the λ_i are distinct so that $q = n$, (2.76) reduces to (2.71). If some of the λ_i are repeated, but the minimum polynomial $m(\lambda)$ has only simple roots (i.e. in eqn (2.61) all $\alpha_i = 1$) eqn (2.76) becomes

$$f(A) = \sum_{k=1}^{q} Z_k\, f(\lambda_k) \qquad (2.77)$$

where the Z_k are defined as in (2.72) except that the upper index in the product is q instead of n.

We end this section with a warning: although the power series (2.69) has been used to define a function of a matrix, it cannot be invariably assumed that properties of the scalar function carry over to the matrix case (see for example Exercise 2.27).

Exercise 2.26.
For what matrices A does the series for $\sin A$ converge? Use (2.71) to determine $\sin A$ if

$$A = \begin{bmatrix} 3 & 2 \\ 2 & 3 \end{bmatrix}.$$

Similarly, write down expressions for A^{100} and A^{-1}.

Exercise 2.27.
If A and B are two $n \times n$ matrices prove that

$$\sin\,(A+B) = \sin A \, \cos B + \cos A \, \sin B$$

only if A and B commute with each other.

Exercise 2.28.
Consider an $(n-1)$th degree polynomial $p(\lambda)$ which takes the values $p(\lambda_k) = p_k$, $k = 1, 2, \ldots, n$, with all the λ_k distinct. By writing

$$p(\lambda) = \sum_{k=1}^{n} (\lambda-\lambda_1)(\lambda-\lambda_2)\cdots(\lambda-\lambda_{k-1})(\lambda-\lambda_{k+1})\cdots(\lambda-\lambda_n)P_k$$

determine the constants P_k, and hence obtain the Lagrange interpolation formula (compare with (2.72)).

Exercise 2.29.

Show that in eqn (2.71) the matrices Z_k satisfy

$$\sum_{k=1}^{n} Z_k = I_n, \quad \sum_{k=1}^{n} \lambda_k^r Z_k = A^r, r = 1, 2, 3, \ldots$$

2.8. Quadratic and Hermitian forms

The scalar function of the state vector x defined by

$$q(x) = x^{\mathrm{T}} Ax = \sum_{i=1}^{n} \sum_{j=1}^{n} a_{ij} x_i x_j$$

$$= a_{11} x_1^2 + a_{22} x_2^2 + 2a_{12} x_1 x_2 + 2a_{13} x_1 x_3 + \ldots, \qquad (2.78)$$

where the x_i and a_{ij} are real, is called a *quadratic form*, since each term in the sum is quadratic in the components of x. It is assumed that in (2.78) A is *symmetric* (i.e. $A^{\mathrm{T}} = A$) and this causes no loss of generality (see Exercise 2.31). The corresponding expression when the x_i and a_{ij} are complex is the *Hermitian form*

$$h(x) = x^* Ax = \sum_{i=1}^{n} \sum_{j=1}^{n} a_{ij} \bar{x}_i x_j, \qquad (2.79)$$

with A now a *Hermitian* matrix ($A^* = A$). Notice that the complex conjugate of h is

$$\bar{h} = x^{\mathrm{T}} \overline{Ax} = (x^* A^* x)^{\mathrm{T}} = h,$$

showing that h is real for all vectors x. We can show similarly that all the characteristic roots λ_i of A in (2.79) are real. For let w_i be a characteristic vector satisfying (2.30), so that

$$w_i^* Aw_i = w_i^* (\lambda_i w_i). \qquad (2.80)$$

However, (2.30) also gives $(Aw_i)^* = (\lambda_i w_i)^*$, or $w_i^* A = w_i^* \bar{\lambda}_i$, since $A^* = A$. Hence

$$w_i^* Aw_i = (w_i^* \bar{\lambda}_i) w_i, \qquad (2.81)$$

and together (2.80) and (2.81) imply $\bar{\lambda}_i = \lambda_i$, since $w_i^* w_i = \| w_i \|_e^2 \neq 0$ by (2.64). Thus all the characteristic roots of a Hermitian matrix are real, and the argument still applies if A is symmetric. Because of this property algorithms for calculating characteristic roots of symmetric and Hermitian matrices are simpler than for general matrices. Also, as we remarked in Sections 2.6, every real symmetric matrix is orthogonally similar to the diagonal matrix of its characteristic roots, and this still holds for Hermitian matrices except that the transformation matrix is then unitary.

In our work on Liapunov stability theory in Chapter 5 we will be interested in Hermitian or quadratic forms $v(x)$ which do not change sign as x varies, so the following definitions are needed:

(i) $v(x)$ is *positive* (*negative*) *definite* if $v(0) = 0$ and $v(x) > 0$ (<0) when $x \neq 0$.

(ii) $v(x)$ is *positive* (*negative*) *semidefinite* if $v(0) = 0$ and $v(x) \geqslant 0$ ($\leqslant 0$) for all values of x, with at least one $x \neq 0$ such that $v(x) = 0$.

Example 2.12. When $n = 2$ the quadratic form

$$q = 2x_1^2 + 3x_2^2$$

is clearly positive definite. However if $n = 3$, q is only positive semi-definite, since although it never takes negative values the choice $x_1 = 0$, $x_2 = 0, x_3 = c$ makes $q = 0$ for any value of c.

A form satisfying neither of (i) nor (ii) above is *indefinite*, and takes both positive and negative values. The terms describing the form are also applied to the matrix A associated with the form. The definitions on definiteness can be extended to scalar functions which are not necessarily quadratic (see Section 5.4).

There are a number of ways of determining the sign properties of a form. One simple approach is to change coordinates by means of $x = Uy$ so that (2.79) becomes

$$(Uy)^* A(Uy) = y^* (U^*AU)y \qquad (2.82)$$

and as stated earlier it is always possible to choose a unitary matrix U so that (2.82) reduces merely to

$$\sum_{i=1}^{n} \lambda_i |y_i|^2. \qquad (2.83)$$

Since U is nonsingular (see Exercise 2.10) $y = 0$ if and only if $x = 0$, so it follows that v will be positive (negative) definite if and only if all

$\lambda_i(A) > 0 \; (< 0)$; positive (negative) semidefinite if and only if all $\lambda_i(A)$ $\geqslant 0 \; (\leqslant 0)$, with at least one $\lambda_i(A) = 0$; and indefinite if and only if at least one $\lambda_i(A) > 0$ and one $\lambda_i(A) < 0$. In fact it is possible to avoid calculation of the λ_i by reducing $v(x)$ to a sum of squares by Lagrange's method (Mirsky 1963, p. 371), the numbers of positive, negative and zero coefficients in the sum being the same as in (2.83).

An alternative approach involves the *principal minors* P_i of A, these being any ith order minors whose principal diagonal is part of the principal diagonal of A. In particular the *leading* principal minors of A are

$$D_1 = a_{11}, \quad D_2 = \begin{vmatrix} a_{11} & a_{12} \\ a_{21} & a_{22} \end{vmatrix}, \quad D_3 = \begin{vmatrix} a_{11} & a_{12} & a_{13} \\ a_{21} & a_{22} & a_{23} \\ a_{31} & a_{32} & a_{33} \end{vmatrix}, \text{etc.}$$

The *Sylvester conditions* state that the Hermitian or quadratic form v is:
   (i) positive definite if and only if $D_i > 0, i = 1, 2, \ldots, n$.
   (ii) negative definite if and only if $(-1)^i D_i > 0, i = 1, 2, \ldots, n$;
   (iii) positive semidefinite if and only if det $A = 0$ and $P_i \geqslant 0$, for *all* principal minors;
   (iv) negative semidefinite if and only if det $A = 0$ and $(-1)^i P_i \geqslant 0$, for *all* principal minors.
If v satisfies none of the above conditions (i)–(iv) then it is indefinite.

Example 2.13. Consider the quadratic form with $n = 3$:

$$v = x_1^2 + 4x_2^2 + 9x_3^2 + 4x_1 x_2 + 12x_2 x_3 + 6x_1 x_3.$$

The matrix of the form is

$$A = \begin{bmatrix} 1 & 2 & 3 \\ 2 & 4 & 6 \\ 3 & 6 & 9 \end{bmatrix}$$

and the principal minors are

$$1, 4, 9, \quad \begin{vmatrix} 1 & 2 \\ 2 & 4 \end{vmatrix} = 0, \quad \begin{vmatrix} 4 & 6 \\ 6 & 9 \end{vmatrix} = 0, \quad \begin{vmatrix} 1 & 3 \\ 3 & 9 \end{vmatrix} = 0, \text{ det } A = 0.$$

Hence by condition (iii) v is positive semidefinite.

A convenient numerical procedure for testing sign properties of $v(x)$ when n is large is provided by writing $A = P^T P$ with P a triangular matrix. An explicit formula is easily derived for the p_{ij} (Barnett and Storey 1970, p. 35) and A is positive definite if and only if all $p_{ii} > 0$.

Exercise 2.30.
A *skew symmetric* real matrix S is defined by $S^T = -S$. If $q = x^T Sx$ show by considering $(q)^T$ that $q \equiv 0$ for all vectors x. Similarly show that $x^* Sx \equiv 0$ if S is *skew Hermitian*, i.e. $S^* = -S$.

Exercise 2.31.
Show that any real matrix A can be written as $A = A_1 + A_2$ where A_1 is symmetric and A_2 is skew symmetric. Hence using the result of the preceding exercise, deduce that $x^T Ax \equiv x^T A_1 x$, all x.

A similar argument applies for complex matrices.

Exercise 2.32.
Let A be a Hermitian matrix, and write it as $A = A_1 + iA_2$, where A_1 and A_2 are real and $i = \sqrt{(-1)}$. Show that A_1 is symmetric and A_2 is skew symmetric. Hence deduce that if A is positive definite, so is A_1.

Exercise 2.33.
Two column n-vectors a and b are said to be *orthogonal* if $a^* b = 0$. Show that if w_i, w_j are characteristic vectors associated with distinct characteristic roots of a Hermitian matrix A then w_i and w_j are orthogonal.

Exercise 2.34.
If A is an $n \times n$ symmetric matrix having all $a_{ij} = 1$, deduce that it has a single nonzero characteristic root equal in value to n (Hint: use (2.29)).

3 Matrix solution of linear systems

The importance of linear models in physical situations was indicated in Chapter 1, and in Section 1.2 we discussed the Laplace and z-transform methods for solving continuous-time and discrete-time equations respectively. However, except for low order systems, the algebraic manipulation required soon becomes very heavy and it is preferable to apply the techniques of matrix functions outlined in Section 2.6. We shall assume initially that our system equations are already in vector-matrix form, and postpone until the last section of this chapter discussion of the relationship with scalar differential or difference equations of the type set out in Section 1.2. The methods described in this chapter may seem rather formal, but of course are applicable to any linear system model, such as those described in the examples and exercises in Chapter 1.

3.1. Solution of uncontrolled system: spectral form

We were able to express the linear examples in Section 1.1 in the matrix form (1.1). To begin with we shall consider systems without the presence of controlled variables, and in this and the following two sections we discuss methods of finding the solution for the state vector $x(t)$ of the nth order system described by

$$\dot{x} = Ax, \tag{3.1}$$

subject to a given initial condition, say

$$x(0) = x_0. \tag{3.2}$$

We shall first assume that all the characteristic roots $\lambda_1, \lambda_2, \ldots, \lambda_n$ of A are distinct. In fact in real-life situations this is not too severe a restriction, since if A does have repeated roots, very small perturbations in a few of its elements (which will only be known to a certain degree of accuracy) will suffice to separate these equal roots. If w_i is a characteristic vector corresponding to λ_i then $w_1, w_2, \ldots, w_n$ are linearly independent (see Section 2.2) so we can express the solution of (3.1) as

$$x(t) = \sum_{i=1}^{n} c_i w_i \qquad (3.3)$$

where the $c_i(t)$ are scalar functions of time. Differentiation of (3.3) and substitution into (3.1) gives

$$\Sigma \dot{c}_i w_i = A \Sigma c_i w_i$$

$$= \Sigma \lambda_i c_i w_i \, ,$$

using (2.30). Hence by the independence of the w_i,

$$\dot{c}_i = \lambda_i c_i, \qquad i = 1, 2, \dots, n,$$

and these equations have the solution

$$c_i(t) = \exp(\lambda_i t) c_i(0), \qquad i = 1, 2 \dots, n,$$

giving

$$x(t) = \sum_{i=1}^{n} c_i(0) \exp(\lambda_i t) w_i \, . \qquad (3.4)$$

This generalizes our informal remarks in Section 1.2 on the solution of (1.7). If W denotes the matrix whose columns are $w_1, w_2, \dots, w_n$ then it is a standard result that the rows $v_1, v_2, \dots, v_n$ of W^{-1} are left characteristic vectors of A. Since we have $v_i w_i = 1$, $v_i w_j = 0$, $i \neq j$, multiplying (3.4) on the left by v_i and setting $t = 0$ in the resulting expression gives $v_i x(0) = c_i(0)$. Thus the solution of (3.1) satisfying (3.2) is

$$x(t) = \sum_{i=1}^{n} (v_i x(0)) \exp(\lambda_i t) w_i \qquad (3.5)$$

Notice that the expression (3.5) depends only upon the initial conditions and the characteristic roots and vectors of A, and for this reason is referred to as the *spectral form* solution (the set $\{\lambda_i\}$ being the *spectrum* of A).

58   *Matrix solution of linear systems*

Example 3.1. Find the general solution of

$$\begin{bmatrix} \dot{x}_1 \\ \dot{x}_2 \end{bmatrix} = \begin{bmatrix} 0 & 1 \\ -2 & -3 \end{bmatrix} \begin{bmatrix} x_1 \\ x_2 \end{bmatrix}$$

It is routine to obtain the characteristic roots and corresponding vectors of A as

$$\lambda_1 = -1, \lambda_2 = -2, \dot{w}_1 = \begin{bmatrix} 1 \\ -1 \end{bmatrix}, \quad w_2 = \begin{bmatrix} 1 \\ -2 \end{bmatrix},$$

$$v_1 = [2,1], v_2 = [-1,-1].$$

Equation (3.5) then gives the general solution as

$$\begin{bmatrix} x_1(t) \\ x_2(t) \end{bmatrix} = (2x_1(0) + x_2(0)) e^{-t} \begin{bmatrix} 1 \\ -1 \end{bmatrix} - (x_1(0) + x_2(0)) e^{-2t} \begin{bmatrix} 1 \\ -2 \end{bmatrix}$$

(3.6)

Exercise 3.1.
Find the general solution of (3.1) subject to (3.2) in each of the following cases:

(a)
$$A = \begin{bmatrix} -1 & -1 \\ 2 & -4 \end{bmatrix}$$

(b)
$$A = \begin{bmatrix} 1 & 0 & -1 \\ 1 & 2 & 1 \\ 2 & 2 & 3 \end{bmatrix}.$$

Exercise 3.2
If $n = 2$ and

$$x(t) = \begin{bmatrix} e^{-t} \\ -2e^{-t} \end{bmatrix} \quad \text{when} \quad x(0) = \begin{bmatrix} 1 \\ -2 \end{bmatrix},$$

$$x(t) = \begin{bmatrix} e^{-2t} \\ -e^{-2t} \end{bmatrix} \quad \text{when} \quad x(0) = \begin{bmatrix} 1 \\ -1 \end{bmatrix},$$

find the general solution of (3.1) subject to (3.2) using the linearity property described in Chapter 1. Hence find also the matrix A.

3.2. Solution of uncontrolled system: exponential matrix

We now present a different approach to solving (3.1) which avoids the need to calculate the characteristic vectors of A. It is based on the idea of generalizing the fact that when $n = 1$ (so that A is a scalar) the solution of (3.1) is simply

$$x(t) = \exp(At)x_0 \qquad (3.7)$$

We define the *exponential matrix* by

$$\exp(At) = I + tA + (t^2/2!)A^2 + (t^3/3!)A^3 + \cdots. \qquad (3.8)$$

The topic of infinite matrix series has already been discussed in Section 2.7 and it follows from (2.69) and (2.70) that since $\exp(zt)$ converges for all finite scalars z and t then the series on the right in (3.8) converges for all finite t and all $n \times n$ matrices A having finite elements. It is clear from (3.8) that $\exp(0) = I$ and that

$$d[\exp(At)]/dt = A \exp(At),$$

so that (3.7) does represent the solution of (3.1). However it is important to realize that properties of the scalar exponential do not necessarily carry over to the matrix case (see Exercises 3.3, 3.4).

Suppose that the initial condition (3.2) is replaced by the slightly more general one

$$x(t_0) = x_0 \qquad (3.9)$$

The solution of (3.1) subject to (3.9) is often written in the control literature as

$$x(t) = \Phi(t, t_0)x_0 \qquad (3.10)$$

where

$$\Phi(t, t_0) = \exp[A(t - t_0)] \qquad (3.11)$$

is called the *state transition* matrix, since it relates the state at any time t to the state at any other time t_0. It is left as an easy exercise for the reader to verify using (3.11), (3.8) and the result of Exercise 3.4 that $\Phi(t,t_0)$ has the following properties:

$$\left.\begin{array}{c} \dfrac{d}{dt}\,\Phi(t,\,t_0) = A\,\Phi(t,\,t_0) \\[2mm] \Phi(t,\,t) = I \\[2mm] \Phi(t_0,\,t) = \Phi^{-1}\,(t,\,t_0) \\[2mm] \Phi(t,\,t_0) = \Phi\,(t,\,t_1)\,\Phi\,(t_1,\,t_0). \end{array}\right\} \qquad (3.12)$$

Evaluation of $\exp(At)$ when all the λ_i are distinct can be achieved by *Sylvester's formula* (2.71) which gives in this case

$$\exp(At) = \sum_{k=1}^{n} Z_k \exp(\lambda_k t) \qquad (3.13)$$

where

$$Z_k = \prod_{\substack{j=1 \\ j \ne k}}^{n} (A - \lambda_j I)/(\lambda_k - \lambda_j). \qquad (3.14)$$

Since the Z_k in (3.14) are constant matrices depending only on A and its characteristic roots, the solution in the form given by (3.7) and (3.13) requires calculation of only the characteristic roots of A. The matrices Z_k have themselves some interesting properties (see Exercises 2.29 and 3.10).

An alternative method of determining $\exp(At)$ was also outlined in Section 2.7. If $r(\lambda)$ is a polynomial of degree at most $n-1$ then as in (2.74)

$$\exp(At) = r(A) \qquad (3.15)$$

where the n coefficients of $r(\lambda)$ are functions of t obtained from the solution of the n linear equations (2.75), namely.

$$\exp(\lambda_i t) = r(\lambda_i), \quad i = 1,2,\ldots,n. \qquad (3.16)$$

Example 3.2. Using the matrix in Example 3.1, eqn (3.14) gives

$$Z_1 = (A - (-2)I)/(-1 - (-2)) = \begin{bmatrix} 2 & 1 \\ -2 & -1 \end{bmatrix}$$

$$Z_2 = (A - (-1)I)/(-2 - (-1)) = \begin{bmatrix} -1 & -1 \\ 2 & 2 \end{bmatrix}$$

Hence by (3.7) and (3.13)

$$x(t) = (e^{-t} Z_1 + e^{-2t} Z_2)x_0 ,$$

which is easily verified to be the same as (3.6).

Alternatively, since $n = 2$, the polynomial $r(\lambda)$ can be written $r(\lambda) = r_0 \lambda + r_1$ and (3.16) then gives

$$\left. \begin{aligned} e^{-t} &= r_1 - r_0 \\ e^{-2t} &= r_1 - 2r_0 \end{aligned} \right\}$$

so that $r_0 = e^{-t} - e^{-2t}$, $r_1 = 2e^{-t} - e^{-2t}$. Hence from (3.15)

$$x(t) = e^{At} x_0$$

$$= (r_1 I + r_0 A)x_0$$

which again easily reduces to (3.6).

It is interesting to note here that taking the Laplace transform of (3.1) subject to (3.2) gives

$$s\bar{x} - x_0 = Ax,$$

or after rearrangement

$$\bar{x}(s) = (sI - A)^{-1} x_0,$$

so that

$$x(t) = \mathcal{L}^{-1} \left\{ (sI - A)^{-1} x_0 \right\}. \tag{3.17}$$

By comparison with (3.7) it then follows that

$$\mathcal{L}^{-1}\left\{ (sI - A)^{-1} \right\} = \exp(At), \tag{3.18}$$

which is a generalization of the well-known result when $n = 1$.

Exercise 3.3.
Prove directly from (3.8) that $\exp(A + B) \neq \exp A \exp B$ for two square matrices A and B unless A and B commute with each other.

Exercise 3.4.
Using the result of the previous exercise, determine the inverse of $\exp A$ and hence deduce that $\exp A$ is nonsingular for any square matrix A.

Exercise 3.5.
$$\text{If } A = \text{diag}[a_1, a_2, \ldots, a_n] \text{ show that}$$
$$\exp A = \text{diag}\ [\exp(a_1), \exp(a_2), \ldots, \exp(a_n)].$$

Exercise 3.6.
Consider the equation of simple harmonic motion $\ddot{z} + \omega^2 z = 0$. Take as state variables $x_1 = z$ and $x_2 = \dot{z}/\omega$, and find the transition matrix $\Phi(t,0)$ using (3.11) and (3.8). (Hint: Find A^2).

Exercise 3.7.
Find the general solution of (3.1) and (3.2) using (3.13) or (3.15) for the two cases where A is given in Exercise 3.1.

Exercise 3.8.
Find the general solution of (3.1) subject to (3.2) when A is the matrix in Exercise 3.1 (a) by determining $(sI - A)^{-1}$ and using eqn (3.17).

Exercise 3.9.
Use the exponential matrix to solve the rabbit-fox environment problem of Exercise 1.4 subject to the same condition as in Exercise 1.7, namely, $a_1/a_3 = a_2/a_4$.

Exercise 3.10.
Consider the expression for $\exp(At)$ in eqn (3.13). By taking Laplace transforms of both sides, or otherwise, show that

$$\sum_{k=1}^{n} Z_k = I_n$$

$$AZ_k = \lambda_k Z_k, Z_k A = \lambda_k Z_k, k = 1, 2, \ldots, n$$

and

$$Z_i Z_j = \delta_{ij} Z_i$$

where δij is the *Kronecker delta* ($\delta_{ij} = 0, i \neq j; \delta_{ij} = 1$).

Exercise 3.11.
Write $J_k(\lambda)$ in (2.60) in the form $\lambda I + K$, and hence show that

$$\exp\{J_k(\lambda)\}t = \exp(\lambda t) \begin{bmatrix} 1 & t & t^2/2! & \cdot & \cdot & t^{k-1}/(k-1)! \\ & 1 & t & & & \cdot \\ & & \cdot & \cdot & \cdot & \\ & & & \cdot & \cdot & \cdot & \cdot \\ & & & & \cdot & \cdot & \cdot \\ & & & & & \cdot & \cdot & t^2/2! \\ & & & & & & \cdot & t \\ 0 & & & & & & & 1 \end{bmatrix}$$

Exercise 3.12.
Verify that the solution of the matrix differential equation

$$\frac{dW}{dt} = AW(t) + W(t)B, \quad W(0) = C,$$

where A and B are square and constant, is $W = \exp(At)C\exp(Bt)$.

3.3. Solution of uncontrolled system: repeated roots

When some of the characteristic roots of A are repeated, evaluation of $\exp(At)$ is more complicated. We use the formula (2.76) with $f(\lambda) = \exp(\lambda t)$ and the constant matrices Z_{kj} are determined as in the following example.

Example 3.3. Find $\exp(At)$ when

$$A = \begin{bmatrix} 4 & -4 & -22 \\ 1 & 0 & -11 \\ 0 & 0 & 2 \end{bmatrix}$$

Since

$$\lambda I - A = \begin{bmatrix} \lambda-4 & 4 & 22 \\ -1 & \lambda & 11 \\ 0 & 0 & \lambda-2 \end{bmatrix}$$

it is easy to verify directly from the definition (see Section 2.5) that the determinantal divisors of $\lambda I - A$ are $d_1 = 1, d_2 = \lambda - 2, d_3 = (\lambda - 2)^3$ so by (2.52) the similarity invariants of A are $i_1 = 1, i_2 = d_2/d_1 = \lambda - 2$, $i_3 = d_3/d_2 = (\lambda - 2)^2$, this last polynomial being the minimum polynomial $m(\lambda)$ of A as stated in Section 2.5. Hence $q = 1, \lambda_1 = 2, \alpha_1 = 2$ in (2.76) which becomes

$$f(A) = Z_{11} f(\lambda_1) + Z_{12} f'(\lambda_1) \tag{3.19}$$

and this expression holds for *any* function $f(\lambda)$. If we choose for simplicity $f(\lambda) = 1$ and $f(\lambda) = \lambda - 2$ then this gives in turn $Z_{11} = I$ and $Z_{12} = A - 2I$. Finally, taking $f(\lambda) = \exp(\lambda t)$ in (3.19) produces

$$\begin{aligned} \exp(At) &= Z_{11} e^{2t} + Z_{12} te^{2t} \\ &= Ie^{2t} + (A - 2I)te^{2t} \\ &= e^{2t} \begin{bmatrix} 1 + 2t & -4t & -22t \\ t & 1 - 2t & -11t \\ 0 & 0 & 1 \end{bmatrix} \end{aligned}$$

Exercise 3.13

Find the general solution of the system

$$\dot{x}_1 = -2x_1 + x_2$$
$$\dot{x}_2 = -x_1 - 4x_2$$

using the exponential matrix.

Exercise 3.14.

Evaluate $\exp(At)$ when

$$A = \begin{bmatrix} 3 & -1 & 1 \\ 2 & 0 & 1 \\ 1 & -1 & 2 \end{bmatrix}$$

3.4. Solution of controlled system

We are now in a position to give an expression for the solution of the constant linear system with control in the state space form of Section 2.5:

$$\dot{x} = Ax + Bu \tag{3.20}$$

where B is an $n \times m$ matrix, and in practice $m \leqslant n$. After multiplication of both sides of (3.20) on the left by $\exp(-At)$, the equation can be written

$$\frac{d}{dt}[\exp(-At)x] = \exp(-At)Bu, \tag{3.21}$$

which on integration produces

$$x(t) = \exp(At)\left[x_0 + \int_0^t \exp(-A\tau)Bu(\tau)d\tau\right]. \tag{3.22}$$

If the initial condition is $x(t_0) = x_0$, integration of (3.21) from t_0 to t and use of the definition of Φ in (3.11) gives

$$x(t) = \Phi(t, t_0)\left[x_0 + \int_{t_0}^t \Phi(t_0, \tau)Bu(\tau)d\tau\right]. \tag{3.23}$$

Thus if $u(t)$ is known for $t \geqslant t_0$, $x(t)$ can be determined by finding the state transition matrix and carrying out the integration in (3.23).

Example 3.4. Consider the equation of motion

$$\frac{d^2z}{dt^2} = u(t)$$

of a unit mass moving in a straight line subject to an external force $u(t)$,

$z(t)$ being the displacement from some fixed point. In state-space form, taking $x_1 = z$ and $x_2 = \dot{z}$ as state variables, this becomes

$$\frac{d}{dt}\begin{bmatrix} x_1 \ (t) \\ x_2 \ (t) \end{bmatrix} = \begin{bmatrix} 0 & 1 \\ 0 & 0 \end{bmatrix}\begin{bmatrix} x_1 \ (t) \\ x_2 \ (t) \end{bmatrix} + \begin{bmatrix} 0 \\ 1 \end{bmatrix}u(t)$$

$$= Ax + Bu, \text{ say.}$$

Since here we have $A^2 = 0$, (3.8) reduces to $\exp(At) = I + At$, so (3.22) gives

$$\begin{bmatrix} x_1 \ (t) \\ x_2 \ (t) \end{bmatrix} = \begin{bmatrix} 1 & t \\ 0 & 1 \end{bmatrix}\begin{bmatrix} x_1 \ (0) \\ x_2 \ (0) \end{bmatrix} + \begin{bmatrix} 1 & t \\ 0 & 1 \end{bmatrix}\int_0^t \begin{bmatrix} 1 & -\tau \\ 0 & 1 \end{bmatrix}\begin{bmatrix} 0 \\ 1 \end{bmatrix}u(\tau)d\tau.$$

Solving for $x_1(t)$ leads to

$$z(t) = z(0) + t\dot{z}(0) + \int_0^t (t-\tau)u(\tau)d\tau, \tag{3.24}$$

where $\dot{z}(0)$ denotes the initial velocity of the mass.

Exercise 3.15.
Simplify (3.24) when $u(t)$ is equal to a constant for all $t \geqslant 0$, to obtain the familiar formula for displacement along a straight line under constant acceleration.

Exercise 3.16.
Determine $\exp(At)$ for the electrically heated oven problem of Example 1.2, assuming that the state equations take the numerical form given in eqn (2.46) in Example 2.5. Suppose that initially the oven interior and jacket are at room temperature T_0, and that at $t = 0$ the heating element is switched on, providing a constant input of magnitude 2 units. Use eqn (3.22) to find an expression for the subsequent inside temperature of the oven.

Exercise 3.17.
Consider the system (3.20) with

$$A = \begin{bmatrix} 1 & 2 \\ 0 & 1 \end{bmatrix}, \qquad B = \begin{bmatrix} 2 \\ 1 \end{bmatrix},$$

and take $u(t)$ to be the unit step function defined in (1.16). Evaluate $\exp(At)$ using the power series definition (3.8) and hence show that the solution of (3.20) subject to $x(0) = [1, 0]^{\mathrm{T}}$ is

$$x(t) = \begin{bmatrix} 1 + 3t + \dfrac{5}{2}t^2 + \dfrac{7}{6}t^3 + \cdots \\[3mm] t + \dfrac{1}{2}t^2 + \dfrac{1}{6}t^3 + \cdots \end{bmatrix} \quad \vdots$$

Exercise 3.18.
Consider $\dot{x} = (A + \epsilon\alpha)x$ where A and α are constant $n \times n$ matrices and ϵ is a parameter. Using (3.22) show that if ϵ is small, then a first approximation for $x(t)$ is $X(t)x_0$ where

$$X(t) = \exp(At)\left[I + \epsilon \int_0^t \exp(-A\tau)\alpha \exp(A\tau)\mathrm{d}\tau\right].$$

Show also that the next approximation produces an additional term of order ϵ^2.

3.5. Time varying systems

Also of considerable importance in many applications are linear systems in which the elements of A and B are continuous functions of time for $t \geqslant 0$. In general it will not be possible to give explicit expressions for solutions and we shall content ourselves with obtaining some general properties. We first consider the uncontrolled case

$$\dot{x}(t) = A(t)x(t), \quad x(0) = x_0, \tag{3.25}$$

and state an existence and uniqueness result:

THEOREM 3.1. If $A(t)$ is continuous for $t \geqslant 0$ then (3.25) has a unique solution for $t \geqslant 0$ given by $x(t) = X(t)x_0$, where $X(t)$ is the unique $n \times n$ matrix satisfying

$$\frac{\mathrm{d}X}{\mathrm{d}t} = A(t)X(t), \quad X(0) = I. \tag{3.26}$$

The proof is straightforward, relying on elementary properties of matrix norms (see Section 2.7), and can be found in Bellman (1970, p. 167).

We can no longer define a matrix exponential, but there is a result corresponding to the fact (Exercise 3.4) that $\exp(At)$ is nonsingular when A is constant:

THEOREM 3.2. In Theorem 3.1 the matrix $X(t)$ is nonsingular.

Proof. Define a matrix $Y(t)$ as the solution of

$$\frac{dY}{dt} = -YA(t), \quad Y(0) = I.$$

Such a matrix exists and is unique by an argument virtually identical to that which is used in the proof of the previous theorem. Now

$$\frac{d}{dt}(YX) = \dot{Y}X + Y\dot{X}$$

$$= -YAX + YAX$$

$$= 0$$

so $Y(t)X(t)$ is equal to a constant matrix, which must be the unit matrix because of the conditions at $t = 0$. Hence $X(t)$ is nonsingular (and its inverse is in fact $Y(t)$).

We can also generalize the idea of the *state transition* matrix, given in (3.11) for time invariant systems by writing

$$\Phi(t, t_0) = X(t)\,X^{-1}(t_0), \tag{3.27}$$

which exists for all $t, t_0 \geqslant 0$ by virtue of the two preceding theorems. It is then easy to verify by direct differentiation that

$$x(t) = \Phi(t, t_0)x_0 \tag{3.28}$$

is the solution of (3.25) with initial condition $x(t_0) = x_0$. The expression (3.28) has the same form as that for the time invariant case, given in (3.10), although of course the transition matrices involved are quite different. However it is most interesting that although in general it is not possible to obtain an analytic expression for the solution of (3.26), and therefore for $\Phi(t, t_0)$ in (3.27), this latter matrix possesses precisely the same properties as those for the constant case given in equations (3.12). This is easily verified using (3.26) and (3.27). A further correspondence with the time invariant case is the following generalization of (3.23):

THEOREM 3.3. The solution of

$$\dot{x}(t) = A(t)x(t) + B(t)u(t), \tag{3.29}$$

subject to the initial condition $x(t_0) = x_0$, is

$$x(t) = \Phi(t, t_0)\left[x_0 + \int_{t_0}^{t} \Phi(t_0, \tau)B(\tau)u(\tau)\, d\tau\right] \tag{3.30}$$

where Φ is defined in (3.27).

Proof. Using the standard method of variation of parameters, put $x = X(t)w(t)$ where $X(t)$ is defined by (3.26). Substitution into (3.29) produces

$$\frac{dx}{dt} = AXw + X\frac{dw}{dt}$$

$$= AXw + Bu.$$

Hence

$$X(t)\frac{dw}{dt} = Bu$$

so

$$\frac{dw}{dt} = X^{-1}(t)Bu$$

which on integration gives

$$w(t) = w(t_0) + \int_{t_0}^{t} X^{-1}(\tau)B(\tau)u(\tau)\, d\tau.$$

The desired expression then follows using $x_0 = X(t_0)w(t_0)$ and (3.27).

The development in this section shows that some of the results on linear systems carry over even when the matrix elements are time varying. This is clearly a useful aspect of the state space approach, since transform methods can only be applied to equations with constant coefficients.

Exercise 3.19.
Show that when $n = 2$ in (3.26),

$$\frac{d}{dt}\left\{\det X(t)\right\} = \text{tr } A(t) \det X(t),$$

and hence deduce that $X(t)$ is nonsingular, $t \geqslant 0$.
  This method can be generalized for arbitrary n.

Exercise 3.20.
Verify using (3.27) that the properties of the transition matrix listed in (3.12) do indeed carry over to the time varying case.

Exercise 3.21.
If $B(t) = \int_0^t A(\tau)d\tau$, verify that the solution of (3.25) is $x(t) = \exp(B(t))x_0$ provided $B(t)$ and $A(t)$ commute with each other for all $t \geqslant 0$.

Exercise 3.22.
Show that if Φ is defined by (3.27) then $[\Phi^{-1}(t, t_0)]^T$ is the transition matrix for the system $\dot{z} = -A^T(t)z$ (the *adjoint* system).

Exercise 3.23.
A system is *self-adjoint* if $A^T(t) = -A(t)$. Show that $\Phi(t, t_0)$ in (3.27) is then an orthogonal matrix.

Exercise 3.24.
Verify that the solution of the matrix differential equation

$$\frac{dW}{dt} = A(t)W(t) + W(t)A^T(t), \quad W(t_0) = C,$$

is $W(t) = \Phi(t, t_0)C\Phi^T(t, t_0)$, using the properties of Φ which is defined in (3.27).
  Compare with Exercise 3.12.

3.6. Discrete-time systems

A general introduction to discrete-time linear systems was given in Section 1.2.2, and the method of z-transforms for solving linear difference equations was outlined. The mathematical model in state variable form is

$$x(k + 1) = A(kT)x(k) + B(kT)u(k) \tag{3.31}$$

where $x(k), u(k)$ denote the values of the state and control vectors $x(kT)$ and $u(kT)$ respectively ($k = 0, 1, 2, \ldots$). The similarity with the continuous-time equation (3.20) is obvious, and the dimensions of A and B are the same. We now develop matrix methods for solution of (3.31). Consider first the situation when there is no control and A is a constant matrix, so (3.31) becomes

$$x(k+1) = Ax(k), x(k_0) = x_0. \qquad (3.32)$$

Clearly

$$x(k_0 + 1) = Ax(k_0)$$
$$x(k_0 + 2) = Ax(k_0 + 1) = A^2 x(k_0), \text{ etc.},$$

and it is easy to see that the solution of (3.32) is simply

$$x(k) = A^{k-k_0} x_0. \qquad (3.33)$$

The matrix A^k can be determined in a similar fashion to the development in Section 3.2 for $\exp(At)$, using either Sylvester's formula (2.71), or eqn (2.74) which is based on the Cayley-Hamilton theorem.

Example 3.5. Find A^k for the matrix A in Example 3.1.
Using (2.74) with $n = 2$ we have

$$A^k = r_0 A + r_1 I$$

and since the characteristic roots of A are -1 and -2, eqn (2.75) gives

$$(-1)^k = -r_0 + r_1, \quad (-2)^k = -2r_0 + r_1.$$

Solving for r_0 and r_1 and substituting produces

$$A^k = (-1)^k Z_1 + (-2)^k Z_2$$

where the Z_k are identical to those found in Example 3.2. This emphasises the fact previously mentioned that the Z_k in Sylvester's formula (2.71) are dependent only on A, not the particular function $f(A)$ being evaluated.
When A has repeated roots the formula (2.76) can again be used.

Example 3.6. Find A^{100} when

$$A = \begin{bmatrix} 2 & -4 \\ 4 & -6 \end{bmatrix}.$$

The development is similar to that in Example 3.3. It is easy to show that A has a repeated root -2, and that its similarity invariants are 1 and $\det(\lambda I - A) = (\lambda + 2)^2$, so as discussed in Section 2.5 its minimum and characteristic polynomials are identical. Hence $q = 1$, $\lambda_1 = -2$, $\alpha_1 = 2$ in (2.76) giving

$$f(A) = Z_{11} f(\lambda_1) + Z_{12} f'(\lambda_1), \qquad (3.34)$$

for any function $f(\lambda)$. Setting $f(\lambda)$ in (3.34) equal to 1 gives $Z_{11} = I$, and $f(\lambda) = \lambda + 2$ gives $Z_{12} = A + 2I$. Then taking $f(\lambda) = \lambda^{100}$ gives

$$A^{100} = (-2)^{100} I + 100 (-2)^{99} (A + 2I)$$

$$= 2^{99} \begin{bmatrix} -398 & 400 \\ -400 & 402 \end{bmatrix}.$$

The *state transition* matrix is now defined by

$$\Phi(k, k_0) = A^{k-k_0} \qquad (3.35)$$

so that the solution of (3.32) can be written

$$x(k) = \Phi(k, k_0) x_0, \qquad (3.36)$$

corresponding to (3.10). It is easy to verify directly from (3.35) that the following properties hold:

$$\left. \begin{array}{l} \Phi(k + 1, k_0) = A\Phi(k, k_0) \\[4pt] \Phi(k, k) = I \\[4pt] \Phi(k_0, k) = \Phi^{-1}(k, k_0), \text{ provided } A \text{ is nonsingular} \\[4pt] \Phi(k, k_0) = \Phi(k, k_1) \Phi(k_1, k_0), \ k \geqslant k_1 \geqslant k_0 \end{array} \right\} \quad (3.37)$$

and these are the discrete analogue of (3.12).

Now return to (3.31) but assume A and B are still time invariant. We have

$$x(k) = A[Ax(k-2) + Bu(k-2)] + Bu(k-1)$$
$$= A^2 x(k-2) + ABu(k-2) + Bu(k-1)$$
$$= A^2[Ax(k-3) + Bu(k-3)] + ABu(k-2) + Bu(k-1)$$

$$\cdot$$
$$\cdot$$
$$\cdot$$

$$= A^{k-k_0}x_0 + \sum_{i=k_0}^{k-1} A^{k-i-1} Bu(i), \tag{3.38}$$

$$= \Phi(k, k_0)\left[x_0 + \sum_{i=k_0}^{k-1} \Phi(k_0, i+1) Bu(i)\right], \tag{3.39}$$

using (3.35) and (3.37). The expression for $x(k)$ in (3.39) corresponds to that in (3.23) for the continuous-time case.

In the case when A and B have time varying elements the development is a little easier than for the differential equation system in Section 3.5. We can write

$$x(k_0 + 1) = A(k_0 T)x_0 ,$$
$$x(k_0 + 2) = A[(k_0 + 1)T] x(k_0 + 1)$$
$$= A[(k_0 + 1)T] A(k_0 T)x_0 ,$$

and a continuation of this process gives the transition matrix as

$$\Phi(k, k_0) = \prod_{i=k_0}^{k-1} A(iT). \tag{3.40}$$

It is a straightforward exercise to verify that the properties (3.37) still hold for (3.40). It is also easy to verify that the solution of (3.31) in the time-varying case is

$$x(k) = \Phi(k, k_0)\left[x_0 + \sum_{i=k_0}^{k-1} \Phi(k_0, i+1)B(iT)u(i)\right], \tag{3.41}$$

where Φ is given by (3.40), and this is the expression corresponding to (3.30).

It is clear from comparison of the preceding results with those obtained earlier in this chapter that there is a close analogy between discrete and continuous linear systems, as we indicated for the two transform methods in Section 1.2. We shall encounter further aspects of this inter-relationship in subsequent chapters.

Exercise 3.25.
Find A^{100}, when A is the matrix in Exercise 3.1(a), by using the expression (2.71).

Exercise 3.26.
By choosing as state variables $x_1(k) = X(k)$, $x_2(k) = X(k+1)$, write the scalar difference equation of Example 1.7 in the form (3.32), and find $\Phi(k, 0)$.

Exercise 3.27.
Find $\Phi(k, 0)$ for the system having the A matrix given in Example 3.6.

Exercise 3.28.
The Fibonacci numbers are $0, 1, 1, 2, 3, 5, 8, 13, \ldots$ each number in the sequence being the sum of the preceding two. These integers arise naturally in a surprisingly large number of biological and other situations (see for example Holland (1972) for an elementary account). Let $X(k)$ denote the $(k+1)$th number, and write the difference equation for X in the form (3.32), as in Exercise 3.26. Find $\Phi(k, 0)$ and hence show that

$$X(k) = \left[k + \binom{k}{3}5 + \binom{k}{5}5^2 + \binom{k}{7}5^3 + \cdots \right] / 2^{k-1},$$

where $\binom{k}{r}$ denotes the usual binomial coefficient.

Exercise 3.29.
By using z-transforms to solve (3.32), deduce using (3.33) that

$$Z^{-1}\{z(zI - A)^{-1}\} = A^k.$$

This is the result corresponding to (3.18), and is the matrix generalization of Example 1.6(b).

3.7. Relationships between state space and classical forms

We have assumed so far in this chapter that the linear system equations
are in vector-matrix form. In fact as we have seen in Chapter 1, classical
linear control theory deals with scalar differential or difference equations
of the forms (1.7) and (1.26). Consider a simplified form of (1.7):

$$z^{(n)} + k_1 z^{(n-1)} + \cdots + k_n z = u(t) \tag{3.42}$$

where as before the superscript denotes differentiation with respect to
t and $u(t)$ is the single control variable. It is easy to write (3.42) in our
matrix form by taking as state variables

$$w_1 = z, w_2 = z^{(1)}, \ldots, w_n = z^{(n-1)}, \tag{3.43}$$

and this can be thought of as a basic step in developing the 'modern'
theory of linear systems. The w_i are called *phase* variables, and since
$\dot{w}_i = w_{i+1}, i = 1, 2, \ldots, n-1$, it is easy to see that (3.42) and (3.43)
lead to the state space form

$$\dot{w} = Cw + du$$

where

$$C = \begin{bmatrix} 0 & 1 & 0 & \cdot & \cdot & \cdot & 0 \\ 0 & 0 & 1 & \cdot & \cdot & \cdot & \cdot \\ \cdot & \cdot & \cdot & \cdot & \cdot & \cdot & \cdot \\ \cdot & \cdot & \cdot & \cdot & \cdot & \cdot & 1 \\ -k_n & -k_{n-1} & -k_{n-2} & \cdot & \cdot & \cdot & -k_1 \end{bmatrix}, \tag{3.45}$$

$$w = [w_1, w_2, \ldots, w_n]^T$$

and

$$d = [0, 0, \ldots, 0, 1]^T \tag{3.46}$$

The matrix C is the *companion form* previously encountered in (2.32),
and its characteristic polynomial is

$$\det(\lambda I - C) = \lambda^n + k_1 \lambda^{n-1} + \cdots + k_n \equiv k(\lambda), \tag{3.47}$$

which has the same coefficients as those in the differential equation
(3.42). As we have seen in eqn (1.10), the polynomial k also arises when
the Laplace transform is applied to the left hand side of (3.42). The

more general right hand side involving derivatives of u as displayed in eqn (1.7) can also be dealt with (see Exercise 3.35; and also Exercise 4.39). We have in fact already applied the transformation (3.43) in some simple cases, for instance in Example 1.1.

Having seen that (3.42) can be put into matrix form, a natural question is to ask whether the converse holds: can any linear system in state space form with a single control variable

$$\dot{x} = Ax + bu \qquad (3.48)$$

be put into the classical form (3.42), or its matrix equivalent defined by (3.43) and (3.44)?

Example 3.7. We saw that in Example 1.2. concerning the electrically heated oven the equations describing the system arose naturally in the matrix form (3.48). Suppose that the values of the constants in (1.4) are as in eqn (2.46) so that eqns (1.2) and (1.3) become

$$\dot{x}_1 = -2x_1 + 2x_2 + u, \dot{x}_2 = x_1 - x_2.$$

Differentiating the second equation we obtain

$$\ddot{x}_2 = \dot{x}_1 - \dot{x}_2$$

$$= (-2x_1 + 2x_2 + u) - (x_1 - x_2)$$

$$= -3x_1 + 3x_2 + u.$$

Hence

$$\ddot{x}_2 + 3\dot{x}_2 = u$$

which has the desired form. We would like to determine when and how such a procedure can be carried out in general. The answer to our questions is provided by the following result:

THEOREM 3.4. A system in the form (3.48), where A is an $n \times n$ constant matrix and b a nonzero column n-vector, can be transformed by a nonsingular transformation $w = Tx$ into the canonical form given by (3.44), and (3.45), and (3.46) provided

$$\text{rank } [b, Ab, A^2 b, \ldots, A^{n-1} b] = n. \qquad (3.49)$$

Conversely, if a nonsingular T exists then (3.49) holds.

Proof. Substitution of $w = Tx$ into (3.48) produces

$$\dot{w} = TAT^{-1} w + Tbu. \qquad (3.50)$$

A proof of the first half of the theorem is established by taking as an explicit expression for the transformation matrix

$$
T = \begin{bmatrix} t \\ tA \\ tA^2 \\ \cdot \\ \cdot \\ \cdot \\ tA^{n-1} \end{bmatrix}, \tag{3.51}
$$

where t is any row n-vector such that T is nonsingular, assuming for the present that at least one suitable t exists. Denote the columns of T^{-1} by $s_1, s_2, \ldots, s_n$ and consider

$$
TAT^{-1} = \begin{bmatrix} tAs_1 & tAs_2 & \cdot & \cdot & tAs_n \\ tA^2s_1 & tA^2s_2 & \cdot & \cdot & tA^2s_n \\ \cdot & \cdot & \cdot & \cdot & \cdot \\ \cdot & \cdot & \cdot & \cdot & \cdot \\ tA^ns_1 & tA^ns_2 & \cdot & \cdot & tA^ns_n \end{bmatrix}.
$$

Comparison with the identity $TT^{-1} = I$, namely

$$
\begin{bmatrix} ts_1 & ts_2 & \cdot & \cdot & ts_n \\ tAs_1 & tAs_2 & \cdot & \cdot & tAs_n \\ \cdot & \cdot & \cdot & \cdot & \cdot \\ \cdot & \cdot & \cdot & \cdot & \cdot \\ tA^{n-1}s_1 & tA^{n-1}s_2 & \cdot & \cdot & tA^{n-1}s_n \end{bmatrix} = \begin{bmatrix} 1 & & & & \\ & 1 & & 0 & \\ & & \cdot & & \\ & 0 & & \cdot & \\ & & & & 1 \end{bmatrix}
$$

then readily establishes that the ith row of TAT^{-1} is the $(i+1)$th row of I ($i = 1, 2, \ldots, n-1$) so TAT^{-1} has the same form as C in (3.45), with last row given by $k_i = -tA^n s_{n-i+1}, i = 1, 2, \ldots, n$. For (3.50) to be identical to (3.44) we must also have $Tb = d$, and substitution of (3.51) into this equation gives

$$
tb = 0, \, tAB = 0, \ldots, \, tA^{n-2}b = 0, \, tA^{n-1}b = 1 \tag{3.52}
$$

or

$$
t[b, Ab, \ldots, A^{n-1}b] = d^{T} \tag{3.53}
$$

which has a unique solution for t in view of (3.49). It only remains to be shown that T in (3.51) is nonsingular, and this is achieved by showing that its rows are linearly independent (see Section 2.2). For suppose that

$$\alpha_1 t + \alpha_2 tA + \cdots + \alpha_n tA^{n-1} = 0 \qquad (3.54)$$

for some scalars α_i. Multiplying (3.54) on the right by b and using (3.52) gives $\alpha_n = 0$. Similarly, multiplying (3.54) on the right successively by $Ab, A^2 b, \ldots, A^{n-1} b$ gives $\alpha_{n-1} = 0, \alpha_{n-2} = 0, \ldots, \alpha_1 = 0$, establishing independence.

To prove the converse of the theorem, if a nonsingular T exists then

$$\begin{aligned}
\text{rank } [b, Ab, \ldots, A^{n-1}b] &= \text{rank } [Tb, TAb, \ldots, TA^{n-1}b] \\
&= \text{rank } [Tb, (TAT^{-1})\, Tb, \ldots, \\
&\qquad\qquad (TAT^{-1})^{n-1} Tb] \\
&= \text{rank } [d, Cd, \ldots, C^{n-1}d] \qquad (3.55)
\end{aligned}$$

and it is easy to verify using (3.45) and (3.46) that this last matrix has the triangular form

$$\tilde{U} = \begin{bmatrix}
0 & 0 & 0 & \cdot & 0 & 1 \\
0 & 0 & 0 & \cdot & 1 & \theta_1 \\
\cdot & \cdot & \cdot & \cdot & \cdot & \cdot \\
\cdot & \cdot & \cdot & \cdot & \cdot & \cdot \\
0 & 0 & 1 & \cdot & \cdot & \theta_{n-3} \\
0 & 1 & \theta_1 & \cdot & \cdot & \theta_{n-2} \\
1 & \theta_1 & \theta_2 & \cdot & \cdot & \theta_{n-1}
\end{bmatrix}, \qquad (3.56)$$

and therefore has full rank.

This completes the proof of the theorem, and T can be constructed using (3.53) and (3.51). However we can also give an explicit expression for the matrix in the transformation $x = T^{-1} w$. Writing

$$U = [b, Ab, \ldots, A^{n-1}b], \qquad (3.57)$$

we have seen in the development of (3.55) that TU is equal to the matrix $\tilde{U}$ in (3.56). This latter matrix has elements given by

$$\theta_i = -\sum_{j=0}^{i-1} k_{j+1}\, \theta_{i-j-1}, i = 1, 2, \ldots, n-1; \theta_0 = 1,$$

and it is straightforward to verify that its inverse is

$$(\bar{U})^{-1} = \begin{bmatrix} k_{n-1} & k_{n-2} & \cdot & \cdot & k_1 & 1 \\ k_{n-2} & k_{n-3} & \cdot & \cdot & 1 & 0 \\ \cdot & \cdot & \cdot & \cdot & \cdot & \cdot \\ \cdot & \cdot & \cdot & \cdot & \cdot & \cdot \\ \cdot & \cdot & \cdot & \cdot & \cdot & \cdot \\ k_1 & 1 & \cdot & \cdot & 0 & 0 \\ 1 & 0 & \cdot & \cdot & 0 & 0 \end{bmatrix} . \quad (3.58)$$

Finally the inverse of T is given explicitly by

$$T^{-1} = U(\bar{U})^{-1}. \quad (3.59)$$

Notice that the k_i in (3.58) are the coefficients in the characteristic equation (3.47) of C. Thus since A is similar to C it is necessary to calculate the characteristic equation of A in order to use (3.59).

Example 3.8. Find the matrix T and the transformed system when

$$A = \begin{bmatrix} 1 & -3 \\ 4 & 2 \end{bmatrix}, \qquad b = \begin{bmatrix} 1 \\ 1 \end{bmatrix} .$$

From (3.52) with $t = [t_1, t_2]$ we have

$$t_1 + t_2 = 0, \quad -2t_1 + 6t_2 = 1$$

whence $t_1 = -1/8, t_2 = 1/8$. Hence from (3.51)

$$T = \tfrac{1}{8} \begin{bmatrix} -1 & 1 \\ 3 & 5 \end{bmatrix}$$

and

$$T^{-1} = \begin{bmatrix} -5 & 1 \\ 3 & 1 \end{bmatrix} .$$

A simple calculation gives

$$TAT^{-1} = \begin{bmatrix} 0 & 1 \\ -14 & 3 \end{bmatrix} .$$

Thus the transformed system is

$$\dot{w}_1 = w_2, \quad \dot{w}_2 = -14w_1 + 3w_2 + u$$

or

$$\dddot{z} - 3\dot{z} + 14z = u.$$

It should be noted that since $C = TAT^{-1}$ then by virtue of the remarks in Section 2.5, a transformation matrix T will exist only if A is nonderogatory. This could also be inferred from the result of Exercise 2.22. In other words, whatever the vector b the system (3.48) cannot be transformed into (3.44) if A is derogatory. In this case a canonical form for the system equations can be obtained by choosing T in (3.50) such that $TAT^{-1} = J$, the Jordan form of A.

A result similar to Theorem 3.4 can now be obtained for systems having zero input and a scalar output, so that the system equations are

$$\dot{x} = Ax \tag{3.60}$$

$$y = cx, \tag{3.61}$$

where A is an $n \times n$ matrix as before, c is a constant row n-vector and $y(t)$ is the output variable.

THEOREM 3.5. Any system described by (3.60) and (3.61) can be transformed by $x = Pv$, with P nonsingular, into the form

$$\dot{v} = Ev, \quad y = fv, \tag{3.62}$$

where

$$E = \begin{bmatrix} 0 & 0 & \cdot & \cdot & \cdot & -e_n \\ 1 & 0 & \cdot & \cdot & \cdot & -e_{n-1} \\ 0 & 1 & \cdot & \cdot & \cdot & \cdot \\ \cdot & \cdot & \cdot & \cdot & \cdot & \cdot \\ \cdot & \cdot & \cdot & \cdot & \cdot & \cdot \\ 0 & 0 & \cdot & \cdot & 1 & -e_1 \end{bmatrix} \tag{3.63}$$

and

$$f = [0, 0, \ldots, 1], \tag{3.64}$$

provided

$$\text{rank}\begin{bmatrix} c \\ cA \\ cA^2 \\ \cdot \\ \cdot \\ cA^{n-1} \end{bmatrix} = n. \tag{3.65}$$

Conversely, if a nonsingular P exists then (3.65) holds.

Proof. This follows along similar lines to the proof of Theorem 3.4, so we do not give all the details. The transformation $x = Pv$ when applied to (3.60) and (3.61) produces $\dot{v} = P^{-1}APv, y = cPv$ so we first require to show that $P^{-1}AP$ has the form (3.63). This is achieved by setting

$$P = [r, Ar, \ldots, A^{n-1}r], \tag{3.66}$$

assuming that some column n-vector r exists which makes P nonsingular. If the rows of P^{-1} are denoted by $q_1, q_2, \ldots, q_n$, then comparison with the elements in the identity $P^{-1}P = I$ establishes that $P^{-1}AP$ has the desired form (3.63) with last column $e_i = -q_{n-i+1}A^n r, i = 1, 2, \ldots, n$. The second requirement, that $cP = f$, holds because of (3.65), and nonsingularity of P is shown by proving that its columns are linearly independent.

The proof of the converse is also similar to that in Theorem 3.4. The matrix P is constructed using (3.66) and the condition $cP = f$.

Notice that E is also called a companion form matrix because its characteristic polynomial is

$$\det(\lambda I - E) = \lambda^n + e_1\lambda^{n-1} + \cdots + e_n, \tag{3.67}$$

which again is identical to the characteristic polynomial of A, by similarity of A and E.

The conditions (3.49) and (3.65) are necessary and sufficient for systems to be transformable into the appropriate canonical forms (3.44) or (3.62), but we shall see at the beginning of the next chapter that these rank conditions possess further important significance.

When we turn to the linear difference equation

$$X(k+n) + k_1X(k+n-1) + \cdots + k_nX(k) = u(k) \tag{3.68}$$

the only modification required is that (3.43) is replaced by

$$w_1(k) = X(k), w_2(k) = X(k+1), \cdots, w_n(k) = X(k+n-1) \tag{3.69}$$

so $w_i(k + 1) = w_{i + 1}(k)$, and (3.68) is equivalent to

$$w(k + 1) = Cw(k) + du(k) \tag{3.70}$$

where C and d are precisely as defined in (3.45) and (3.46). We have in fact already used a simple case of (3.69) in Exercises 3.26 and 3.28.

Theorems 3.4 and 3.5 now carry over with no changes other than that (3.44) is replaced by (3.70), and similarly in (3.48), (3.60), and (3.62) $x(k + 1)$ and $v(k + 1)$ replace derivatives.

Exercise 3.30.

Find the matrix T in Theorem 3.4 and the transformed system for each of the cases where the matrices are as given in Exercise 3.1 and the corresponding vectors b are

$$(a) \quad b = \begin{bmatrix} 1 \\ 3 \end{bmatrix} \qquad\qquad (b) \quad b = \begin{bmatrix} 1 \\ 0 \\ 1 \end{bmatrix} .$$

Exercise 3.31.

Two platforms P_1 and P_2 are connected to each other and to a fixed support by springs and dampers as shown, and a control force $u(t)$ is applied to P_1.

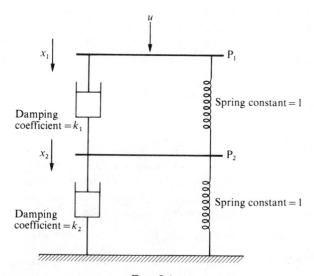

FIG. 3.1

The forces exerted by the dampers are proportional to velocity, and the springs obey Hooke's law. Assume that the masses of the platforms and the other components can be neglected, and that the platforms remain horizontal. Derive the state equations in the form (3.48), taking the displacements x_1 and x_2 from equilibrium as state variables. Find the condition to be satisfied by k_1 and k_2 for there to exist a nonsingular transformation of variables which puts the equations into the form (3.44). If $k_1 = \frac{1}{2}, k_2 = \frac{1}{4}$ determine T and the transformed system.

Exercise 3.32.
Find the matrix P in Theorem 3.5 and the transformed system when

$$A = \begin{bmatrix} 1 & 2 & 0 \\ 3 & -1 & 1 \\ 0 & 2 & 0 \end{bmatrix}, \qquad c = [0, 0, 2].$$

Exercise 3.33.
Prove the converse of Theorem 3.5.

Exercise 3.34.
Verify that when A is a scalar multiple of the unit matrix then it is not possible to transform it by a nonsingular transformation into either (3.45) or (3.63).

Exercise 3.35.
Show that if

$$z = [\beta_n - k_n\beta_0, \beta_{n-1} - k_{n-1}\beta_0, \ldots, \beta_1 - k_1\beta_0] w + \beta_0 u$$

where w satifies (3.44), then z satisfies (3.42) with the right hand side replaced by

$$\beta_0 u^{(n)} + \beta_1 u^{(n-1)} + \cdots + \beta_{n-1} u^{(1)} + \beta_n u.$$

(Compare with eqn 1.7.)

Exercise 3.36.
If V denotes the matrix in (3.65), show that the inverse of the transformation matrix in Theorem 3.5 can be written as $P^{-1} = (\bar{U})^{-1} V$, where $(\bar{U})^{-1}$ is as stated in (3.58) but with the k_i replaced by the e_i in (3.67), $i = 1, 2, \ldots, n - 1$.

4 Linear control systems

The material in the previous chapter on solution of linear systems is of course applicable to any area where linear equations arise, and no use was made of the fact that some of the variables represented control terms. We have now done enough groundwork, however, to be able to concentrate our attention on some important ideas which are peculiar to control theory. This chapter can therefore be regarded as a fundamental one in the development of state space theory, and most of the results have been obtained within the last fifteen years. We discuss exclusively continuous-time systems until Section 4.7, where it is pointed out that the basic theorems carry over to discrete-time systems with only minor modification.

4.1 Controllability

As was mentioned during the discussion of the examples in Chapter 1, an essential first step in dealing with many control problems is to determine whether a desired objective can be achieved by manipulating the chosen control variables. If not, then either the objective will have to be modified or control will have to be applied in some different fashion. For example, economists would dearly like to know whether the rate of inflation can be controlled by altering taxes, the money supply, bank lending rate, and so on.

Here we discuss the general property of being able to transfer a system from any given state to any other by means of a suitable choice of control functions. Specifically, the linear time varying system S_1 defined by

$$\dot{x} = A(t)x(t) + B(t)u(t) \tag{4.1}$$

$$y = C(t)x(t) \tag{4.2}$$

where A is $n \times n$, B is $n \times m$ and C is $r \times n$, is said to be *completely controllable* (*c.c.*) if for any t_0, any initial state $x(t_0) = x_0$ and any given final state x_f there exists a finite time $t_1 > t_0$ and a control $u(t)$, $t_0 \leqslant t \leqslant t_1$, such that $x(t_1) = x_f$. The qualifying term 'completely' implies that the definition holds for *all* x_0 and x_f, and several other types of controllability can be defined – for example, complete output controllability requires attainment of arbitrary final output. The control $u(t)$ is assumed *piecewise continuous* in the interval t_0 to t_1, that is, continuous except at a finite number of points in the interval.

Example 4.1. Suppose a wheel is rotating on an axle, the total moment of inertia being J, and it is required to bring the system to rest by applying a braking torque $u(t)$. The equation of motion is

$$J\dot{x}_1 = u$$

where $x_1(t)$ is the angular velocity. Integrating we obtain

$$x_1(t_1) = x_1(t_0) + (1/J) \int_{t_0}^{t_1} u(t)\,dt$$

and since $x_1(t_1) = 0$ we must choose $u(t)$ so that

$$\int_{t_0}^{t_1} u(t)\,dt = -Jx_1(t_0).$$

Clearly this requirement can be satisfied for any value of $x_1(t_0)$ by taking

$$u(t) = -Jx_1(t_0)/(t_1 - t_0)$$

so the system is c.c. However, it is apparent (and intuitively obvious in this very simple example) that there are an infinite number of suitable choices for $u(t)$, and to make the control force unique we would have to add an additional requirement, such as bringing the wheel to rest as quickly as possible or with minimum expenditure of energy.

Example 4.2. Consider the system described by

$$\dot{x}_1 = a_1 x_1 + a_2 x_2 + b_1 u$$
$$\dot{x}_2 = a_3 x_2.$$

Clearly by inspection this is not c.c., since $u(t)$ has no influence on $x_2(t)$, which is entirely determined by the second equation and $x_2(t_0)$.

From the expression (3.30) for the solution of (4.1) we have

$$x_f = \Phi(t_1, t_0) \left[x_0 + \int_{t_0}^{t_1} \Phi(t_0, \tau) B(\tau) u(\tau)\,d\tau \right] \qquad (4.3)$$

or, rearranging and using the third property in (3.12),

$$0 = \Phi(t_1, t_0) \left[\{ x_0 - \Phi(t_0, t_1) x_f \} + \int_{t_0}^{t_1} \Phi(t_0, \tau) B(\tau) u(\tau) \, d\tau \right] \ .$$

Since $\Phi(t_1, t_0)$ is nonsingular it follows that if $u(t)$ transfers x_0 to x_f, it also transfers $x_0 - \Phi(t_0, t_1) x_f$ to the origin in the same time interval. Since x_0 and x_f are arbitrary, it therefore follows that in the definition the given final state can be taken to be the null vector without loss of generality.

For time invariant systems the initial time t_0 in the controllability definition can be set equal to zero, and a general algebraic criterion can be derived:

THEOREM 4.1. The constant system

$$\dot{x} = Ax + Bu \tag{4.4}$$

(or the *pair* $[A, B]$) is c.c. if and only if the $n \times nm$ *controllability matrix*

$$U = [B, AB, A^2 B, \ldots, A^{n-1} B] \tag{4.5}$$

has rank n.

Proof.

Necessity. We suppose (4.4) is c.c. and wish to prove rank $U = n$. This is done by assuming rank $U < n$, which leads to a contradiction. For then there will exist a constant row n-vector $q \neq 0$ such that

$$qB = 0, qAB = 0, \ldots, qA^{n-1} B = 0. \tag{4.6}$$

In the expression (3.22) for the solution of (4.4) subject to $x(0) = x_0$ set $t = t_1$, $x(t_1) = 0$ to obtain, since $\exp(At_1)$ is nonsingular,

$$-x_0 = \int_0^{t_1} \exp(-A\tau) Bu(\tau) \, d\tau. \tag{4.7}$$

Now as in (3.15), $\exp(-A\tau)$ can be expressed as some polynomial $r(A)$ in A having degree at most $n - 1$, so (4.7) becomes

$$-x_0 = \int_0^{t_1} (r_0 I + r_1 A + \cdots + r_{n-1} A^{n-1}) Bu(\tau) \, d\tau. \tag{4.8}$$

Multiplying (4.8) on the left by q and using (4.6) gives $qx_0 \equiv 0$. Since (4.4) is c.c. this must hold for *any* vector x_0, which implies $q = 0$, thus contradicting the assumption that rank $U < n$.

Sufficiency. We now assume rank $U = n$, and again using (3.22) we have

$$\exp(-At_1)x(t_1) = x_0 + \int_0^{t_1} r(A)Bu(\tau)\,d\tau \qquad (4.9)$$

where the coefficients of r will be functions of τ. Carrying out the integration in (4.9) will produce

$$\exp(-At_1)x(t_1) = x_0 + (s_0 B + s_1 AB + \cdots + s_{n-1} A^{n-1}B). \qquad (4.10)$$

Since rank $U = n$ it follows that for *any* given x_0 it will be possible to choose the s_i (and hence by implication $u(\tau)$) so that the right hand side of (4.10) is identically zero, giving $x(t_1) \equiv 0$. This establishes that (4.4) is c.c. since the conditions of the definition are satisfied.

COROLLARY 4.1. If rank $B = p$, the condition in Theorem 4.1 reduces to

$$\text{rank } [B, AB, \ldots, A^{n-p}B] = n.$$

Proof. Define the matrix

$$U_k = [B, AB, \ldots, A^k B], \quad k = 0,1,2,\ldots.$$

If rank $U_\ell = $ rank $U_{\ell+1}$ it follows that all the columns of $A^{\ell+2}B$ must be linearly dependent on those of U_ℓ. This then implies that all the columns of $A^{\ell+2}B, A^{\ell+3}B, \ldots$ must also be linearly dependent on those of U_ℓ, so that rank $U_\ell = $ rank $U_{\ell+1} = $ rank $U_{\ell+2} = \ldots$. Hence the rank of U_k increases by at least one when k is increased by one, until the maximum value of rank U_k is attained when $k = \ell$. Since rank $U_0 = $ rank $B = p$, and rank $U_k \leqslant n$ it follows that $p + \ell \leqslant n$, giving $\ell \leqslant n - p$ as required.

Example 4.3. Consider again Example 1.2 describing an electrically-heated oven, and let the constants be as in Example 2.5 so that the equations are

$$\dot{x} = \begin{bmatrix} -2 & 2 \\ 1 & -1 \end{bmatrix} x + \begin{bmatrix} 1 \\ 0 \end{bmatrix} u. \qquad (4.11)$$

The controllability matrix (4.5) is

$$U = \begin{bmatrix} 1 & -2 \\ 0 & 1 \end{bmatrix}$$

which has rank 2, so the system is c.c. That is, it is possible to control
(in the sense of our definition) the temperatures of both the oven interior
and the jacket by means of the heating coil in the jacket. However, this
does not tell us how the control can be applied to satisfy given objectives.

When $m = 1$, so that B reduces to a column vector b, the condition on
U in (4.5) becomes identical to that in (3.49). For this reason a system
described by (3.44), (3.45), and (3.46) is said to be in *controllable* canonical form, since Theorem 3.4 can now be restated as:

THEOREM 4.2. A system in the form (3.48) can be transformed into
the canonical form (3.44) if and only if it is c.c.

Notice the important point that if the system model is taken to be in
the classical form (3.42), then by virtue of Theorem 4.2 this automatically assumes that the system is c.c. Thus the concept of controllability
could not be appreciated until linear systems in vector–matrix form
were studied, and this is one of the reasons why controllability considerations have only recently been taken into account. Note also that
another remark on Theorem 3.4 can now be interpreted as stating that if
A is derogatory, (3.48) cannot be c.c. for *any* vector b.

Theorem 4.1 gives a criterion for determining whether a constant
linear system is c.c., but gives no help in determining a control vector
which will carry out a required alteration of states. We now give an explicit expression for such a vector for both constant and time varying
systems.

THEOREM 4.3. The system S_1 is c.c. if and only if the $n \times n$ symmetric *controllability* matrix

$$U(t_0, t_1) = \int_{t_0}^{t_1} \Phi(t_0, \tau) B(\tau) B^T(\tau) \Phi^T(t_0, \tau) \, d\tau. \qquad (4.12)$$

where Φ is defined in (3.27), is nonsingular. In this case the control

$$u(t) = -B^T(t) \Phi^T(t_0, t) U^{-1}(t_0, t_1) [x_0 - \Phi(t_0, t_1) x_f], \qquad (4.13)$$

defined on $t_0 \leqslant t \leqslant t_1$, transfers $x(t_0) = x_0$ to $x(t_1) = x_f$.

Proof.

Sufficiency. If $U(t_0, t_1)$ is assumed nonsingular then the control
defined by (4.13) exists. It is then straightforward to show that S_1 is c.c.
by verifying that substitution of (4.13) into the solution (3.30) of (4.1)

does indeed give $x(t_1) = x_f$, as required (use the property $\Phi(t_1, t_0)\Phi(t_0, t_1) = I$).

Necessity. We need to show that if S_1 is c.c. then $U(t_0, t_1)$ is non-singular. First notice that if α is an arbitrary constant column n-vector then from (4.12) since U is symmetric we can construct the quadratic form

$$\alpha^T U\alpha = \int_{t_0}^{t_1} \theta^T (\tau, t_0) \theta (\tau, t_0) \, \mathrm{d}\tau$$

$$= \int_{t_0}^{t_1} \| \theta \|_e^2 \, \mathrm{d}\tau$$

$$\geqslant 0, \tag{4.14}$$

where $\theta(\tau, t_0) = B^T(\tau) \Phi^T(t_0, \tau)\alpha$, so that $U(t_0, t_1)$ is positive semi-definite. Suppose there exists some $\hat{\alpha} \neq 0$, such that $\hat{\alpha}^T U(t_0, t_1)\hat{\alpha} = 0$. Eqn (4.14) with $\theta = \hat{\theta}$ when $\alpha = \hat{\alpha}$ then implies

$$\int_{t_0}^{t_1} \| \hat{\theta} \|_e^2 \, \mathrm{d}\tau = 0$$

which in turn implies, using the properties of norms (see Section 2.7) that $\hat{\theta}(\tau, t_0) \equiv 0, t_0 \leqslant \tau \leqslant t_1$. However, by assumption S_1 is c.c. so there exists a control $v(t)$, say, making $x(t_1) = 0$ if $x(t_0) = \hat{\alpha}$. Hence from (4.3) it follows that

$$\hat{\alpha} = - \int_{t_0}^{t_1} \Phi(t_0, \tau) B(\tau) v(\tau) \, \mathrm{d}\tau.$$

Therefore

$$\| \hat{\alpha} \|_e^2 = \hat{\alpha}^T \hat{\alpha} = - \int_{t_0}^{t_1} v^T(\tau) B^T(\tau) \Phi^T(t_0, \tau)\hat{\alpha} \, \mathrm{d}\tau$$

$$= - \int_{t_0}^{t_1} v^T(\tau) \hat{\theta}(\tau, t_0) \, \mathrm{d}\tau$$

$$= 0,$$

which contradicts the assumption that $\hat{\alpha} \neq 0$. Hence $U(t_0, t_1)$ is positive definite and is therefore nonsingular.

Since Theorem 4.3 shows that controllability of S_1 is independent of the matrix C, we shall often refer to the controllability of the *pair* $[A, B]$

instead of that of S_1. The control function (4.13) which transfers the system from (x_0, t_0) to (x_f, t_1) requires calculation of the transition matrix and the controllability matrix (4.12). This is not too difficult for constant linear systems, although rather tedious, and moderates the objection raised at the end of Example 4.3. Of course there will in general be many other suitable control vectors which achieve the same result, but the expression (4.13) has an additional interesting property:

THEOREM 4.4 If $\hat{u}(t)$ is any other control taking (x_0, t_0) to (x_f, t_1) then

$$\int_{t_0}^{t_1} \| \hat{u}(\tau) \|_e^2 \, d\tau > \int_{t_0}^{t_1} \| u(\tau) \|_e^2 \, d\tau$$

where $u(\tau)$ is given by (4.13), provided $\hat{u} \not\equiv u$.

Proof. Since both u and $\hat{u}$ satisfy (4.3), we obtain after subtraction

$$0 = \int_{t_0}^{t_1} \Phi(t_0, \tau) B(\tau) \, [\hat{u}(\tau) - u(\tau)] \, d\tau.$$

Multiplication of this equation on the left by

$$[x_0 - \Phi(t_0, t_1) x_f]^T \, [U^{-1} (t_0, t_1)]^T$$

and use of (4.13) gives

$$\int_{t_0}^{t_1} u^T(\tau) \, [u(\tau) - \hat{u}(\tau)] \, d\tau = 0. \tag{4.15}$$

Therefore

$$\int_{t_0}^{t_1} (u - \hat{u})^T \, (u - \hat{u}) \, d\tau = \int_{t_0}^{t_1} [\| \hat{u} \|_e^2 + \| u \|_e^2 - 2 u^T \hat{u}] \, d\tau$$

$$= \int_{t_0}^{t_1} [\| \hat{u} \|_e^2 - \| u \|_e^2] \, d\tau,$$

using (4.15), so

$$\int_{t_0}^{t_1} \| \hat{u} \|_e^2 \, d\tau = \int_{t_0}^{t_1} [\| u \|_e^2 + \| u - \hat{u} \|_e^2] \, d\tau$$

$$> \int_{t_0}^{t_1} \| u \|_e^2 \, d\tau$$

provided $u \not\equiv \hat{u}$, as required.

This result can be interpreted as showing that the control (4.13) is 'optimal', in the sense that it minimizes the integral

$$\int_{t_0}^{t_1} \| u(\tau) \|_{\mathrm{e}}^2 \, d\tau = \int_{t_0}^{t_1} (u_1{}^2 + \cdots + u_m{}^2) \, d\tau,$$

over the set of all controls which transfer (x_0, t_0) to (x_f, t_1), and this integral can be thought of as a measure of control 'energy' involved.

If the system is not c.c., it would be misleading to call it 'uncontrollable', since the implication of our definition is that for a non-c.c. system there are only *certain* final states which cannot be achieved by any choice of control. We can however modify the argument used in Theorem 4.3 to show how such final states can be attained when S_1 is not c.c.

THEOREM 4.5. If, for a given x_f, there exists a constant column n-vector γ such that

$$U(t_0, t_1) \, \gamma = x_0 - \Phi^{\mathrm{T}}(t_0, t_1) x_f \qquad (4.16)$$

then the control

$$u(t) = -B^{\mathrm{T}}(t) \, \Phi^{\mathrm{T}}(t_0, t) \gamma$$

transfers the system (4.1) from $x(t_0) = x_0$ to $x(t_1) = x_f$.

Proof. Substitution of the given $u(t)$ into (3.30) with $t = t_1$ produces

$$x(t_1) = \Phi(t_1, t_0) \left[x_0 - \int_{t_0}^{t_1} \Phi(t_0, \tau) B(\tau) B^{\mathrm{T}}(\tau) \Phi^{\mathrm{T}}(t_0, \tau) \gamma \, d\tau \right]$$

$$= \Phi(t_1, t_0) [x_0 - U(t_0, t_1)\gamma] \qquad \text{by (4.12)}$$

$$= \Phi(t_1, t_0) \Phi(t_0, t_1) x_f \qquad \text{by (4.16)}$$

$$= x_f, \text{ as required.}$$

When S_1 is c.c., U is nonsingular and the expression for $u(t)$ in Theorem 4.5 reduces to (4.13). It can also be shown (Brockett 1970, p.77) that the converse of this theorem is true, namely that only states x_f for which (4.16) holds can be reached.

For time invariant systems a convenient form of Theorem 4.5 is as follows (for a proof, see Rosenbrock 1970, p.167):

THEOREM 4.6. A given state $x_0 = x(0)$ can be transferred into another state x_f provided both x_0 and x_f lie in the subspace spanned by the columns of U in (4.5).

A further aspect of controllability is now indicated. Let $P(t)$ be an $n \times n$ matrix which is continuous and nonsingular for all $t \geqslant t_0$. Then the system S_2 obtained from S_1 by the transformation

$$\hat{x}(t) = P(t) x(t) \tag{4.17}$$

is said to be *algebraically equivalent* to S_1.

THEOREM 4.7. If $\Phi(t, t_0)$ is the state transition matrix for S_1 then $P(t) \Phi(t, t_0)P^{-1}(t_0) = \hat{\Phi}(t, t_0)$ is the state transition matrix for S_2.

Proof. From Section 3.5. we recall that $\Phi(t, t_0)$ is the unique matrix satisfying

$$\dot{\Phi}(t, t_0) = A(t) \Phi(t, t_0), \Phi(t_0, t_0) = I,$$

and is nonsingular. Clearly $\hat{\Phi}(t_0, t_0) = I$, and differentiation of (4.17) and use of (4.1) gives

$$
\begin{aligned}
d\hat{x}/dt &= \dot{P}x + P\dot{x} \\
&= (\dot{P} + PA)x + PBu \\
&= (\dot{P} + PA)P^{-1} \hat{x} + PBu
\end{aligned}
\tag{4.18}
$$

To establish the theorem we must show that $\hat{\Phi}$ is the transition matrix for (4.18), i.e.

$$\frac{d}{dt}[P(t)\Phi(t, t_0)P^{-1}(t_0)] = [\{\dot{P}(t) + P(t)A(t)\}P^{-1}(t)] P(t)\Phi(t, t_0)P^{-1}(t_0)$$

and this is left as an easy exercise for the reader.

One of the important properties of the transformation of state variables in (4.17) is that it preserves controllability:

THEOREM 4.8. If S_1 is c.c. then so is S_2.

Proof. From (4.18) we have that the system matrices for S_2 are

$$\hat{A}(t) = [\dot{P}(t) + P(t)A(t)]P^{-1}(t), \hat{B}(t) = P(t)B(t) \tag{4.19}$$

so the controllability matrix (4.12) for S_2 is

$$\hat{U}(t_0, t_1) = \int_{t_0}^{t_1} \hat{\Phi}(t_0, \tau) \hat{B}(\tau) \hat{B}^{\mathrm{T}}(\tau) \hat{\Phi}^{\mathrm{T}}(t_0, \tau) \, d\tau$$

$$= \int_{t_0}^{t_1} P(t_0) \Phi(t_0, \tau) P^{-1}(\tau) P(\tau) B(\tau) B^{\mathrm{T}}(\tau) P^{\mathrm{T}}(\tau)$$

$$\times (P^{-1}(\tau))^{\mathrm{T}} \Phi^{\mathrm{T}}(t_0, \tau) P^{\mathrm{T}}(t_0) \, d\tau$$

$$= P(t_0) U(t_0, t_1) P^{\mathrm{T}}(t_0) \qquad (4.20)$$

using (4.19) and Theorem 4.7. Thus $\hat{U}$ is nonsingular since the matrices U and $P(t_0)$ in (4.20) each have rank n.

When A, B, and C are time invariant P is also time invariant, and (4.17) is the usual definition of equivalence transformation in matrix theory. The following important result on system decomposition then holds:

THEOREM 4.9. When S_1 is time invariant then if U in (4.5) has rank $n_1 < n$ there exists a system algebraically equivalent to S_1 having the form

$$\frac{d}{dt} \begin{bmatrix} x^{(1)} \\ x^{(2)} \end{bmatrix} = \begin{bmatrix} A_1 & A_2 \\ 0 & A_3 \end{bmatrix} \begin{bmatrix} x^{(1)} \\ x^{(2)} \end{bmatrix} + \begin{bmatrix} B_1 \\ 0 \end{bmatrix} u \quad (4.21)$$

$$y = [C_1 \ C_2] x$$

where $x^{(1)}, x^{(2)}$ have orders n_1 and $n - n_1$ respectively and $[A_1, B_1]$ is c.c.

We shall postpone the proof of this until a later section (see the proof of Theorem 4.23). However, comparing with Example 4.2, it is clear that in (4.21) the vector $x^{(2)}$ is completely unaffected by u. Thus the state space has been divided into two parts, one being c.c. and the other *uncontrollable*.

Exercise 4.1.
Verify that the system in Example 1.1 is c.c.

Exercise 4.2.
Re-interpret the result of Exercise 3.31 in the light of Theorem 4.2.

Exercise 4.3.
Two pendulums are connected by a spring as shown.

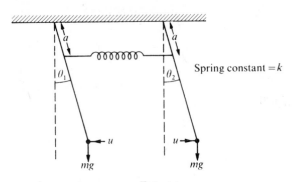

FIG. 4.1

The masses of the rods, which have unit lengths, can be neglected. Equal
and opposite control forces $u(t)$ are applied to the particles, which have
mass m. Write down the equations of motion for *small* oscillations so that
θ_i^2 and higher powers can be neglected. Take $x_1 = \theta_1 + \theta_2, x_2 = \theta_1 - \theta_2$,
$x_3 = \dot{x}_1, x_4 = \dot{x}_2$ as state variables and hence deduce that the system is
not c.c.

   Notice that if the control forces were not equal the system would be
c.c.

Exercise 4.4.
Consider again the problem of two connected masses moving on a smooth
horizontal plane, described in Exercise 1.2. Suppose now that in addition
to the springs the masses are joined by dampers as shown, the forces as
usual being proportional to velocity with coefficients d_1 and d_2.

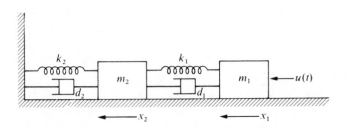

FIG. 4.2

Take the same state variables as before and derive the state equations in the form (4.4). If $m_1 = m_2 = 1, d_1 = d_2 = 1$ and $k_2 = \frac{1}{4}$, determine under what conditions the system is c.c.

Exercise 4.5.
A platform is supported by springs and dampers as shown, it being assumed that the forces they produce act at the end points P and Q, and that x_1 and x_2 are the displacements of these points from equilibrium.

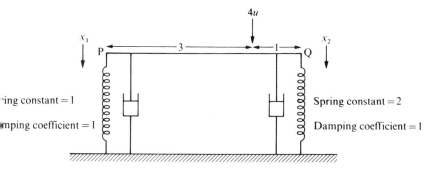

FIG. 4.3

This could be thought of as a simple representation of a vehicle suspension system. The forces exerted by the dampers are proportional to velocity and the springs obey Hooke's law. Assume that the mass of the platform can be neglected, so that the spring motions can be regarded as independent. If a control force $4u(t)$ is applied one quarter the way along from one end, show that the system equations are

$$\frac{d}{dt}\begin{bmatrix} x_1 \\ x_2 \end{bmatrix} = \begin{bmatrix} -1 & 0 \\ 0 & -2 \end{bmatrix}\begin{bmatrix} x_1 \\ x_2 \end{bmatrix} + \begin{bmatrix} 1 \\ 3 \end{bmatrix} u.$$

Verify that the system is c.c. If the ends of the platform are each given an initial displacement of 10 units, find using (4.13) a control function which returns the system to equilibrium at $t = 1$.

Exercise 4.6.
If in the system (3.48) A has repeated characteristic roots but nevertheless the Jordan form of A is a diagonal matrix, show that (3.48) is not c.c.

Exercise 4.7.
If the pair $[A, B]$ is c.c. show that $[A + BK, B]$ is also c.c. for any matrix K having appropriate dimensions. (Hint: do *not* use Theorem 4.1).

Exercise 4.8.
Using the matrix A in Exercise 3.1(a), find for what vectors b the system (3.48) is not c.c. Using Laplace transforms investigate what happens to $\bar{x}(s)$ in these cases.

Exercise 4.9.
By taking A to be the companion matrix

$$
\begin{bmatrix}
0 & 0 & -a_3 \\
1 & 0 & -a_2 \\
0 & 1 & -a_1
\end{bmatrix},
$$

assumed nonsingular, of a third degree polynomial $a(\lambda)$, and $b = [0, -k, 1]^T$, deduce using (4.5) that $a(\lambda)$ is divisible by $\lambda - k$ if and only if the pair $[A, b]$ is not c.c.

Exercise 4.10.
Prove that $U(t_0, t_1)$ defined in (4.12) satisfies the matrix differential equation

$$
\dot{U}(t, t_1) = A(t)U(t, t_1) + U(t, t_1)A^T(t) - B(t)B^T(t), \quad U(t_1, t_1) = 0.
$$

Exercise 4.11.
In the preceding exercise let A and B be time invariant, and put $W(t, t_1) = U(t, t_1) - U_0$ where the constant matrix U_0 satisfies

$$
AU_0 + U_0 A^T = BB^T.
$$

Write down the solution of the resulting differential equation for W using the result in Exercise 3.24, and hence show that

$$
U(t, t_1) = U_0 - \exp[A(t - t_1)] U_0 \exp[A^T(t - t_1)].
$$

Exercise 4.12.
If

$$\dot{x} = \begin{bmatrix} 1 & 2 & -1 \\ 0 & 1 & 0 \\ 1 & -4 & 3 \end{bmatrix} x + \begin{bmatrix} 0 \\ 0 \\ 1 \end{bmatrix} u$$

find a basis for the set of vectors which can be reached from the origin.

Exercise 4.13.
Show that the result in Theorem 4.4 still holds if the measure of control energy is

$$\int_{t_0}^{t_1} u^{\mathrm{T}}(\tau) R(\tau) u(\tau) \mathrm{d}\tau$$

where $R(t)$ is a positive definite symmetric matrix, and (4.13) is replaced by

$$u(t) = -R^{-1}(t)B^{\mathrm{T}}(t)\Phi^{\mathrm{T}}(t_0, t)U_1^{-1}(t_0, t_1)\,[x_0 - \Phi(t_0, t_1)x_{\mathrm{f}}]$$

where

$$U_1(t_0, t_1) = \int_{t_0}^{t_1} \Phi(t_0, \tau)B(\tau)R^{-1}(\tau)B^{\mathrm{T}}(\tau)\Phi^{\mathrm{T}}(t_0, \tau)\,\mathrm{d}\tau.$$

4.2. Observability.

Closely linked to the idea of controllability is that of observability, which in general terms means that it is possible to determine the state of a system by measuring only the output. For example, a political party which wins most votes in a national election usually claims that its policies are supported by a majority of the electorate; but can the state of opinion of the voters on a particular point at issue be determined from the overall election result?

Our precise definition is that the system S_1 described by (4.1) and (4.2) is *completely observable* (*c.o.*) if for any t_0 and any initial state $x(t_0) = x_0$ there exists a finite time $t_1 > t_0$ such that knowledge of $u(t)$ and $y(t)$ for $t_0 \leqslant t \leqslant t_1$ suffices to determine x_0. There is in fact no loss in generality in assuming $u(t)$ is identically zero throughout the interval.

Example 4.4. Consider the system described by

$$\dot{x}_1 = a_1 x_1 + b_1 u$$
$$\dot{x}_2 = a_2 x_2 + b_2 u$$
$$y = x_1.$$

The first equation shows that $x_1(t)$ ($= y(t)$) is completely determined by $u(t)$ and $x_1(t_0)$. Thus it is impossible to determine $x_2(t_0)$ by measuring the output, so the system is not c.o.

Notice that application of Theorem 4.1 easily shows that the system is c.c. provided $a_1 \neq a_2, b_1 \neq 0, b_2 \neq 0$.

The result corresponding to the general controllability criterion of Theorem 4.3 is:

THEOREM 4.10. The system S_1 is c.o. if and only if the symmetric *observability matrix*

$$V(t_0, t_1) = \int_{t_0}^{t_1} \Phi^T(\tau, t_0) C^T(\tau) C(\tau) \Phi(\tau, t_0) \, d\tau, \qquad (4.22)$$

where Φ is defined in (3.27), is nonsingular.

Proof.

Sufficiency. Assuming $u(t) \equiv 0, t_0 \leqslant t \leqslant t_1$, we have from (3.28)

$$y(t) = C(t)\Phi(t, t_0)x_0. \qquad (4.23)$$

Multiply (4.23) on the left by $\Phi^T(t, t_0)C^T(t)$ and integrate to obtain

$$\int_{t_0}^{t_1} \Phi^T(\tau, t_0) C^T(\tau) y(\tau) \, d\tau = V(t_0, t_1) x_0,$$

so that if $V(t_0, t_1)$ is nonsingular the initial state is

$$x_0 = V^{-1}(t_0, t_1) \int_{t_0}^{t_1} \Phi^T(\tau, t_0) C^T(\tau) y(\tau) \, d\tau, \qquad (4.24)$$

so S_1 is c.o.

Necessity. We now assume S_1 is c.o. and prove that $V(t_0, t_1)$ is non-singular. The argument follows along very similar lines to those used in the proof of the second part of Theorem 4.3. First, if α is an arbitrary column n-vector,

$$\alpha^T V\alpha = \int_{t_0}^{t_1} [C(\tau)\,\Phi(\tau, t_0)\alpha]^T [C(\tau)\Phi(\tau, t_0)\alpha]\; d\tau$$

$$\geqslant 0$$

so $V(t_0, t_1)$ is positive semidefinite. Next, suppose there exists an $\hat{\alpha}$ such that $\hat{\alpha}^T V\hat{\alpha} = 0$. It then follows as before that $C(\tau)\Phi(\tau, t_0)\,\hat{\alpha} \equiv 0$, $t_0 \leqslant \tau \leqslant t_1$. From (4.23) this implies that when $x_0 = \hat{\alpha}$ the output is identically zero throughout the time interval, so that x_0 cannot be determined in this case from a knowledge of y. This contradicts the assumption that S_1 is c.o. Hence $V(t_0, t_1)$ is positive definite, and there-fore nonsingular.

Notice that when S_1 is c.o., (4.24) provides an explicit expression for the initial state in terms of the output and the transition and observability matrices.

Since the observability of S_1 is independent of B, we shall refer to the observability of the *pair* $[A, C]$. We have seen in Exercise 3.22 that $\phi^T(t_0, t)$ is the transition matrix for the system having state matrix $-A^T(t)$. By comparing eqns (4.12) and (4.22) we can therefore see that the controllability matrix (4.12) is identical to the observability matrix (4.22) associated with the pair $[-A^T(t), B^T(t)]$. Conversely, the observ-ability matrix (4.22) is identical to the matrix (4.12) associated with the pair $[-A^T(t), C^T(t)]$. We have thus established:

THEOREM 4.11. (*Duality*) The system S_1 defined in (4.1) and (4.2) is c.c. if and only if the *dual* system

$$\left.\begin{aligned}\dot{x}(t) &= -A^T(t)x(t) + C^T(t)u(t)\\y(t) &= B^T(t)x(t)\end{aligned}\right\} \tag{4.25}$$

is c.o.; and conversely.

If the matrices have complex elements, transpose in (4.25) is replaced by conjugate transpose. This duality theorem is extremely useful, since it enables us to deduce immediately from a controllability result the corresponding one on observability (and conversely). For example, to obtain the observability criterion for the time invariant case, we simply apply Theorem 4.1 to (4.25) to obtain (after transposition of (4.5), which does not affect its rank):

THEOREM 4.12. When A, B, and C are time-invariant the system S_1 is c.o. if and only if the observability matrix

$$V = \begin{bmatrix} C \\ CA \\ CA^2 \\ \cdot \\ \cdot \\ \cdot \\ CA^{n-1} \end{bmatrix} \tag{4.26}$$

has rank n.

Example 4.5. Consider again Example 1.2 describing an electrically heated oven, and let the state equations be as given in (4.11). Suppose that as stated in Example 2.5 it is only possible to measure $y = x_1$, the jacket (excess) temperature. Then the observability matrix in (4.26) is

$$\begin{bmatrix} 1 & 0 \\ -2 & 2 \end{bmatrix}$$

which has rank 2. Thus the system is c.o., that is, it is possible to determine the temperature of the oven interior from a knowledge of $u(t)$ and $x_1(t)$.

It is worth noting that in the scalar output case (i.e. $r = 1$) if $u = 0$ $y(t)$ is known in the form

$$\sum_{i=1}^{n} \gamma_i \exp(\lambda_i t),$$

assuming that all the characteristic roots λ_i of A are distinct, then x_0 can be obtained more easily than by using (4.24). For suppose that $t_0 = 0$ and consider the solution of $\dot{x} = Ax$ in the spectral form (3.5), namely

$$x(t) = \sum_{i=1}^{n} (v_i x(0)) \exp(\lambda_i t) w_i.$$

We have

$$y(t) = \sum_{i=1}^{n} (v_i x(0)) (cw_i) \exp(\lambda_i t),$$

and equating coefficients of the exponential terms gives

$$v_i x(0) = \gamma_i / (cw_i), i = 1, \ldots, n.$$

This represents n linear equations for the n unknown components of $x(0)$ in terms of the γ_i and left and right characteristic vectors of A. Notice that because $[A, c]$ is c.o., no term cw_i is zero (see Exercise 4.20) and a unique solution for $x(0)$ therefore exists since the v_i are linearly independent.

For the scalar output case we also see that V in (4.26) is identical to the matrix in (3.65), so Theorem 3.5 can be restated as:

THEOREM 4.13. A system in the form (3.60) and (3.61) can be transformed into the canonical form (3.62) if and only if it is c.o.

For this reason a system described by (3.62), (3.63), and (3.64) is often said to be in *observable* canonical form.

Again by duality the result corresponding to Theorem 4.9 is:

THEOREM 4.14. When S_1 is time invariant then if V in (4.26) has rank $n_1 < n$ there exists a system algebraically equivalent to S_1 having the form

$$\left. \frac{d}{dt} \begin{bmatrix} x^{(1)} \\ x^{(2)} \end{bmatrix} = \begin{bmatrix} A_1 & 0 \\ A_2 & A_3 \end{bmatrix} \begin{bmatrix} x^{(1)} \\ x^{(2)} \end{bmatrix} + \begin{bmatrix} B_1 \\ B_2 \end{bmatrix} u \atop y = C_1 x^{(1)} \right\} \quad (4.27)$$

where $x^{(1)}, x^{(2)}$ have orders n_1 and $n - n_1$ respectively and $[A_1, C_1]$ is c.o.

As in Example 4.4, we see that in (4.27) y is completely unaffected by $x^{(2)}$ which is therefore said to be *unobservable,* and the state space has been divided into two parts with respect to observability.

We close this section with a decomposition result which effectively combines together Theorems 4.9 and 4.14 to show that a linear time-invariant system can be split up into *four* mutually exclusive parts, respectively (1) c.c. but unobservable (2) c.c. and c.o. (3) uncontrollable and unobservable (4) c.o. but uncontrollable (see Zadeh and Desoer, 1963, p. 505).

THEOREM 4.15. When S_1 is time-invariant it is algebraically equivalent to

$$\frac{d}{dt} \begin{bmatrix} x^{(1)} \\ x^{(2)} \\ x^{(3)} \\ x^{(4)} \end{bmatrix} = \begin{bmatrix} A^{11} & A^{12} & A^{13} & A^{14} \\ 0 & A^{22} & 0 & A^{24} \\ 0 & 0 & A^{33} & A^{34} \\ 0 & 0 & 0 & A^{44} \end{bmatrix} \begin{bmatrix} x^{(1)} \\ x^{(2)} \\ x^{(3)} \\ x^{(4)} \end{bmatrix} + \begin{bmatrix} B^1 \\ B^2 \\ 0 \\ 0 \end{bmatrix} u$$

$$y = C^2 x^{(2)} + C^4 x^{(4)}$$

where the superscripts refer to the stated classifications.

Exercise 4.14.
If the output in the spring-mass system described in Exercise 1.2 is taken to be $y = x_2$, is the system c.o.?

Exercise 4.15.
Consider again the rabbit–fox environment problem described in Exercise 1.4. If it is possible to count only the *total* number of animals, can the individual numbers of rabbits and foxes be determined?

Exercise 4.16.

In the circuit shown in Fig. 4.4 take the state variables to be the voltage x_1 across the capacitor and the current x_2 through the inductor. The input voltage u is the control variable and the current y can be regarded as the output. Derive the equations describing the system, and show that if $R_1 R_2 C = L$ it is not c.c. and not c.o.

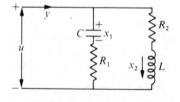

FIG. 4.4

Exercise 4.17.
Using the matrix in Exercise 3.1 (*a*), find for what vectors *c* the pair
[*A, c*] is not c.o. By using the solution of (3.1) obtained, investigate
what happens to $y(t)$ in these cases.

Exercise 4.18.
Bearing in mind the result of the preceding exercise, does it follow that
if some of the exponential terms present in $x(t)$ are missing from $y(t)$
then the system is not c.o.?

Exercise 4.19.
For the system $\dot{x} = Ax$ with A matrix as in Exercise 3.1 (*a'*) and $y = [1,2]x$
find $x(0)$ if $y(t) = -20 \exp(-3t) + 21 \exp(-2t)$.

Exercise 4.20.
Suppose that the pair [*A, c*] is c.o., where *c* is a row *n*-vector, and that
all the characteristic roots of *A* are distinct. If the right characteristic
vectors of *A* are $w_1, \ldots, w_n$ show that $cw_i \neq 0, i = 1, 2, \ldots, n$.

Exercise 4.21.
If in the system described by (3.60) and (3.61) *A* has repeated characteristic roots, but the Jordan form of *A* is a diagonal matrix, show that the
system is not c.o. (compare with Exercise 4.6).

Exercise 4.22.
Prove that $V(t_0, t_1)$ defined in (4.22) satisfies the differential equation

$$\dot{V}(t, t_1) = -A^{\mathrm{T}}(t)V(t, t_1) - V(t, t_1)A(t) - C^{\mathrm{T}}(t)C(t), \quad V(t_1, t_1) = 0.$$

Compare with Exercise 4.10.

Exercise 4.23.
Prove directly the necessity of the condition in Theorem 4.12. (Hint:
assume rank $V < n$ and obtain a contradiction).

Exercise 4.24.
Show that if the initial state of a constant system which is not c.o.
satisfies $Vx(0) \equiv 0$, where V is defined in (4.26), then $y(t) \equiv 0$ for all
$t \geqslant 0$. (Hint: it can be assumed that the system is in the form (4.27).)

Exercise 4.25.
Obtain the result corresponding to Theorem 4.8 by expressing the observability matrix $\hat{V}(t_0, t_1)$ in terms of $V(t_0, t_1)$.

†4.3. Controllability and polynomials

We now discuss some interesting relationships involving controllability and polynomials for time invariant systems. By duality, corresponding results can also be obtained in terms of observability. Some of the ideas have already been hinted at in Exercises 4.8 and 4.17.

Let A be in the companion form (3.63), i.e.

$$A = \begin{bmatrix} 0 & 0 & \cdot & \cdot & -k_n \\ 1 & 0 & \cdot & \cdot & -k_{n-1} \\ \cdot & \cdot & \cdot & \cdot & \cdot \\ \cdot & \cdot & \cdot & \cdot & \cdot \\ 0 & 0 & \cdot & 1 & -k_1 \end{bmatrix} \qquad (4.28)$$

then the basic Theorem 4.1 on constant systems can be stated in the following form:

THEOREM 4.16. The pair $[A, B]$ is c.c. if and only if the set of polynomials

$$k(\lambda) \equiv \det(\lambda I - A) = \lambda^n + k_1 \lambda^{n-1} + \cdots + k_n$$

and

$$p_i(\lambda) = b_{ni}\lambda^{n-1} + b_{n-1,i}\lambda^{n-2} + \cdots + b_{1i}, i = 1, 2, \ldots, m$$

where $B = [b_{ij}]$, is relatively prime. Furthermore, the columns of the controllability matrix in (4.5) are a re-ordering of the columns of

$$[p_1(A), p_2(A), \ldots, p_m(A)]$$

where

$$p_i(A) = b_{ni} A^{n-1} + \cdots + b_{1i}I.$$

Proof. For the general case this relies on a theorem on polynomial matrices and is too lengthy to give here, so we refer the reader to Barnett

(1971, p.41). When $m = 1$, the argument is straightforward and the steps have been indicated in Exercises 2.11 and 2.12. First, if the roots of $k(\lambda)$ (which are the characteristic roots of A) are $\lambda_1, \lambda_2, \ldots, \lambda_n$ then

$$\det p_1(A) = p_1(\lambda_1) p_1(\lambda_2) \cdots p_1(\lambda_n)$$

so that $p_1(A)$ is singular if and only if $p_1(\lambda_j) = 0$ for at least one j; in other words, if and only if $p_1(\lambda)$ and $k(\lambda)$ have a common factor. To complete the proof, let e_i and r_i denote the ith columns of I and $p_1(A)$ respectively. Using (4.28) it is easy to show that

$$r_1 = [b_{11}, b_{21}, \ldots, b_{n1}]^\mathrm{T} \equiv B.$$

Also, $e_i = A e_{i-1}$ and $p_1(A)$ and A commute with each other, so

$$r_i = p_1(A)e_i = p_1(A)Ae_{i-1} = Ap_1(A)e_{i-1} = Ar_{i-1}.$$

Hence $p_1(A) = [B, AB, \ldots, A^{n-1}B]$ which is the controllability matrix (4.5).

   Theorem 4.16 can be extended to give a simple method of calculating the greatest common divisor of $a(\lambda)$ and the $p_i(\lambda)$ if $[A, B]$ is not c.c. (See Barnett 1971, p.43). In particular, the degree of the g.c.d. is equal to the rank defect of the controllability matrix (4.5). This is a special case of another result (Rosenbrock 1970, p.85) which states that for any $n \times n$ matrix A, the rank defect of (4.5) is equal to the degree of the nth determinantal divisor (see Section 2.5) of the $n \times (n + m)$ polynomial matrix $[\lambda I - A, B]$. When $m = 1$ we can relate this to the Laplace transform representation of the solution of (4.4). This was obtained in eqn. (2.41) as

$$\bar{x}(s) = (sI - A)^{-1} B\bar{u}(s). \tag{4.29}$$

If we write

$$(sI - A)^{-1} B = \frac{1}{k(s)} \begin{bmatrix} q_1(s) \\ \cdot \\ \cdot \\ \cdot \\ q_n(s) \end{bmatrix},$$

then

$$[sI - A, B] = [sI - A] \begin{bmatrix} & q_1/k \\ & \cdot \\ I_n & \cdot \\ & q_n/k \end{bmatrix}. \qquad (4.30)$$

The $n \times n$ minors of the matrix product on the right in (4.30) are just $\det(sI - A) = k(s), q_1(s), \ldots, q_n(s)$ so that these polynomials are relatively prime if and only if the pair $[A, B]$ is c.c. In other words, for systems with a scalar input we have the interesting interpretation that complete controllability is equivalent to there being no common factors between numerators and denominator in the vector transfer function $(sI - A)^{-1} B$ in (4.29).

Example 4.6. In Exercise 4.8 with

$$A = \begin{bmatrix} -1 & -1 \\ 2 & -4 \end{bmatrix}, b = \begin{bmatrix} b_1 \\ b_2 \end{bmatrix}$$

the controllability matrix U in (4.5) has determinant

$$\det[b, Ab] = (2b_1 - b_2)(b_1 - b_2).$$

Also

$$(sI - A)^{-1} b = \frac{1}{s^2 + 5s + 6} \begin{bmatrix} s + 4 & -1 \\ 2 & s + 1 \end{bmatrix} \begin{bmatrix} b_1 \\ b_2 \end{bmatrix}$$

$$= \frac{1}{(s + 3)(s + 2)} \begin{bmatrix} (s + 4)b_1 - b_2 \\ (s + 1)b_2 + 2b_1 \end{bmatrix}$$

The pair $[A, b]$ is not c.c. if $b_2 = 2b_1$ or $b_2 = b_1$, in which cases there are common factors $s + 2$ and $s + 3$ respectively in the vector transfer function.

Exercise 4.26. Use the Cayley–Hamilton theorem to show that if

$$b(\lambda) = b_0 \lambda^n + b_1 \lambda^{n-1} + \cdots + b_n$$

then
$$b(A) = [\beta, A\beta, \ldots, A^{n-1}\beta]$$

where A is given by (4.28) and
$$\beta = [b_n - b_0 k_n, b_{n-1} - b_0 k_{n-1}, \ldots, b_1 - b_0 k_1]^T.$$

Exercise 4.27.
Using the notation of Exercises 2.12 and 2.13 deduce that the pair $[C, r]$ is c.o. if and only if $k(\lambda)$ and $\beta(\lambda)$ are relatively prime.

Exercise 4.28.
If $k'(\lambda)$ denotes the derivative of $k(\lambda)$ with respect to λ, and A is defined in (4.28), deduce that $k'(A)$ is nonsingular if and only if $k(\lambda)$ has no repeated zeros.

4.4. Linear feedback

In Chapter 1 we discussed the importance of the idea of feedback, mainly in the context of single-input single-output systems. We now study feedback using state space representations, and our first result provides an extremely important link with controllability. Consider the time invariant system
$$\dot{x} = Ax + Bu. \tag{4.31}$$

Suppose that we apply *linear (state) feedback*, that is each control variable is a *linear* combination of the state variables, so that
$$u = Kx \tag{4.32}$$

where K is a constant $m \times n$ *feedback* (or *gain*) *matrix*. The resulting *closed loop* system obtained by substituting (4.32) into (4.31) is
$$\dot{x} = (A + BK)x. \tag{4.33}$$

Assume that as is usual in applications A and B are real, and let $\Lambda_n = \{\theta_1, \theta_2, \ldots, \theta_n\}$ be an *arbitrary* set of n complex numbers such that any which are not purely real occur in conjugate pairs.

THEOREM 4.17. If the pair $[A, B]$ is c.c. then there exists a real matrix K such that the characteristic roots of $A + BK$ are the set Λ_n.

In view of the development in Section 3.2 it follows that the solution of (4.33) depends on the characteristic roots of $A + BK$, so provided

(4.31) is c.c. the theorem tells us that using linear feedback it is possible
to exert a considerable influence on the time behaviour of the closed loop
system by suitably choosing the θ_i. A further comment on this point will
be made at the end of the section. However, it should be noted that it is
not, in general, possible to choose K in order to give $A + BK$ an arbitrary
Jordan form..

The theorem gives us a new and most interesting insight into the
meaning of linear feedback in state space terms. For example, if a single-
input single-output system is in the classical form (3.42), then application
of Theorem 4.17 to the equivalent matrix representation (3.44) shows
that in general u will be a linear combination of *all* the phase variables,
that is of $z, z^{(1)}, \ldots, z^{(n-1)}$, not just a multiple of the output z alone.
If (4.31) is not c.c. then it follows from Theorem 4.9 that only n_1 of the
characteristic roots of the closed loop system can be arbitrarily chosen
as members of a set A_{n_1}, since A_3 in (4.21) is unaffected by the feedback.

The theorem is very recent, the first general proof being given by
Wonham in 1967. We shall present a somewhat different argument which
is nevertheless rather lengthy, so we first consider the case when there is
only a single control variable, and give a proof which includes a method
of constructing K.

Proof when m = 1. Since (4.31) is c.c. it follows from Theorems 4.2 and
3.4 that there exists a nonsingular transformation $w = Tx$ such that (4.31)
is transformed into $\dot{w} = Cw + du$ where C and d are given by (3.45) and
(3.46) respectively. The feedback control $u = \kappa w$ where

$$\kappa = [\kappa_n, \kappa_{n-1}, \ldots, \kappa_1]$$

produces the closed loop matrix $C + d\kappa$ which has the same companion
form as C but with last row $- [\gamma_n, \gamma_{n-1}, \ldots, \gamma_1]$, where

$$\kappa_i = k_i - \gamma_i, i = 1, 2, \ldots, n. \tag{4.34}$$

Since

$$C + d\kappa = T(A + b\kappa T)T^{-1} \tag{4.35}$$

it follows that the desired matrix is $K = \kappa T$, the κ_i being given by (4.34).
In this equation the k_i are the coefficients in the characteristic polynomial of A, i.e.

$$\det (\lambda I - A) = \lambda^n + k_1 \lambda^{n-1} + \cdots + k_n, \tag{4.36}$$

and the γ_i are obtained by equating coefficients of λ in

$$\lambda^n + \gamma_1 \lambda^{n-1} + \cdots + \gamma_n \equiv \prod_{i=1}^{n} (\lambda - \theta_i). \qquad (4.37)$$

The realness of K follows from that of κ and T.

Notice that (4.35) shows that in the single control variable case the closed loop matrix $A + b\kappa T$ is similar to a companion form matrix, and so in nonderogatory (see Section 2.5). This provides an illustration of our earlier remark that the closed loop matrix cannot be made to take an arbitrary Jordan form. Notice also that if in the preceding argument the canonical form involving C, d is replaced by the observable canonical form in Theorem 3.5, we obtain:

COROLLARY 4.2. If the pair $[A, c]$ is c.o., where c is a real row n-vector, then there exists a real column n-vector ℓ such that the characteristic roots of $A + \ell c$ are the set Λ_n.

This result can also be deduced from Theorem 4.17 using the duality Theorem 4.11.

Example 4.7. Consider the matrices A and b given in Example 3.8. The characteristic equation of A is

$$\lambda^2 - 3\lambda + 14 = 0$$

which has roots $3/2 \pm i\sqrt{(47)}/2$. Suppose we wish the characteristic roots of the closed loop system to be -1 and -2, so that the corresponding polynomial is $\lambda^2 + 3\lambda + 2$. From (4.34), (4.36), and (4.37) we have

$$\kappa_1 = k_1 - \gamma_1 = -3 - 3 = -6,$$
$$\kappa_2 = k_2 - \gamma_2 = 14 - 2 = 12.$$

Hence using the matrix T in Example 3.8,

$$K = \kappa T$$
$$= \tfrac{1}{8} [12, -6] \begin{bmatrix} -1 & 1 \\ 3 & 5 \end{bmatrix}$$
$$= -[15/4, 9/4].$$

It is easy to verify that

$$A + bK = \tfrac{1}{4} \begin{bmatrix} -11 & -21 \\ 1 & -1 \end{bmatrix}$$

does have the desired roots.

Before proving Theorem 4.17 for $m > 1$ we need a preliminary result.

LEMMA 4.1. *If the pair $[A, B]$ is c.c. and the columns of B, assumed non-zero, are $b_1, b_2, \ldots, b_m$, then there exist real matrices $K_i, i = 1, 2, \ldots, m$, such that the pairs $[A + BK_i, b_i]$ are c.c.*

Proof. For convenience consider the case $i = 1$. Since the matrix U in (4.5) has full rank, it is possible to select from its columns at least one set of n vectors which are linearly independent (see Section 2.2). Define an $n \times n$ matrix M by choosing such a set as follows:

$$M = [b_1, Ab_1, \ldots, A^{r_1 - 1} b_1, b_2, Ab_2, \ldots, A^{r_2 - 1} b_2, \ldots]$$

where r_i is the smallest integer such that $A^{r_i} b_i$ is linearly dependent on all the preceding vectors, the process continuing until n columns of U are taken. Define an $m \times n$ matrix N having its r_1 th column equal to e_2, the second column of I_m, its $(r_1 + r_2)$th column equal to e_3, its $(r_1 + r_2 + r_3)$th column equal to e_4 and so on, all its other columns being zero. It is then not difficult to show that the desired matrix in the statement of the Lemma is $K_1 = NM^{-1}$. This is established by comparing terms on both sides of the expression $K_1 M \equiv N$, from which it follows that

$$b_1, (A + BK_1)b_1, (A + BK_1)^2 b_1, \ldots, (A + BK_1)^{n-1} b_1$$

are linearly independent, so by Theorem 4.1 the pair $[A + BK_1, b_1]$ is c.c.

It is worth remarking that the matrix M defined above can be used as a transformation giving a canonical form for (4.31) with $m > 1$ (see Chen 1970, Chapter 7 where fuller details of the proof of Lemma 4.1 can also be found).

Proof of Theorem 4.17 for $m > 1$. Let K_1 be the matrix in the proof of Lemma 4.1 and define an $m \times n$ matrix K' having as its first row some vector k, and all its other rows zero. Then the control

$$u = (K_1 + K')x \tag{4.38}$$

leads to the closed loop system

$$\dot{x} = (A + BK_1)x + BK'x$$
$$= (A + BK_1)x + b_1kx,$$

where b_1 is the first column of B. Since the pair $[A + BK_1, b_1]$ is c.c. it now follows from the proof of the theorem when $m = 1$ that k can be chosen so that the characteristic roots of $A + BK_1 + b_1k$ are the set Λ, so the desired feedback control is indeed (4.38).

If $y = Cx$ is the output vector in (4.2) then again by duality we can immediately deduce from Theorem 4.17:

COROLLARY 4.3. If the pair $[A, C]$ is c.o. then there exists a real matrix L such that the characteristic roots of $A + LC$ are the set Λ_n.

It is interesting to relate the feedback theorem to the transfer function for the scalar input and output case defined in (1.14), namely

$$g(s) = \frac{\beta_0 s^m + \beta_1 s^{m-1} + \cdots + \beta_m}{s^n + k_1 s^{n-1} + \cdots + k_n}.$$

It is easy to verify (see Exercise 4.39) that

$$g(s) = r(sI - C)^{-1}d \qquad (4.39)$$

where C is the companion form matrix in (3.45), d the column vector in (3.46) and

$$r = [\beta_m, \ldots, \beta_1, \beta_0, 0, \ldots, 0],$$

so $g(s)$ is the transfer function for the state space system

$$\dot{x} = Cx + du, y = rx.$$

As in the proof of Theorem 4.17 when $m = 1$, linear state feedback affects only the last row of C, which contains the coefficients of the denominator of the transfer function. In other words, linear feedback enables the poles of the closed loop transfer function to be arbitrarily located in the complex s-plane, but leaves the zeros unaltered. This fact does not hold when $m > 1$, when in general the zeros are also affected.

We now establish a relationship between the characteristic equations of closed loop and open loop linear systems with multivariable control. As in (2.44) the open loop system is described by

$$\bar{y}(s) = C(sI - A)^{-1}B\bar{u}(s)$$
$$= G(s)\bar{u}(s)$$

where $G(s)$ is the $r \times m$ open loop transfer function matrix. The closed loop system considered is of the form shown in Fig. 4.5.

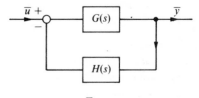

FIG. 4.5

This is the multivariable version of Fig. 1.8 and the equation corresponding to (1.15) is

$$(I_r + G(s)H(s))\bar{y}(s) = G(s)\bar{u}(s). \qquad (4.40)$$

If it is assumed that $r = m$, so $G(s)$ and $H(s)$ are square, then as in Exercise 1.5 a unity feedback loop can be used.

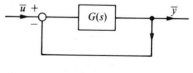

FIG. 4.6

In Fig. 4.6 we have

$$(I_m + G(s))\bar{y}(s) = G(s)\bar{u}(s)$$

where by analogy with the scalar case in Section 1.2.1, $I_m + G(s)$ is termed the *return difference* matrix. In state space terms the control is

$$u(t) = -y(t)$$
$$= -Cx(t)$$

so that the closed loop system is

$$\dot{x} = (A - BC)x.$$

An interesting relationship between the two systems is the following:

THEOREM 4.18. The ratio of the characteristic equations of the closed loop and open loop systems is equal to the determinant of the return difference matrix, i.e.

$$\frac{\det (sI_n - A + BC)}{\det (sI_n - A)} = \det [I_m + G(s)] \tag{4.41}$$

$$= \det [I_m + C(sI - A)^{-1}B].$$

Proof.

$$\det (sI - A + BC) = \det [(sI - A)\{I + (sI - A)^{-1}BC\}]$$

$$= \det (sI - A) \det [I + (sI - A)^{-1}BC]$$

$$= \det (sI - A) \det [I + C(sI - A)^{-1}B],$$

$$= \det (sI - A) \det [I + G(s)],$$

the penultimate step following from the fact that for any two matrices X and Y having dimensions $n \times m$ and $m \times n$ respectively then

$$\det (I_n + XY) = \det (I_m + YX) \tag{4.42}$$

(see Exercise 2.3).

The proof of Theorem 4.17 for $m > 1$ given earlier does not provide a practical way of constructing the feedback matrix K in (4.32). However, we can use (4.42) to derive a simple method due to MacFarlane:

THEOREM 4.19. Let all the characteristic roots λ_i of A be distinct and let $W = [w_1, w_2, \ldots, w_n]$, where w_i is a characteristic vector corresponding to λ_i. With linear feedback $u = -Kx$, suppose that the characteristic roots of A and of $A - BK$ are ordered so that those of $A - BK$ are to be $\mu_1, \mu_2, \ldots, \mu_p, \lambda_{p+1}, \ldots, \lambda_n$ ($p \leqslant n$). Then provided $[A, B]$ is c.c. a suitable matrix is

$$K = fg\widetilde{W} \tag{4.43}$$

where $\widetilde{W}$ consists of the first p rows of W^{-1}, and

$$g = [\alpha_1/\beta_1, \alpha_2/\beta_2, \ldots, \alpha_p/\beta_p], \tag{4.44}$$

$$\alpha_i = \prod_{\substack{j=1}}^{p} (\lambda_i - \mu_j) \Big/ \prod_{\substack{j=1 \\ j \neq i}}^{p} (\lambda_i - \lambda_j), p > 1, \tag{4.45}$$

$$\beta = [\beta_1, \beta_2, \ldots, \beta_p]^T = \widetilde{W}Bf, \tag{4.46}$$

f being any column m-vector such that all $\beta_i \neq 0$.

Proof. Since only the first p characteristic roots of the closed and open loop systems differ, eqn (4.41) gives

$$\det \left[I + K(sI - A)^{-1}B \right] = \prod_{i=1}^{p} (s - \mu_i) \Big/ \prod_{i=1}^{p} (s - \lambda_i). \qquad (4.47)$$

Furthermore since $A = WA_dW^{-1}$, where $A_d = \text{diag}\,[\lambda_1, \ldots, \lambda_n]$, (see (2.31)) we have

$$
\begin{aligned}
\det \left[I + K(sI - A)^{-1}B \right] &= \det \left[I + (sI - A)^{-1}BK \right] \\
&= \det \left[I + W(sI - A_d)^{-1}W^{-1}Bfg\bar{W} \right] \\
&= 1 + (g\bar{W})\left[W(sI - A)^{-1}W^{-1}Bf \right] \qquad (4.48)
\end{aligned}
$$

where the first and last steps follow from (4.42). Using the definition of $\bar{W}$ the right side of (4.48) becomes

$$
\begin{aligned}
1 &+ g(sI - \bar{A}_d)^{-1}\bar{W}Bf \\
&= 1 + g(sI - \bar{A}_d)^{-1}\beta \qquad (4.49)
\end{aligned}
$$

where $\bar{A}_d = \text{diag}\,[\lambda_1, \lambda_2, \ldots, \lambda_p]$. Hence by (4.47) and (4.49) we have

$$1 + g(sI - \bar{A}_d)^{-1}\beta = \prod_{1}^{p} (s - \mu_i)/(s - \lambda_i) \qquad (4.50)$$

$$= 1 + \sum_{i=1}^{p} \alpha_i/(s - \lambda_i), \qquad (4.51)$$

where the α_i given in (4.45) are obtained by expansion of (4.50) into the partial fractions (4.51) (note that when $p = 1$, $\alpha_1 = \lambda_1 - \mu_1$). Clearly

$$(sI - \bar{A}_d)^{-1} = \text{diag}\,[1/(s - \lambda_1), \ldots, 1/(s - \lambda_p)],$$

so the expression (4.44) for the elements of g follows from (4.51). Since the system is c.c., $\bar{W}B$ has no zero rows (see Exercise 4.37) and this ensures the existence of a suitable f.

The method can be extended to the case when A has repeated roots. Note that the relative simplicity of the expression for K is due to the fact that the matrix on the right in (4.43) has rank one.

Example 4.8. Consider the matrix A given in Example 3.1, and let $b = [2, 1]^T$. We have $\lambda_1 = -1, \lambda_2 = -2$ and

$$W = \begin{bmatrix} 1 & 1 \\ -1 & -2 \end{bmatrix}, \qquad W^{-1} = \begin{bmatrix} 2 & 1 \\ -1 & -1 \end{bmatrix}.$$

Suppose that $\mu_1 = -3, \mu_2 = -4$, so $\tilde{W} = W^{-1}$. From (4.45), $\alpha_1 = 6$, $\alpha_2 = -2$, and (4.46) gives

$$\begin{bmatrix} \beta_1 \\ \beta_2 \end{bmatrix} = \begin{bmatrix} 2 & 1 \\ -1 & -1 \end{bmatrix} \begin{bmatrix} 2 \\ 1 \end{bmatrix} f = \begin{bmatrix} 5f_1 \\ -3f_1 \end{bmatrix}.$$

Hence we can take $f_1 = 1$, which results in

$$g = [6/5, 2/3]$$

using (4.44). Finally, from (4.43), the desired feedback matrix is

$$K = 1.[6/5, 2/3] W^{-1}$$
$$= [26/15, 8/15]. \tag{4.52}$$

The reader should verify that the characteristic roots of $A - bK$ are as specified.

Example 4.9. Let b in the preceding example be replaced by

$$B = \begin{bmatrix} 2 & 1 \\ 1 & 0 \end{bmatrix},$$

everything else remaining unaltered. From (4.46) we now obtain

$$\begin{bmatrix} \beta_1 \\ \beta_2 \end{bmatrix} = \begin{bmatrix} 5f_1 & + & 2f_2 \\ -3f_1 & - & f_2 \end{bmatrix}$$

so that $f_1 = 1, f_2 = 0$ gives K with first row identical to (4.52) and second row zero. However $f_1 = 1, f_2 = -1$ gives $\beta_1 = 3, \beta_2 = -2$ so that $g_1 = 2$, $g_2 = 1$, and from (4.43) we now have

$$K = \begin{bmatrix} 1 \\ -1 \end{bmatrix} \begin{bmatrix} 2 & 1 \end{bmatrix} W^{-1}$$

$$= \begin{bmatrix} 3 & 1 \\ -3 & -1 \end{bmatrix},$$

and again the reader can verify that $A - BK$ has the roots -3 and -4.

Methods for controlling systems by prespecifying the closed loop system characteristic roots are often called *modal control* techniques, the name *mode* being given to the terms $\exp(\lambda_i t)w_i$ in the expression (3.5) for the solution of a linear system. Much effort has been put into this approach (Porter and Crossley 1972) but there are a number of disadvantages which arise in practical applications. For example, there is no means of directly correlating the time behaviour of the closed loop system with the specified values of the poles since, as we have mentioned, there is no control over the closed loop zeros (see MacFarlane (1972) for further discussion).

Exercise 4.29.
Using the matrices in Exercise 3.30(*a*), use the method of Theorem 4.17 to find a 1×2 matrix K such that the closed loop system has characteristic roots -4 and -5.

Exercise 4.30.
Repeat the procedure of the preceding exercise using the matrices in Exercise 3.30(*b*) so as to make the closed loop system characteristic roots $-1, -1 \pm 2i$.

Exercise 4.31.
Verify that the method of Theorem 4.17 when applied to Example 4.8 produces the same matrix K.

Exercise 4.32.

If

$$A = \begin{bmatrix} 0 & 1 & 0 \\ 0 & 0 & 1 \\ 6 & -11 & 6 \end{bmatrix}, \qquad B = \begin{bmatrix} 1 & 0 \\ 0 & 1 \\ 1 & 1 \end{bmatrix}$$

find using Theorem 4.19 a suitable matrix K which makes the characteristic roots of $A - BK$ equal to $1, 1, 3$.

Exercise 4.33.

Consider yet again the rabbit–fox environment problem of Exercise 1.4. It was seen in Exercise 1.7 that if $a_1 - a_4 > 0$ in eqns (1.6) then in general the animal populations increase without limit as $t \to \infty$. Suppose for simplicity that the values of the constants are such that the system equations are

$$\dot{x}_1 = 2x_1 - 3x_2, \quad \dot{x}_2 = 2x_1 - x_2.$$

It is decided to control the environment by introducing linear feedback in the form of a disease which is fatal to rabbits but does not affect foxes, thereby reducing the rate of growth of the rabbit population by an amount kx_1. Find the smallest value of k which prevents the 'population explosion' from occurring (assuming arbitrary initial population sizes).

Exercise 4.34.

Consider

$$\dot{x} = Ax + bu, \quad u = cx$$

where b and c are respectively column and row n-vectors. Let b be a right characteristic vector of A corresponding to a root λ. Show that b and $\lambda + cb$ are corresponding characteristic vector and root of the closed loop system.

If on the contrary b is arbitrary but c is a left characteristic vector of A corresponding to λ, show that c and $\lambda + cb$ are corresponding characteristic vector and root of the closed loop system.

Exercise 4.35.

In the preceding exercise let b and c be respectively right and left characteristic vectors of A corresponding to the root λ. Assuming that all the characteristic roots of A are distinct, show that the other roots and vectors of the closed loop system are just the remaining roots and vectors of A.

Exercise 4.36.

Let all the characteristic roots of A be distinct and let W be the matrix defined in Theorem 4.19. By applying the transformation $x = W\xi$ to (4.31) deduce that u_j can influence ξ_i if and only if $p_{ij} \neq 0$, where the p_{ij} are defined by $b_i = \sum_{j=1}^{n} p_{ji}w_j$, b_i denoting the ith column of B. Note that as in Section 3.1 it follows that $p_{ji} = v_j b_i$ where v_j are left characteristic vectors of A.

If $Q_j = [b_j, Ab_j, A^2 b_j, \ldots, A^{n-1} b_j]$

it can be verified that $Q_j = WP_j M^T$ where M is the Vandermonde matrix defined in Exercise 2.15 and $P_j = \text{diag } [p_{1j}, p_{2j}, \ldots, p_{nj}]$. Hence deduce that rank Q_j is equal to the number of modes which can be controlled independently by the input u_j.

Exercise 4.37.

Using the notation in Theorem 4.19, deduce that if $\widetilde{W}B$ has a zero row than the associated controllability matrix (4.5) has rank less than n.

4.5. State observers

Unfortunately the usefulness of Theorem 4.17 in many real-life problems is limited, since the feedback control (4.32) involves all state variables and in practice it is often impossible to measure all the x_i. Instead, if as before the measured output is the column r-vector

$$y = Cx, \tag{4.53}$$

then linear *output feedback*

$$u = Ky = KCx \tag{4.54}$$

is applied, but is no longer possible to preassign all the closed-loop characteristic roots. However, if C has rank r, B has rank m and the system is c.c. and c.o, then it has recently been shown (Sridhar and Lindorff 1973) using an argument similar to that in the proof of Theorem 4.19 that a matrix K exists such that at least $s = \max(m, r)$

of the characteristic roots of the closed loop system matrix $A + BKC$
are arbitrarily close to any set Λ_s.

Instead of looking at methods for choosing K in (4.54) we consider a
different approach and show how the concept of observability can be
applied to obtain state feedback. If the system described by (4.31) and
(4.53) is c.o. then because of the definition in Section 4.2 it is possible,
at least in theory, to determine the state vector x from a knowledge of
y and u. A system whose inputs are u and y and whose output $\hat{x}(t)$
is an approximation to the state vector $x(t)$ is called a *state observer* (or
estimator). Since the original system is assumed c.o., by Corollary 4.3
there exists a matrix L such that the characteristic roots of $A + LC$ can
be made equal to a set $\Lambda_n = \{\theta_i\}$. In particular it follows that all the θ_i
can be taken to have negative real parts, so that if we then set $x_d(t) =$
$x(t) - \hat{x}(t)$ and take

$$\dot{x}_d = (A + LC)x_d, \qquad (4.55)$$

this ensures that $x_d(t) \to 0$ as $t \to \infty$, irrespective of $x_d(0)$ (see Section
5.2, Theorem 5.1). Thus $\hat{x}(t) \to x(t)$ as $t \to \infty$, as required, and (4.55)
shows that $\hat{x}$ must satisfy

$$\frac{d}{dt}(x - \hat{x}) = (A + LC)(x - \hat{x})$$

so

$$d\hat{x}/dt = \dot{x} - (A + LC)(x - \hat{x})$$
$$= Ax + Bu - (A + LC)(x - \hat{x})$$
$$= (A + LC)\hat{x} - Ly + Bu. \qquad (4.56)$$

Thus (4.56) represents a mathematical model for the desired state
observer, having inputs y and u and output $\hat{x}$.

Example 4.10. Consider the case of scalar control variable and output,
let the matrices A and b be as in Example 3.8, and take $C = [2,3]$. To
find the 2×1 matrix L we use a procedure similar to that given in the
proof of Theorem 4.17 for $m = 1$, but commencing with the observable
canonical form in Theorem 3.5. The transformation is $v = P^{-1}x$, where
from the result of Exercise 3.36 we have

$$P^{-1} = \begin{bmatrix} e_1 & 1 \\ 1 & 0 \end{bmatrix} \begin{bmatrix} C \\ CA \end{bmatrix},$$

where

$$\lambda^2 + e_1\lambda + e_2 \equiv \det(\lambda I - A) \equiv \lambda^2 - 3\lambda + 14.$$

This gives

$$P^{-1} = \begin{bmatrix} 8 & -9 \\ 2 & 3 \end{bmatrix},$$

so the matrices in (3.62) are

$$E = P^{-1} AP = \begin{bmatrix} 0 & -14 \\ 1 & 3 \end{bmatrix},$$

$$f = CP = [0, 1].$$

Suppose that the characteristic roots of the observer system matrix $A + LC$ are to be -3 and -4, so that its characteristic equation is $\lambda^2 + 7\lambda + 12$. Since

$$A + LC = P(E + P^{-1} Lf) P^{-1}$$

and $E + P^{-1}Lf$ is in companion form its last column must be $[-12, -7]^{\mathrm{T}}$, i.e.

$$\begin{bmatrix} -14 \\ 3 \end{bmatrix} + P^{-1} L = \begin{bmatrix} -12 \\ -7 \end{bmatrix}.$$

Hence $L = [-2, -2]^{\mathrm{T}}$, the matrix required for constructing the observer system (4.56).

An important point which is now demonstrated is that although the feedback matrix K was obtained in Section 4.4 with respect to the actual state x, use of linear feedback $u = K\hat{x}$ instead of $u = Kx$ still results in the closed loop system having the desired set of characteristic roots. To see this, put $u = K\hat{x}$ in (4.31) and (4.56) and combine these two equations in the form

$$\frac{\mathrm{d}}{\mathrm{d}t}\begin{bmatrix} x \\ \hat{x} \end{bmatrix} = \begin{bmatrix} A & BK \\ -LC & (A + LC + BK) \end{bmatrix}\begin{bmatrix} x \\ \hat{x} \end{bmatrix}. \qquad (4.57)$$

Apply a similarity transformation to the matrix in (4.57) as follows:

$$
\begin{bmatrix} I & 0 \\ I & -I \end{bmatrix} \begin{bmatrix} A & BK \\ -LC & A+LC+BK \end{bmatrix} \begin{bmatrix} I & 0 \\ I & -I \end{bmatrix} \begin{bmatrix} A+BK & -BK \\ 0 & A+LC \end{bmatrix} \quad (4.58)
$$

Since the right hand side of (4.58) is block diagonal, this shows that the characteristic roots of the system in (4.57) are just those of $A + BK$ (as required), together with the known and also predetermined roots of the observer system matrix $A + LC$. Thus the use of the state observer enables all the roots of the closed loop system to be preassigned even though only the output y can be measured.

It can also be shown that the dimension of the observer system can be reduced to $n -$ rank C (see Chen 1970, p.295).

Exercise 4.38.
Using the matrices A and c in Exercise 3.32, find a matrix L such that $A + Lc$ has characteristic roots $-3, -4$, and -5.

4.6. Realization of constant systems

We defined in (2.44) the transfer function matrix $G(s)$ associated with a time-invariant system. In practice it often happens that the mathematical description of a system in terms of differential equations is not known, but $G(s)$ can be determined from experimental measurements or other considerations. It is then useful to find a system in our usual linear state space form to which $G(s)$ corresponds. For example, an analogue simulator can then be constructed – this is essentially a device (usually electronic) which duplicates the behaviour of the physical system and thus can be conveniently used to study its properties.

In formal terms, given an $r \times m$ matrix $G(s)$ whose elements are rational functions of s, we wish to find constant matrices A, B, C having dimensions $n \times n$, $n \times m$ and $r \times n$ respectively such that

$$
G(s) = C(sI - A)^{-1}B,
$$

and the system equations will then be (4.31) and (4.53). The triple $\{A, B, C\}$ is termed a *realization* of $G(s)$ of *order n*, and is not, of course, unique. Amongst all such realizations some will include matrices A having least dimensions – these are called *minimal* realizations, since the corresponding systems involve the smallest possible number of state variables. Notice that since each element in

$$(sI - A)^{-1} = \text{Adj}(sI - A)/\det(sI - A)$$

has the degree of the numerator less than that of the denominator it follows that $C(sI - A)^{-1}B \to 0$ as $s \to \infty$, and we shall assume that any given $G(s)$ also has this property, $G(s)$ then being termed *proper*.

Example 4.11. Consider the scalar transfer function

$$g(s) = \frac{2s + 7}{s^2 - 5s + 6}.$$

As in (4.39), one realization of g is

$$A = \begin{bmatrix} 0 & 1 \\ -6 & 5 \end{bmatrix}, b = \begin{bmatrix} 0 \\ 1 \end{bmatrix}, c = [7, 2].$$

It is also easy to verify that a quite different triple is

$$A = \begin{bmatrix} 2 & 0 \\ 0 & 3 \end{bmatrix}, b = \begin{bmatrix} 1 \\ 1 \end{bmatrix}, c = [-11, 13]. \tag{4.59}$$

In fact both these realizations are minimal, and there is in consequence a simple relationship between them, as will be shown later.

We begin our development with a generalization of the result of (4.39), an example of which has just been given. This enables us to write down a simple realization for a transfer function matrix, although it will not in general be minimal.

THEOREM 4.20. Let

$$g(s) = s^q + g_1 s^{q-1} + \cdots + g_q \tag{4.60}$$

be the monic least common denominator of all the elements $g_{ij}(s)$ of $G(s)$, and let

$$g(s) G(s) = s^{q-1} G_0 + s^{q-2} G_1 + \cdots + G_{q-1}, \tag{4.61}$$

the G_i being constant $r \times m$ matrices. Then a realization of $G(s)$ is

$$
A = \begin{bmatrix} 0 & I_m & 0 & \cdot & & 0 \\ 0 & 0 & I_m & \cdot & & \cdot \\ \cdot & \cdot & \cdot & \cdot & & \cdot \\ \cdot & \cdot & \cdot & \cdot & & I_m \\ -g_q I_m & -g_{q-1} I_m & \cdot & & \cdot & -g_1 I_m \end{bmatrix}, B = \left.\begin{bmatrix} 0 \\ 0 \\ \cdot \\ \cdot \\ 0 \\ I_m \end{bmatrix}\begin{matrix} \\ \\ q \\ \text{blocks} \\ \\ \end{matrix}\right\} (4.62)
$$

$$
C = [G_{q-1}, G_{q-2}, \ldots, G_0].
$$

Furthermore, the pair $[A, B]$ is c.c.

Proof. Let F denote the companion matrix of $g(s)$ in the form (2.32). Clearly $A = F \otimes I_m$, so that

$$
\begin{aligned}
(sI_{mq} - A)^{-1} &= [sI_q \otimes I_m - F \otimes I_m]^{-1} \\
&= [(sI_q - F) \otimes I_m]^{-1} \\
&= (sI_q - F)^{-1} \otimes I_m,
\end{aligned} \tag{4.63}
$$

using the result of Exercise 2.2. Also

$$
B = e_q \otimes I_m, \tag{4.64}
$$

where e_q denotes the last column of I_q, so (4.63) and (4.64) give

$$
(sI - A)^{-1} B = [(sI_q - F)^{-1} \otimes I_m] [e_q \otimes I_m]
$$

$$
= [(sI_q - F)^{-1} e_q] \otimes I_m, \text{ by } (2.5),
$$

$$
= \begin{bmatrix} 1 \\ s \\ s^2 \\ \cdot \\ \cdot \\ s^{q-1} \end{bmatrix} \otimes I_m / g(s), \tag{4.65}
$$

using the expression given in Exercise 4.39 for the last column of $(sI_q - F)^{-1} = \text{Adj } (sI_q - F)/g(s)$. Finally, combining (4.65) and the expression for C in (4.62) we have

$$C(sI - A)^{-1}B = [G_{q-1}, G_{q-2}, \cdots, G_0] \begin{bmatrix} I_m \\ sI_m \\ \cdot \\ \cdot \\ s^{q-1}I_m \end{bmatrix} /g(s)$$

$$= G(s),$$

by virtue of (4.61), showing that $\{A, B, C\}$ is a realization of $G(s)$. †
That $[A, B]$ is c.c. can be seen from the fact that the controllability matrix (4.5) is

$$[B, AB, \ldots, A^{mq-1}B] = \begin{bmatrix} 0 & 0 & 0 & \cdot & \cdot & I_m & X & \cdot & X \\ 0 & 0 & \cdot & \cdot & \cdot & X & X & \cdot & X \\ \cdot & \cdot & \cdot & \cdot & \cdot & \cdot & \cdot & \cdot & \cdot \\ \cdot & \cdot & I_m & \cdot & \cdot & \cdot & \cdot & \cdot & \cdot \\ \cdot & I_m & X & \cdot & \cdot & \cdot & \cdot & \cdot & \cdot \\ I_m & X & X & \cdot & \cdot & \cdot & \cdot & \cdot & \cdot \end{bmatrix}$$

(X denoting nonzero terms) and so clearly has rank equal to mq, the dimension of A.

As we have already seen in Example 4.11, when $m = 1$ the matrices A and B in (4.62) reduce to C and d in the controllable canonical form in Theorem 3.4. For a similar generalization of the observable canonical form in Theorem 3.5, see Exercise 4.44. Notice also that when $G(s)$ is a scalar transfer function (i.e. $r = m = 1$) then (4.62) is minimal provided any common factors between numerator and denominator have been removed (see Exercise 4.41).

It is now appropriate to return to the idea of algebraic equivalence defined in (4.17), and discuss its implications for the realization problem. Since A, B, and C are constant P is also constant, and the transformation $\hat{x} = Px$ in (4.17) produces a system with matrices

$$\hat{A} = PAP^{-1} \quad \hat{B} = PB, \quad \hat{C} = CP^{-1}. \tag{4.66}$$

† This part of the proof is due to H. K. Wimmer.

THEOREM 4.21. If $\{A, B, C\}$ represents a c.c. (c.o.) system then so does $\{\hat{A}, \hat{B}, \hat{C}\}$.

Proof. The controllability part follows as a special case of Theorem 4.8. Alternatively, using (4.66) we have

$$\text{rank } [\hat{B}, \hat{A}\hat{B}, \ldots, (\hat{A})^{n-1}\hat{B}] = \text{rank } (P [B, AB, \ldots, A^{n-1}B]) = n$$

since P is nonsingular, so $[\hat{A}, \hat{B}]$ is c.c. if $[A, B]$ is by Theorem 4.1. The observability condition follows similarly (see also Exercise 4.25).

Not only are controllability and observability properties preserved under algebraic equivalence, but it is also easy to prove Theorem 4.22 (see Exercise 4.45).

THEOREM 4.22. If two systems are algebraically equivalent then their transfer function matrices are identical, i.e.

$$C(sI - A)^{-1} B = \hat{C}(sI - \hat{A})^{-1} \hat{B}.$$

We can now prove the central result of this section, which links together the three basic concepts of controllability, observability, and realization.

THEOREM 4.23. A realization $\{A, B, C\}$ of a given transfer function matrix $G(s)$ is minimal if and only if $[A, B]$ is c.c. and $[A, C]$ is c.o.

Proof.

Sufficiency. Let U and V be the controllability and observability matrices in (4.5) and (4.26) respectively. We wish to show that if these both have rank n then $G(s)$ has least order n. Suppose that there exists a realization $\{\bar{A}, \bar{B}, \bar{C}\}$ of $G(s)$ with $\bar{A}$ having order $\bar{n}$. Since

$$C(sI - A)^{-1} B = \bar{C}(sI - \bar{A})^{-1} \bar{B}$$

it follows (see Exercise 4.45) that

$$C \exp (At)B = \bar{C} \exp (\bar{A}t)\bar{B}$$

which implies, using the series (3.8), that

$$CA^i B = \bar{C} \bar{A}^i \bar{B}, \ i = 0, 1, 2, \ldots . \tag{4.67}$$

Consider the product

$$VU = \begin{bmatrix} C \\ CA \\ \cdot \\ \cdot \\ CA^{n-1} \end{bmatrix} [B, AB, \ldots, A^{n-1}B]$$

$$= \begin{bmatrix} CB & CAB & \cdot & \cdot & CA^{n-1}B \\ \cdot & & \cdot & & \cdot \\ \cdot & & \cdot & & \cdot \\ CA^{n-1} & CA^{n}B & & & CA^{2n-2}B \end{bmatrix}$$

$$= \begin{bmatrix} \tilde{C} \\ \tilde{C}\tilde{A} \\ \cdot \\ \cdot \\ \tilde{C}\tilde{A}^{n-1} \end{bmatrix} [\tilde{B}, \tilde{A}\tilde{B}, \ldots, \tilde{A}^{n-1}\tilde{B}], \text{ using (4.67)}$$

$$= V_1 U_1, \text{ say.} \tag{4.68}$$

By assumption V and U both have rank n, so the matrix $V_1 U_1$ also has rank n. However, the dimensions of V_1 and U_1 are respectively $r_1 n \times \tilde{n}$ and $\tilde{n} \times m_1 n$, where r_1 and m_1 are positive integers, so that the rank of $V_1 U_1$ cannot be greater than $\tilde{n}$. That is, $n \leqslant \tilde{n}$, so there can be no realization of $G(s)$ having order less than n.

Necessity. We show that if the pair $[A, B]$ is not c.c. then there exists a realization of $G(s)$ having order less than n. The corresponding part of the proof involving observability follows by duality.

Let the rank of U in (4.5) be $n_1 < n$ and let $u_1, u_2, \ldots, u_{n_1}$ be any set of n_1 linearly independent columns of U. Consider the transformation $\hat{x} = Px$ with the $n \times n$ matrix P defined by

$$P^{-1} = [u_1, u_2, \ldots, u_{n_1}, u_{n_1+1}, \ldots, u_n], \tag{4.69}$$

where the columns $u_{n_1+1}, \ldots, u_n$ are any vectors which make the matrix in (4.69) nonsingular. Since U has rank n_1 it follows that all its columns can be expressed as a linear combination of the basis $u_1, u_2, \ldots, u_{n_1}$. The matrix $AU = [AB, A^2B, \ldots]$ contains all but the first m

columns of U, so in particular it follows that the vectors Au_i, $= 1, 2, \ldots,$ n_1 can be expressed in terms of the same basis. Multiplying both sides of (4.69) on the left by P shows that Pu_i is equal to the ith column of I_n. Combining these facts together we obtain

$$\hat{A} = PAP^{-1}, \text{ by (4.66),}$$

$$= P[Au_1, \ldots, Au_{n_1}, \ldots, Au_n]$$

$$= \begin{bmatrix} A_1 & A_2 \\ 0 & A_3 \end{bmatrix}$$

where A_1 is $n_1 \times n_1$. Similarly, since $u_1, \ldots, u_{n_1}$ also forms a basis for the columns of B we have from (4.66) and (4.69)

$$\hat{B} = PB = \begin{bmatrix} B_1 \\ 0 \end{bmatrix}$$

where B_1 is $n_1 \times m$. Writing $\hat{C} = CP^{-1} = [C_1, C_2]$, by Theorem 4.22 we have

$$G(s) = \hat{C}(sI - \hat{A})^{-1}\hat{B}$$

$$= [C_1 \; C_2] \begin{bmatrix} sI - A_1 & -A_2 \\ 0 & sI - A_3 \end{bmatrix}^{-1} \begin{bmatrix} B_1 \\ 0 \end{bmatrix}$$

$$= [C_1 \; C_2] \begin{bmatrix} (sI - A_1)^{-1} & (sI - A_1)^{-1}A_2(sI - A_3)^{-1} \\ 0 & (sI - A_3)^{-1} \end{bmatrix} \begin{bmatrix} B_1 \\ 0 \end{bmatrix}$$

$$= C_1 (sI - A_1)^{-1} B_1$$

showing that $\{A_1, B_1, C_1\}$ is a realization of $G(s)$ having order $n_1 < n$. This contradicts the assumption that $\{A, B, C\}$ is minimal, so $[A, B]$ must be c.c.

Notice that the necessity part of the preceding proof, together with Exercise 4.49, establishes Theorem 4.9.

Example 4.12. Consider the electrical network in Exercise 4.16 (Fig. 4.4). Using x_1 and x_2 as state variables and y as the scalar output, standard techniques for circuits give

$$A = \begin{bmatrix} -1/R_1 C & 0 \\ 0 & -R_2/L \end{bmatrix}, b = \begin{bmatrix} 1/R_1 C \\ 1/L \end{bmatrix}, c = [-1/R_1, 1]$$

and $y = cx + u/R_1$.

After Laplace transformation we obtain

$$\bar{y}(s) = \{c(sI - A)^{-1}b + 1/R_1\}\, \bar{u}(s)$$

and hence

$$g(s) = \frac{(R_1^2 C - L)s + (R_1 - R_2)}{(R_1^2 Cs + R_1)(Ls + R_2)} + \frac{1}{R_1}$$

By the result of Exercise 4.16 it follows, using the theorem just proved, that the above triple $\{A, b, c\}$ is a minimal realization for $g(s)$ if and only if $L \neq R_1 R_2 C$. In fact it is easy to verify that when $L = R_1 R_2 C$ there is a common factor between numerator and denominator of $g(s)$.

Of course for any given $G(s)$ there are an infinite number of minimal realizations satisfying the conditions of Theorem 4.23. However, we now show that the relationship between *any* two minimal realizations is just that of algebraic equivalence:

THEOREM 4.24. If $\{A, B, C\} = R$ is a minimal realization of $G(s)$ then $\{\hat{A}, \hat{B}, \hat{C}\} = \hat{R}$ is also minimal realization if and only if (4.66) holds.

Proof.

Sufficiency. If (4.66) holds, then by Theorem 4.22, $\hat{R}$ is certainly a realization and is minimal since $\hat{A}$ has the same dimensions as A.

Necessity. Let $U, \hat{U}, V, \hat{V}$ be controllability and observability matrices (4.5) and (4.26) associated with the minimal realizations R and $\hat{R}$. We show that (4.66) holds by demonstrating that the transformation matrix is

$$P = (\hat{V}^{\mathrm{T}} \hat{V})^{-1}\, \hat{V}^{\mathrm{T}} V. \tag{4.70}$$

Since V and $\hat{V}$ are associated with minimal realizations, by Theorem 4.23 they both have rank n, so that the matrix on the right in (4.70) certainly exists, and is nonsingular. Since A and $\hat{A}$ have the same dimensions we can deduce from (4.68) that

$$VU = \hat{V}\hat{U}, \qquad (4.71)$$

and by a very similar argument, using (4.67), that

$$VAU = \hat{V}\hat{A}\hat{U}. \qquad (4.72)$$

Multiplying (4.71) on the left by $(\hat{V}^T \hat{V})^{-1} \hat{V}^T$ gives

$$PU = \hat{U} \qquad (4.73)$$

i.e. $\qquad P[B, AB, \cdots] = [\hat{B}, \hat{A}\hat{B}, \cdots]$

so that $PB = \hat{B}$, P being defined by (4.70). From (4.73) it is clear that

$$P = \hat{U}U^T (UU^T)^{-1}. \qquad (4.74)$$

Using (4.74) shows that multiplication of (4.71) on the right by $U^T(UU^T)^{-1}$ gives $V = \hat{V}P$, whence from (4.26) $C = \hat{C}P$. Finally, it is left as an exercise for the reader to use (4.70), (4.72), and (4.74) to verify that $PA = \hat{A}P$, which completes the proof that (4.66) holds.

We do not have room in this book to discuss the general problem of efficient construction of minimal realizations. For example, one method is to use the c.o. realization given in Exercise 4.44 and then reduce it to a realization which also c.c. by the procedure indicated in the second part of the proof of Theorem 4.23. For further details we refer the reader to Barnett (1971, p. 58), Chen (1970, p.235), and Rosenbrock (1970, p. 116) and merely give here one simple but nevertheless useful result:

THEOREM 4.25. Let the denominators of the elements $g_{ij}(s)$ of $G(s)$ have only simple zeros $s_1, s_2, \ldots, s_p$. Define

$$K_i = \lim_{s \to s_i} (s - s_i)G(s), \quad i = 1, 2, \ldots, p \qquad (4.75)$$

and let $r_i = \text{rank } K_i$. If L_i and M_i are $r \times r_i$ and $r_i \times m$ matrices respectively, each having rank r_i, such that

$$K_i = L_iM_i, \qquad (4.76)$$

then a minimal realization of $G(s)$ is

$$A = \begin{bmatrix} s_1 I_{r_1} & & & 0 \\ & s_2 I_{r_2} & & \\ & & \ddots & \\ 0 & & & s_p I_{r_p} \end{bmatrix}, B = \begin{bmatrix} M_1 \\ M_2 \\ \cdot \\ \cdot \\ M_p \end{bmatrix} \Bigg\} \qquad (4.77)$$

$$C = [L_1, L_2, \ldots, L_p].$$

Proof. Eqn (4.75) is equivalent to the representation of G in partial fractions in the form

$$G(s) = \sum_{i=1}^{p} K_i/(s - s_i). \qquad (4.78)$$

Using the matrices in (4.77) we have

$$C(sI - A)^{-1} B = C \text{ diag } [I_{r_1}/(s - s_1), I_{r_2}/(s - s_2), \ldots, I_{r_p}/(s - s_p)] B$$

$$= \Sigma L_i M_i /(s - s_i)$$

$$= \Sigma K_i/(s - s_i), \text{ by } (4.76)$$

$$= G(s) \qquad \text{by } (4.78).$$

To prove that the realization (4.77) is minimal it is necessary to show that it is c.c. and c.o. (Theorem 4.23). The controllability matrix is

$$[B, AB, \ldots, A^{n-1}B] = \begin{bmatrix} M_1 & s_1 M_1 & s_1^2 M_1 & \cdot & s_1^{n-1} M_1 \\ M_2 & s_2 M_2 & s_2^2 M_2 & \cdot & \cdot \\ \cdot & \cdot & \cdot & \cdot & \cdot \\ \cdot & \cdot & \cdot & \cdot & \cdot \\ M_p & s_p M_p & s_p^2 M_p & \cdot & s_p^{n-1} M_p \end{bmatrix} \quad (4.79)$$

where $n = r_1 + r_2 + \cdots + r_p$. Using the facts that M_i has rank r_i and all the s_i are distinct it follows that the matrix in (4.79) has full rank (see Exercise 4.51). The observability condition is proved similarly.

Example 4.13. In the scalar transfer function in Example 4.11 the denominator is

$$s^2 - 5s + 6 = (s - 2)(s - 3).$$

Thus (4.75) gives

$$K_1 = \lim_{s \to 2} \frac{(s - 2)(2s + 7)}{(s - 2)(s - 3)} = -11, \; r_1 = 1$$

$$K_2 = \lim_{s \to 3} \frac{(s - 3)(2s + 7)}{(s - 2)(s - 3)} = 13, \; r_2 = 1.$$

Taking $L_1 = K_1, M_1 = 1, L_2 = K_2, M_2 = 1$ in (4.76) then produces a minimal realization (4.77) which is precisely that in (4.59). However

$$b = \begin{bmatrix} m_1 \\ m_2 \end{bmatrix}, \qquad c = [-11/m_1, 13/m_2]$$

can be used instead, still giving a minimal realization for arbitrary nonzero values of m_1 and m_2.

Notice that (4.75) can be used to evaluate the order of minimal realizations of $G(s)$ without actually determining a realization, since the order is the dimension of A in (4.77), namely $\sum_{i=1}^{p} r_i$. However, calculation of the r_i involves the same disadvantage as using Theorem 4.25 in general, namely the need to calculate the s_i. An alternative method of finding the least order of $G(s)$ which does not rely on any knowledge of the s_i is obtained by arguing as follows. The realization in (4.62) is c.c. but not in general c.o. By Theorem 4.14, (4.62) is therefore algebraically equivalent to

$$\left\{ \begin{bmatrix} A_1 & 0 \\ A_2 & A_3 \end{bmatrix}, \; \begin{bmatrix} B_1 \\ B_2 \end{bmatrix}, \; [C_1, 0] \right\} \qquad (4.80)$$

where $[A_1, C_1]$ is c.o., and by Theorem 4.22 the triple in (4.80) is a realization of $G(s)$. It is easy to verify that $\{A_1, B_1, C_1\}$ is also a realization of $G(s)$ (compare with the second part of the proof of Theorem 4.23). From Theorem 4.21 we know that (4.80) is c.c., which implies that $[A_1, B_1]$ is also c.c. Hence $\{A_1, B_1, C_1\}$ is a minimal realization of $G(s)$, since it is both c.c. and c.o. Therefore the least order of G is equal to the dimension of A_1. Finally, from Theorem 4.14, this dimension is equal to the rank of the observability matrix (4.26) with A and C as given in (4.62).

•

Exercise 4.39.
If C, d, and k are as defined in (3.45), (3.46), and (3.47), and $\beta(s) = \beta_0 s^{n-1} + \beta_1 s^{n-2} + \cdots + \beta_{n-1}$, verify that a realization of $\beta(s)/k(s)$ is $\{C, d, r\}$ where $r = [\beta_{n-1}, \beta_{n-2}, \ldots, \beta_0]$. (Hint: By considering the product $(sI - C)\mathrm{Adj}(sI - C)$ show that the last column of $\mathrm{Adj}(sI - C)$ is $[1, s, s^2, \ldots, s^{n-1}]^{\mathrm{T}}$).

Show that the realization is minimal if $\beta(s)$ and $k(s)$ are relatively prime. (Use the result of Exercise 4.27).

Exercise 4.40.
Deduce from the result of the preceding exercise that a realization of $\beta(s)/k(s)$ is $\{C^{\mathrm{T}}, r^{\mathrm{T}}, d^{\mathrm{T}}\}$ and that this is c.o. but not c.c. if $\beta(s)$ and $k(s)$ are not relatively prime.

Exercise 4.41.
Let A be an arbitrary $n \times n$ matrix with characteristic polynomial $q(s)$, and let

$$c(sI - A)^{-1}b = t(s)/q(s) \equiv g(s)$$

where c is $1 \times n$ and b is $n \times 1$. Prove that $\{A, b, c\}$ is a minimal realization of $g(s)$ if and only if $t(s)$ and $q(s)$ are relatively prime.

Exercise 4.42.
Using the notation in Theorem 4.16, let

$$G(s) = \frac{1}{k(s)} \begin{bmatrix} p_1(s) \\ \cdot \\ \cdot \\ \cdot \\ p_m(s) \end{bmatrix}$$

and assume that the polynomials $k(s), p_1, \ldots, p_m$ are relatively prime. Generalize the result of Exercise 4.39 by verifying that a minimal realization of $G(s)$ is $\{C, d, E\}$ where C, d are defined in (3.45) and (3.46), and

$$E = \begin{bmatrix} b_{11} & \cdot & \cdot & b_{n1} \\ \cdot & & & \cdot \\ \cdot & & & \cdot \\ b_{1m} & \cdot & \cdot & b_{nm} \end{bmatrix}.$$

Exercise 4.43.
Using Theorem 4.25, write down a minimal realization for a scalar transfer function whose denominator has only simple zeros.

Exercise 4.44.
Let $G(s)$ and $g(s)$ be as defined in (4.60) and (4.61). Deduce that $\{A^T, B, C\}$, where A is defined in (4.62),

$$B = \begin{bmatrix} G_{q-1} \\ \cdot \\ \cdot \\ G_1 \\ G_0 \end{bmatrix}, \quad C = [0, 0, \ldots, I_m],$$

is a realization of $G(s)$, and that $[A, C]$ is c.o.

Exercise 4.45.
Using (4.66) prove Theorem 4.22, and hence deduce that

$$C\{\exp(At)\}B = \hat{C}\{\exp(\hat{A}t)\}\hat{B}.$$

Exercise 4.46.
Use Theorem 4.25 to obtain a minimal realization of

$$\frac{1}{g(s)} \begin{bmatrix} (s^2 + 6) & (s^2 + s + 4) \\ (2s^2 - 7s - 2) & (s^2 - 5s - 2) \end{bmatrix}$$

where $g(s) = s^3 + 2s^2 - s - 2$.

Exercise 4.47.

Show that the order of a minimal realization of

$$\frac{1}{s^2 + 3s + 2} \begin{bmatrix} (s+2) & 2(s+2) \\ -1 & (s+1) \end{bmatrix}$$

is three. (Notice the fallacy of assuming that the order is equal to the degree of the common denominator).

Exercise 4.48.

If $\{A_1, B_1, C_1\}$ and $\{A_2, B_2, C_2\}$ are realizations of $G_1(s)$ and $G_2(s)$, show that

$$A = \begin{bmatrix} A_1 & B_1 C_2 \\ 0 & A_2 \end{bmatrix}, \quad B = \begin{bmatrix} 0 \\ B_2 \end{bmatrix}, \quad C = [C_1 \ 0]$$

is a realization of $G_1(s)G_2(s)$, assuming that this product exists.

Exercise 4.49.

Verify that in the second part of the proof of Theorem 4.23 the pair $[A_1, B_1]$ is c.c.

Exercise 4.50.

Show that the transfer function matrix of the system in Theorem 4.15 depends only on the c.c. and c.o. part. This result shows that the uncontrollable and unobservable part of the state space representation is lost when the transfer function matrix description is used.

Exercise 4.51.

In (4.79) let $p = 2, r_1 = 2, r_2 = 2$ for simplicity. By considering the linear independence of the rows of the matrix on the right in (4.79) show that it has full rank.

Exercise 4.52.

Verify that algebraic equivalence in (4.66) can be written as the transformation

$$\begin{bmatrix} P & 0 \\ 0 & I \end{bmatrix} \begin{bmatrix} sI - A & B \\ -C & 0 \end{bmatrix} \begin{bmatrix} P^{-1} & 0 \\ 0 & I \end{bmatrix} = \begin{bmatrix} sI - \hat{A} & \hat{B} \\ -\hat{C} & 0 \end{bmatrix}$$

(this is called *system similarity* – see Rosenbrock (1970) for a development of linear control theory in terms of polynomial and rational matrices).

4.7. Discrete-time systems

So far in this chapter we have discussed only systems described by linear differential equations. In fact the definitions of controllability and observability given in Sections 4.1 and 4.2 carry over to systems described by the linear difference equations (3.31) with only minor obvious modifications.

When A and B in (3.31) are time invariant the controllability and observability criteria are the same as those for the continuous time case given in Theorems 4.1 and 4.2 respectively (Rubio 1971, p. 234) with one important exception. This is the situation when the discrete-time system A-matrix is singular. The discrete-time version of the argument in the first part of the proof of Theorem 4.1 breaks down because the corresponding transition matrix A^k is also singular (Exercise 2.11), whereas $\exp(At)$ is nonsingular for all matrices A (Exercise 3.4). It is necessary to define a new concept: the linear system

$$x(k+1) = Ax(k) + Bu(k) \qquad (4.81)$$

is *completely reachable* (from the origin) if given any state x_f there exist an integer $N > 0$ and a control sequence $u(0), u(1), \ldots, u(N-1)$ such that if $x(0) = 0$ then $x(N) = x_f$. When A in (4.81) is singular this is not the same as complete controllability, which requires that given any state x_0 there exist an $N > 0$ and a control sequence such that if $x(0) = x_0$ then $x(N) = 0$. In this case the discrete analogue of Theorem 4.1 is that (4.81) is completely reachable if and only if

$$\text{rank } [B, AB, \ldots, A^{n-1}B] = n$$

and the set of reachable states is a subset of the set of controllable states (Kalman, Falb, and Arbib 1969, p.41). For the continuous time system (4.4) the concepts of reachability and controllability are completely equivalent.

To deal with the realization problem we apply z-transforms to (4.81) to obtain, using (1.30) and assuming $x(0) = 0$.

$$z\tilde{x}(z) = A\tilde{x}(z) + B\tilde{u}(z). \qquad (4.82)$$

Rearranging (4.82) gives

$$\bar{x}(z) = (zI - A)^{-1}B\bar{u}(z)$$

so the output $y(k) = Cx(k)$ has z-transform

$$\bar{y}(z) = C(zI - A)^{-1}B\bar{u}(z). \tag{4.83}$$

Thus the transfer function matrix in (4.83) relating $\bar{y}(z)$ and $\bar{u}(z)$ has exactly the same form as that for the continuous-time case. The theory developed in Section 4.6 therefore carries over directly for (4.81) virtually without modification, although in view of our remarks on the case when A is singular, Theorem 4.23 should be interpreted as stating that a realization is minimal if and only if the matrices (4.5) and (4.26) have full rank. When linear feedback $u(k) = Kx(k)$ is applied to (4.81) the closed loop matrix is again $A + BK$, so the methods of Section 4.4 also apply to discrete-time systems.

Exercise 4.53.
It was seen in the buffalo population model in Exercise 1.13 that under natural conditions the numbers would grow without limit. In fact due to indiscriminate slaughter the number of animals was reduced from 60 million in 1830 to only 200 in 1887.

Suppose that a controlled slaughter policy had been adopted, killing for food S_{k+1} adult females in year $k+1$ so that (1.33) becomes

$$F_{k+2} = 0 \cdot 95F_{k+1} + 0 \cdot 12F_k - S_{k+1}.$$

If linear feedback $S_{k+1} = pF_{k+1}$ is used, show that the total population would remain constant even if 7 per cent of adult females were killed each year. Also, find an expression for the number of adult females in the steady state in this case.

What difference would it make if there were a year's delay in completing the buffalo census, so that $S_{k+1} = pF_k$?

As a footnote, a single buffalo carcase would provide enough meat (250 kg) for at least 10 people for a whole year!

Exercise 4.54.
Show using (3.39) that when A is nonsingular, then if the control sequence $u(k_0), \ldots, u(N-1)$ transfers $x(k_0) = x_0$ to $x(N) = x_f$, it also transfers $x_0 - A^{k_0 - N}x_f$ to the origin in the same time interval.

Exercise 4.55.

Verify using (3.41) that the control sequence

$$u(i) = -B^T (iT)\Phi^T (0, i+1)W^{-1} (0, N)[x_0 - \Phi(0, N)x_f],$$

$i = 0, 1, 2, \ldots, N-1$, where Φ is defined in (3.40) and

$$W(0, N) = \sum_{i=0}^{N-1} \Phi(0, i+1)B(iT)B^T (iT) \Phi^T (0, i+1)$$

is assumed nonsingular, transfers the system described by (3.31) from $x(0) = x_0$ to $x(N) = x_f$.

†4.8. Realization of time varying systems

We now return to systems described by eqns (4.1) and (4.2). Once again, as in the case of the transition matrix for time varying systems discussed in Section 3.5, we find that many of the properties established for time-invariant systems in Section 4.6 still hold. However, as is to be expected, we cannot give analytical methods for calculation of realizations.

As in the constant case assume that $x_0 = 0$. Then using (3.30) the output is

$$\begin{aligned}
y(t) &= C(t)x(t) \\
&= C(t) \int_{t_0}^{t} \Phi(t, \tau)B(\tau)u(\tau)\mathrm{d}\tau \\
&= \int_{t_0}^{t} K(t, \tau)u(\tau)\mathrm{d}\tau
\end{aligned}$$

where Φ is the transition matrix defined in (3.27). The matrix

$$K(t, \tau) = C(t)\Phi(t, \tau)B(\tau) \tag{4.84}$$

is called the *weighting pattern* matrix. For a given $K(t, \tau)$ the realization problem is now to find a triple $\{A(t), B(t), C(t)\}$ such that (4.84) is satisfied. The notion of minimality of a realization is the same as before, that A should have least possible dimension. The relationship with the case when A, B, and C are constant is obtained by noting that by (3.11) the transition matrix is then

$$\Phi(t, \tau) = \exp [A (t - \tau)], \tag{4.85}$$

and the Laplace transform of the right side of (4.84) is $C(sI - A)^{-1}B$, using the expression for $\mathcal{L}\{\exp(At)\}$ in (3.18). In this constant case substitution of (4.85) into (4.84) gives

$$K(t, \tau) = C(t) \exp(At) \exp(-A\tau)B(\tau)$$

showing that $K(t, \tau)$ can be written as a product of functions of t and τ. We now establish that this holds even when A, B, and C are time varying.

THEOREM 4.26. A realization exists for a matrix $K(t, \tau)$ if and only if it can be expressed in the form

$$K(t, \tau) = L(t)M(\tau) \tag{4.86}$$

where L and M are matrices having finite dimensions.

Proof. From (3.27) and (4.84) if K possesses a realization then

$$K(t, \tau) = C(t)X(t)X^{-1}(\tau)B(\tau),$$

where $X(t)$ is defined in (3.26), so (4.86) is certainly a necessary condition.
    Conversely, if (4.86) holds then a realization of $K(t, \tau)$ is $\{0_n, M(t), L(t)\}$ where 0_n denotes an $n \times n$ zero matrix, since then $\Phi(t, \tau) = I$.

It is interesting that the fundamental result on controllability and observability established in Theorem 4.23 still holds in the time varying case.

THEOREM 4.27. A realization $R = \{A(t), B(t), C(t)\}$, of $K(t, \tau)$ is minimal if and only if it is c.c. and c.o.

Proof.

Necessity. We assume that the pair $[A(t), B(t)]$ is not c.c. and show that the realization R is then not minimal. A similar argument applies if $[A, C]$ is assumed not c.o. Suppose that A is $n \times n$ and that the controllability matrix $U(t_0, t_1)$ in (4.12) has rank $p < n$. Since, as was shown in the proof of Theorem 4.3, $U(t_0, t_1)$ is positive semidefinite, there exists a nonsingular matrix T such that

$$TUT^{\mathrm{T}} = \begin{bmatrix} I_p & 0 \\ 0 & 0 \end{bmatrix} \tag{4.87}$$

(see Exercise 2.23). Consider the algebraic equivalence transformation with $P(t)$ in (4.17) taken to be $TX(t_0)X^{-1}(t)$, where $X(t)$ is defined by

(3.26). It is easy to verify (see Exercise 4.58) that under this transformation R becomes $\hat{R} = \{O_n, \hat{B}(t), \hat{C}(t)\}$ where $\hat{B}(t) = P(t)B(t)$ and $\hat{C}(t) = C(t)P^{-1}(t)$. Furthermore (see Exercise 4.57) $\hat{R}$ is also a realization of $K(t, \tau)$. From (4.20) the controllability matrix associated with $\hat{R}$ is

$$\hat{U} = P(t_0) U(t_0, t_1)P^T(t_0)$$
$$= TUT^T \tag{4.88}$$

and since $\Phi = I$ for $\hat{R}$ we also have from (4.12)

$$\hat{U} = \int_{t_0}^{t_1} \hat{B}(\tau)\hat{B}^T(\tau)d\tau. \tag{4.89}$$

From (4.87), (4.88), and (4.89) it follows that

$$\hat{B} = \begin{bmatrix} \beta \\ 0 \end{bmatrix}$$

where β has dimensions $p \times m$. This implies that $[0_p, \beta, \gamma]$, where γ is $r \times p$, is a realization of K, and this contradicts the minimality of R.

Sufficiency. We now assume that R is c.c. and c.o. and show that there cannot exist a realization R_1 of K having order $n_1 < n$. First, by again applying the result of Exercise 4.58 we can assume that such a realization has the form $R_1 = \{0_{n_1}, B_1(t), C_1(t)\}$. It similarly follows that under the transformation $P = X^{-1}(t)$, R becomes $\bar{R} = \{0_n, \bar{B}(t), \bar{C}(t)\}$ and remains c.c. and c.o. (see Theorem 4.8). Since

$$K(t, \tau) \equiv C_1(t)B_1(\tau) = \bar{C}(t)\bar{B}(\tau),$$

multiplying the second and third terms in this expression on the left and right by $\bar{C}^T(t)$ and $\bar{B}^T(\tau)$ respectively and integrating with respect to t and τ gives

$$W_1 W_2 = \bar{V}\bar{U} \tag{4.90}$$

where

$$W_1 = \int_{t_0}^{t_1} \bar{C}^T(t)C_1(t)dt, \qquad W_2 = \int_{t_0}^{t_1} B_1(\tau)\bar{B}^T(\tau)d\tau$$

and $\bar{V}$ and $\bar{U}$ are the observability and controllability matrices for $\bar{R}$ defined in (4.22) and (4.12) respectively. By assumption $\bar{V}$ and $\bar{U}$ have rank n, so $\bar{V}\bar{U}$ also has rank n. However, W_1 and W_2 have dimensions

$n \times n_1$ and $n_1 \times n$ respectively, so that rank $(W_1 W_2) \leqslant n_1$. Hence (4.90) implies that $n_1 \geqslant n$, showing that R is minimal.

It can also be shown by a similar argument that if rank $(UV) = q < n$ then the least order of realizations of $K(t, \tau)$ is equal to q.

Again following the time invariant case (Theorem 4.24) the relationship between minimal realizations is that of algebraic.equivalence, defined in (4.17).

THEOREM 4.28. If $R = \{A(t), B(t), C(t)\}$ is a minimal realization of $K(t, \tau)$ then $\hat{R} = \{\hat{A}(t), \hat{B}(t), \hat{C}(t)\}$ is also a minimal realization if and only if

$$\hat{A} = \dot{P}P^{-1} + PAP^{-1}, \hat{B} = PB, \hat{C} = CP^{-1} \qquad (4.91)$$

where $P(t)$ is continuous and nonsingular.

The proof follows along similar lines to that of Theorem 4.27.

An interesting question is under what conditions a given weighting matrix has a time invariant realization:

THEOREM 4.29. A given matrix $K(t, \tau)$ has a realization $\{A, B, C\}$ in which A, B, C are constant matrices if and only if (4.86) holds and if in addition

$$K(t, \tau) = K(t + s, \tau + s), t_0 \leqslant t, \tau, s \leqslant t_1.$$

Unfortunately the proof does not provide a practical method of constructing such a realization, so will also be omitted. A good source for these proofs and other material on realization of time varying systems is the review by Silverman (1971).

Exercise 4.56.
Verify that in Theorem 4.26 suitable matrices are $L(t) = C(t) \Phi(t, t_0)$ and $M(t) = \Phi(t_0, \tau) B(\tau)$, where $\Phi(t, t_0)$ is defined in (3.27).

Exercise 4.57.
Show, using Theorem 4.7, that if two realizations are algebraically equivalent then the corresponding weighting pattern matrices are identical

Exercise 4.58.
Show that if $P(t)$ in (4.17) is taken to be $EX^{-1}(t)$, where $X(t)$ is defined in (3.26) and E is a constant nonsingular matrix, then $\{A(t), B(t), C(t)\}$ is transformed into $\{0, P(t) B(t), C(t)P^{-1}(t)\}$.

Exercise 4.59.

Show that the system

$$\dot{x} = Ax + \{\exp(Dt)\}Bu, \quad y = C\{\exp(-Dt)\}x$$

where A, B, C, and D are constant matrices and $AD = DA$, possesses a constant realization.

5 Stability

In contrast with the preceding two chapters our treatment of stability will apply to systems described by sets of linear *or* nonlinear equations. As is to be expected, however, it is once again for linear systems that our most explicit results will be obtained. Stability theory is a vast subject and to keep this chapter within a reasonable length it has been necessary to omit many proofs and finer points of detail. Where possible, however, references have been given to standard textbooks which can be consulted if further material is required.

5.1. Definitions

Consider the system described by

$$\dot{x} = f(x, t) , \tag{5.1}$$

where as before $x(t)$ is the state vector and f is a vector having components $f_i(x_1, x_2, \ldots, x_n, t), i = 1, 2, \ldots, n$. We shall assume that the f_i are continuous and satisfy standard conditions, such as having continuous first partial derivatives so that the solution of (5.1) exists and is unique for given initial conditions (see, for example, Brauer and Nohel 1969). If the f_i do not depend explicitly on t, eqn (5.1) is called *autonomous* (otherwise, *nonautonomous*). If $f(c, t) = 0$ for all t, where c is some constant vector, then it follows at once from (5.1) that if $x(t_0) = c$ then $x(t) = c$, all $t \geqslant t_0$. Thus solutions starting at c remain there, and c is said to be an *equilibrium* or *critical* point (or state). Clearly, by introducing new variables $x_i' = x_i - c_i$ we can arrange for the equilibrium point to be transferred to the origin; we shall assume that this has been done for any equilibrium point under consideration (there may well be several for a given system (5.1)) so that we then have $f(0, t) = 0, t \geqslant t_0$. We shall also assume that there is no other constant solution in the neighbourhood of the origin, so this is an *isolated* equilibrium point.

Example 5.1.
The intuitive idea of stability in a dynamical setting is that for "small" perturbations from the equilibrium state at some time t_0,

subsequent motions $x(t)$, $t > t_0$, should not be too 'large'. Suppose that Fig. 5.1 represents a ball resting in equilibrium on a sheet of metal bent into various shapes with cross-sections as shown. If frictional forces can be neglected then small perturbations lead to:

(a) oscillatory motion about equilibrium;

(b) the ball moving away without returning to equilibrium;

(c) oscillatory motion about equilibrium, unless the initial perturbation is so large that the ball is forced to oscillate about the new equilibrium position on the left, or to fall off at the right.

If friction is taken into account then the oscillatory motions steadily decrease until the equilibrium state is returned to.

Clearly there is no single concept of stability, and very many different definitions are possible (see for example Willems 1970, p. 3). We shall consider for the present only the following fundamental statements;

An equilibrium state $x = 0$ is said to be:

(i) *stable* if for any positive scalar ϵ there exists a positive scalar δ such that† $\| x(t_0) \|_e < \delta$ implies $\| x(t) \|_e < \epsilon, t \geqslant t_0$.

(ii) *asymptotically stable* if it is stable and if in addition $x(t) \to 0$ as $t \to \infty$.

(iii) *unstable* if it is not stable; that is, there exists an $\epsilon < 0$ such that for every $\delta > 0$ there exists an $x(t_0)$ with $\| x(t_0) \| < \delta$, $\| x(t_1) \| \geqslant \epsilon$ for some $t_1 > t_0$. If this holds for every $x(t_0)$ in $\| x(t_0) \| < \delta$ the equilibrium is *completely unstable*.

The definition (i) is often called 'stability in the sense of Liapunov' (stability *i.s.L.*) after the Russian mathematician Liapunov, whose important work of 1892 features prominently in current control theory literature on stability problems and will be described in Section 5.4.

In Example 5.1, case (a) in Fig. 5.1 represents stability i.s.L. if friction is ignored, and asymptotic stability if friction is taken into account, whereas case (b) represents instability. If the metal sheet in Fig. 5.1(a) were thought to extend indefinitely then if friction is present the

† Throughout this chapter the Euclidean norm will be used, so the suffix e will henceforth be dropped.

ball would eventually return to equilibrium no matter how large the disturbance. This is an illustration of asymptotic stability *in the large,* which means that *every* motion converges to a single equilibrium point as $t \rightarrow \infty$, and clearly does not apply to case (c) in Fig. 5.1. Asymptotic stability in the large implies that all motions are bounded. Generally, $x = 0$ is said to be *bounded* or *Lagrange stable* if there exists a constant

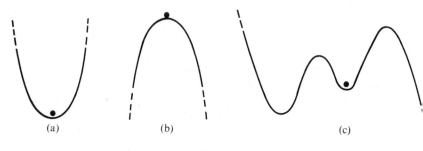

$$\text{(a)} \qquad\qquad \text{(b)} \qquad\qquad\qquad \text{(c)}$$

FIG. 5.1

b, which may depend on t_0 and $x(t_0)$, such that $\| x(t) \| \leqslant b$ for all $t \geqslant t_0$.

Regarded as a function of t in the n-dimensional state space, the solution $x(t)$ of (5.1) is called a *trajectory* or *motion*. In two dimensions we can give the definitions a simple geometrical interpretation. If the origin O is stable, then given the outer circle C, radius ϵ, there exists an inner circle C_1, radius δ_1, such that trajectories starting within C_1 never leave C. If O is asymptotically stable then there is some circle C_2, radius δ_2, having the same property as C_1 but in addition trajectories starting inside C_2 tend to O as $t \rightarrow \infty$.

Some further remarks can be made at this stage:

(1) Notice that we refer to the stability of an equilibrium state of (5.1), not the system itself, as different equilibrium points may have different stability properties.

(2) A weakness of the definition of stability i.s.L. for practical purposes is that only the *existence* of some positive δ is required, so δ may be very small compared to ϵ – in other words, only very small disturbances from equilibrium may be allowable.

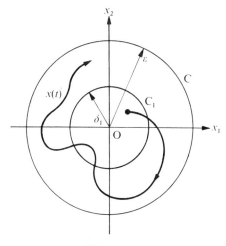

FIG. 5.2

(3) In engineering applications asymptotic stability is more desirable
than stability, since it ensures eventual return to equilibrium,
whereas stability allows continuing deviations 'not too far' from
the equilibrium state.

Some further aspects of stability are now illustrated.

Example 5.2. We again return to the rabbit–fox environment problem
described in Exercises 1.4 and 1.7. The eqns (1.6) have a single equilibrium point at the origin. With arbitrary initial numbers $x_1(0)$ and
$x_2(0)$ of rabbits and foxes respectively the solution of eqn (1.6) is
found to be

$$x_1(t) = [a_2 x_2(0) - a_4 x_1(0) + e^{dt} (a_1 x_1(0) - a_2 x_2(0))]/d,$$

where $d = a_1 - a_4$, and $a_1/a_3 = a_2/a_4$, with a similar expression for $x_2(t)$.
If $d > 0$, $x_1(t)$ and $x_2(t)$ tend to infinity as $t \to \infty$, so the origin is
unstable. If $d < 0$, both $x_1(t)$ and $x_2(t)$ approach constant values as
$t \to \infty$, and it is intuitively obvious that the origin is stable. This could
be verified formally by showing that the condition of the definition is
satisfied, but we shall see in Section 5.2 that linear equations like (1.6)
can be tested directly.

Example 5.3. Consider the system described by

$$\dot{x}_1 = x_1^2 \qquad (5.2)$$

It is clear that the solution exists and is unique, and in fact by integrating we easily obtain

$$-1/x_1 = t - 1/x_1^0$$

where $x_1(0) = x_1^0$. Hence

$$x_1(t) = \frac{1}{(1/x_1^0) - t}$$

so that if $x_1^0 > 0$, $x_1(t) \to \infty$ as $t \to 1/x_1^0$. The solution of the differential equation (5.2) is said to 'escape' to infinity in a finite time, or to have a *finite escape time*. We shall henceworth exclude this situation and assume that (5.1) has a finite solution for all finite $t \geqslant t_0$, for otherwise (5.1) cannot be a mathematical model of a real-life situation.

Example 5.4. We demonstrate that the original is a stable equilibrium point for the system described by

$$\dot{x}_1 = x_1 (1 - 2t) \qquad (5.3)$$

by determining explicitly the scalar δ in the definition. Integrating (5.3) and using $x_1(t_0) = x_1^0$ gives

$$x_1(t) = x_1^0 \exp(t - t^2) \exp(t_0^2 - t_0). \qquad (5.4)$$

The condition $|x_1(t)| < \epsilon$ in (5.4) leads to

$$|x_1^0| < \epsilon \exp(t^2 - t) \exp(t_0 - t_0^2). \qquad (5.5)$$

Since $\exp(t^2 - t)$ has a minimum value of $\exp(-\frac{1}{4})$ when $t = \frac{1}{2}$, it follows from (5.5) that we can take $\delta = \epsilon \exp[-(t_0 - \frac{1}{2})^2]$. In general

δ will depend upon ϵ, but in this example it is also a function of the initial time. If δ is independent of t_0, the stability is called *uniform*.

The following two examples illustrate the *local* nature of the definition of stability i.s.L., mentioned in Remark (2) above.

Example 5.5. Consider the equation

$$\dot{x}_1 = \begin{cases} x_1 - 2, & x_1 > 2 \\ \\ 0, & x_1 \leqslant 2 \end{cases} \tag{5.6}$$

The solution of (5.6) is easily found to be

$$\begin{aligned} x_1(t) &= 2 + (x_1^0 - 2) \exp(t - t_0) && \text{if } x_1^0 > 2, \\ &= x_1^0 && \text{if } x_1^0 \leqslant 2 \end{aligned} \tag{5.7}$$

where as before $x_1(t_0) = x_1^0$. The condition $|x_1(t)| < \epsilon$ is implied by $|x_1^0| < 2$ when $\epsilon \geqslant 2$, for then by (5.7) $|x_1(t)| = |x_1^0| < 2 < \epsilon$. When $\epsilon < 2$, $|x_1(t)| < \epsilon$ is implied by $|x_1^0| < \epsilon$, for then again $|x_1(t)| = |x_1^0| < \epsilon$. Thus according to the definition the origin is a stable equilibrium point. However, (5.7) shows that if $x_1^0 > 2$ then $x_1(t) \to \infty$, so for initial perturbations $x_1^0 > 2$ from equilibrium motions are certainly unstable in a practical sense.

Example 5.6. Consider

$$\dot{x}_1 = f(t) x_1$$

where

$$\begin{aligned} f(t) &= \text{\ln } 10, && 0 \leqslant t \leqslant 10 \\ &= -1, && t > 10. \end{aligned}$$

The solution is

$$\begin{aligned} x_1(t) &= 10^t x_1^0, && 0 \leqslant t \leqslant 10 \\ &= 10^{10} \exp(10 - t) x_1^0, \, t > 10. \end{aligned} \tag{5.8}$$

Clearly $x_1(t) \to 0$ as $t \to \infty$, and the origin is asymptotically stable. However, if x_1^0 changes by a very small amount, say 10^{-5}, then the corresponding change in $x_1(t)$ in (5.8) is relatively large – for example when $t = 20$, the change in $x_1(t)$ is $10^{10} \exp(10 - 20). 10^{-5} \approx 4.5$.

Examples 5.5 and 5.6 show that an equilibrium point may be stable according to Liapunov's definitions and yet the system's behaviour may be unsatisfactory from a practical point of view. The converse situation is also possible, and this has led to a definition of 'practical stability' being coined for systems which are unstable in Liapunov's sense but have an acceptable performance in practice, namely that for *pre-specified* deviations from equilibrium the subsequent motions also lie within specified limits (La Salle and Lefschetz 1961, p. 121).

Example 5.7. The equation of motion of a simple pendulum consisting of a mass m suspended from a fixed point by a rod whose weight can be neglected is

$$m\ell^2 \, d^2\theta/dt^2 = -mg\ell \sin\theta.$$

For simplicity assume $g/\ell = 1$ and take as state variables $x_1 = \theta$, $x_2 = \dot{\theta}$ to obtain

$$\dot{x}_1 = x_2, \qquad \dot{x}_2 = -\sin x_1. \tag{5.9}$$

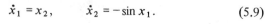

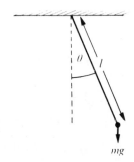

FIG. 5.3

The origin of these coordinates is an equilibrium point, and from (5.9)

$$dx_1/dx_2 = -x_2/\sin x_1$$

which on integration gives

$$x_2{}^2 = 2\cos x_1 + a$$

where a is determined by the initial conditions. Routine analysis shows that the trajectories in the x_1, x_2 plane (the *phase* plane), for various initial conditions, are as indicated below.

The origin is clearly a stable equilibrium point. However, if the initial conditions are outside the hatched region (for example the point P) then this produces a trajectory for which x_1 diverges to infinity.

Exercise 5.1.
Determine the equilibrium point (other than the origin) of the system described by

$$\dot{x}_1 = x_1 - 2x_1 x_2$$
$$\dot{x}_2 = -2x_2 + x_1 x_2$$

Apply a transformation of coordinates which moves this point to the origin, and find the new system equations.

The equations are an example of a predator–prey population model due to Volterra and used in biology, and are more general than the simple linear rabbit–fox model of Exercise 1.4.

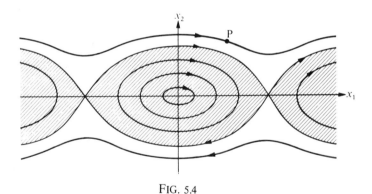

FIG. 5.4

Exercise 5.2.
Show by solving the equations explicitly and applying the definition that the origin is a stable equilibrium point for the system

$$\dot{x}_1 = ax_1 - x_2, \quad \dot{x}_2 = x_1 + ax_2$$

with $a \leqslant 0$, $x_1(t_0) = \alpha$, $x_2(t_0) = \beta$.

Exercise 5.3.

If the oscillations of the simple pendulum in Example 5.7 are assumed sufficiently small so that θ^2 and higher powers are neglected, and if $g/\ell = k$, obtain the equation of trajectories and sketch them in the phase plane.

Exercise 5.4.

Verify that for the inverted pendulum problem in Exercise 1.3 the origin is an equilibrium point.

5.2. Algebraic criteria for linear systems

5.2.1. Continuous time

Before studying nonlinear systems we return to the general continuous-time linear system

$$\dot{x} = Ax, \tag{5.10}$$

where A is a constant $n \times n$ matrix, and (5.10) may represent the closed or open loop system. The only equilibrium point of (5.10) is the origin, so it is meaningful to refer to the stability of the *system* (5.10). The two basic results on which the development of linear system stability theory relies are now given.

THEOREM 5.1. The system (5.10) is asymptotically stable if and only if A is a *stability* matrix, i.e. all the characteristic roots λ_k of A have negative real parts; (5.10) is unstable if any $\Re(\lambda_k) > 0$; and completely unstable if all $\Re(\lambda_k) > 0$.

Proof. From (3.7) the solution of (5.10) subject to $x(0) = x_0$ is

$$x(t) = \exp(At)x_0. \tag{5.11}$$

From (2.76) with $f(\lambda) = e^{\lambda t}$ we have

$$\exp(At) = \sum_{k=1}^{q} (Z_{k1} + Z_{k2}t + \cdots + Z_{k\alpha_k}t^{\alpha_k - 1}) \exp(\lambda_k t)$$

where the $Z_{k\ell}$ are constant matrices determined entirely by A. Using properties of norms (see Section 2.7) we obtain

$$\| \exp{(At)} \| \leqslant \sum_{k=1}^{q} \sum_{\ell=1}^{\alpha k} t^{\ell-1} \| \exp{(\lambda_k t)} \| \, \| Z_{k\ell} \|$$

$$= \sum \sum t^{\ell-1} \exp{[\Re(\lambda_k)t]} \, \| Z_{k\ell} \| \qquad (5.12)$$

$$\to 0 \text{ as } t \to \infty$$

provided $\Re(\lambda_k) < 0$, all k, since (5.12) is a finite sum of terms, each of which $\to 0$ as $t \to \infty$. From (5.11)

$$\| x(t) \| \leqslant \| \exp{(At)} \| \, \| x_0 \|,$$

so the system is asymptotically stable.

If any $\Re(\lambda_k)$ is positive then it is clear from the expression for $\exp{(At)}$ that $\| x(t) \| \to \infty$ as $t \to \infty$, so the origin is unstable.

If some of the λ_k are purely imaginary the situation is more complicated:

THEOREM 5.2. Suppose all the characteristic roots of A have non-positive real parts. Let $\lambda_1, \lambda_2, \ldots, \lambda_\ell$ be those characteristic roots of A having zero real parts, and let β_i be the highest power of $(\lambda - \lambda_i)$ amongst the elementary divisors of $\lambda I - A$, $i = 1, 2, \ldots, \ell$. Then the origin of (5.10) is stable but not asymptotically stable if $\beta_1 = \beta_2 = \cdots = \beta_\ell = 1$; unstable if there is at least one $\beta_i > 1$.

We do not give a proof of this result (see for example Lehnigk, 1966, p. 20) but instead illustrate the important point that Theorem 5.2 does *not* mean that the roots $\lambda_1, \ldots, \lambda_\ell$ may not occur more than once if the system is to be stable.

Example 5.8. The matrix

$$A_1 = \begin{bmatrix} i & 0 \\ 0 & i \end{bmatrix}$$

has characteristic root i with multiplicity two. The solution of (5.10) is

$$x_1(t) = c_1 \exp{(it)}, \qquad x_2(t) = c_2 \exp{(it)}$$

(the c_i are constants) so the system is clearly stable. Using the definitions in Section 2.5 the elementary divisors of A_1 are found to be $\lambda - i, \lambda - i$ so $\beta_1 = \beta_2 = 1$.

If however we consider the matrix

$$A_2 = \begin{bmatrix} i & 0 \\ 1 & i \end{bmatrix}$$

the roots of A_2 are again i, i but the elementary divisors are $1, (\lambda - i)^2$ so $\beta_1 = 2$. It is easy to verify that the solution of (5.10) in this case is

$$x_1(t) = c_3 \exp{(it)}, x_2(t) = c_4 \exp{(it)} + c_3 t \exp{(it)}$$

showing that the origin is indeed unstable.

In fact (see Exercise 2.24) the stability condition on the β_i in Theorem 5.2 is equivalent to requiring that all the Jordan blocks $J(\lambda_i), i = 1, 2, \ldots , \ell$ in the Jordan form (2.59) of A must have order one. This is clearly illustrated in the above example, where

$$A_1 = \text{diag}[J_1(i), J_i(i)], \qquad A_2 = J_2(i).$$

In particular if all the roots $\lambda_1, \ldots , \lambda_\ell$ are distinct then the origin is stable.

Example 5.9. In Example 5.2 the system matrix is

$$A = \begin{bmatrix} a_1 & -a_2 \\ a_3 & -a_4 \end{bmatrix}$$

by inspection of (1.6). It is easy to show that

$$\det(\lambda I - A) = \lambda(\lambda - d)$$

using the condition $a_1/a_3 = a_2/a_4$. Hence A has a single zero root, so the system is stable provided $d \ (= a_1 - a_4)$ is negative.

The two preceding theorems apply if A is real or complex, so the stability determination of (5.10) can be carried out by computing the λ_k using one of the powerful standard computer programs now available. However, if n is small (say less than six), or if some of the elements of A are in parametric form, or if access to a digital computer is not possible, then the classical results given below are useful.

Because of its practical importance the linear system stability problem has attracted attention for a considerable time, an early study being by Maxwell in 1868 in connection with the governing of steam engines. The original formulation of the problem was not of course in matrix terms, the system model being (3.42). This is equivalent to working with the characteristic polynomial of A, which we shall write in this section as

$$\det(\lambda I - A) \equiv \lambda^n + a_1 \lambda^{n-1} + \cdots + a_{n-1}\lambda + a_n = a(\lambda), \quad (5.13)$$

and this is identical to $k(\lambda)$ in (3.47) when the system equation is (3.42). The first solutions giving necessary and sufficient conditions for all the roots of $a(\lambda)$ in (5.13) to have negative real parts were given by Cauchy in 1831, Sturm in 1836, and Hermite in 1854, but we give here a well-known theorem due to Hurwitz in 1895 for the case when all the a_i are real (for a good account of the history of the problem see Fuller 1974).

THEOREM 5.3. The $n \times n$ *Hurwitz* matrix associated with $a(\lambda)$ in (5.13) is

$$H = \begin{bmatrix} a_1 & a_3 & a_5 & \cdot & \cdot & \cdot & a_{2n-1} \\ 1 & a_2 & a_4 & \cdot & \cdot & \cdot & a_{2n-2} \\ 0 & a_1 & a_3 & \cdot & \cdot & \cdot & a_{2n-3} \\ 0 & 1 & a_2 & \cdot & \cdot & \cdot & a_{2n-4} \\ \cdot & \cdot & \cdot & \cdot & \cdot & \cdot & \cdot \\ \cdot & \cdot & \cdot & \cdot & \cdot & \cdot & \cdot \\ 0 & 0 & 0 & \cdot & \cdot & \cdot & a_n \end{bmatrix} \quad (5.14)$$

where $a_r = 0, r > n$. Let H_i denote the ith leading principal minor of H. Then all the roots of $a(\lambda)$ have negative real parts ($a(\lambda)$ is a *Hurwitz* polynomial) if and only if $H_i > 0, i = 1, 2, \ldots, n$.

We shall not give a proof, which usually involves complex variable theory (see Gantmacher 1959, 2 pp.177, 190). However, some remarks on an alternative way of obtaining Theorem 5.3 will be given later in Section 5.5.

Of course a disadvantage of Theorem 5.3 is the need to evaluate determinants of increasing order, and a convenient way of avoiding this is due to Routh whose work was published before that of Hurwitz, in 1877.

For simplicity consider the case $n = 3$. It is then easy to verify that

$$\begin{bmatrix} 1 & 0 & 0 \\ (-1/a_1) & 1 & 0 \\ -a_1/(a_3-a_1a_2) & a_1{}^2/(a_3-a_1a_2) & 1 \end{bmatrix} \begin{bmatrix} a_1 & a_3 & 0 \\ 1 & a_2 & 0 \\ 0 & a_1 & a_3 \end{bmatrix}$$

$$= \begin{bmatrix} r_{11} & r_{12} & r_{13} \\ 0 & r_{21} & r_{22} \\ 0 & 0 & r_{31} \end{bmatrix} \qquad (5.15)$$

where $r_{11} = H_1, r_{21} = H_2/H_1, r_{31} = H_3/H_2$. Similarly in general

$$\Lambda H = R, \qquad (5.16)$$

where H is given by (5.14), and as in (5.15) the matrices Λ and R are lower and upper triangular respectively. By considering leading principal minors in (5.16) it can then be deduced that in general

$$r_{11} = H_1, \quad r_{i1} = H_i/H_{i-1}, \quad i = 2, 3, \ldots, n, \qquad (5.17)$$

which leads to:

THEOREM 5.4. The criterion $H_i > 0, i = 1, \ldots, n$ of Theorem 5.3 is equivalent to the condition that all the numbers $r_{i1}, i = 0, 1, 2, \ldots, n$ in the first column of the *Routh array*

r_{01}	r_{02}	r_{03}	$\cdot$	$\cdot$	$\cdot$
r_{11}	r_{12}	r_{13}	$\cdot$	$\cdot$	$\cdot$
r_{21}	r_{22}	r_{23}	$\cdot$	$\cdot$	$\cdot$
$\cdot$	$\cdot$	$\cdot$	$\cdot$	$\cdot$	$\cdot$
$r_{i-2,1}$	$\cdot$	$\cdot$	$r_{i-2,j}$	$r_{i-2,j+1}$	$\cdot$
$r_{i-1,1}$	$\cdot$	$\cdot$	$r_{i-1,j}$	$r_{i-1,j+1}$	$\cdot$
r_{i1}	$\cdot$	$\cdot$	r_{ij}	$r_{i,j+1}$	$\cdot$
$\cdot$	$\cdot$	$\cdot$	$\cdot$	$\cdot$	$\cdot$

$$(5.18)$$

be positive, where

$$\{r_{01}, r_{02}, r_{03}, \ldots\} = \{1, a_2, a_4, \ldots\}$$
$$\{r_{11}, r_{12}, r_{13}, \ldots\} = \{a_1, a_3\ a_5, \ldots\}$$
(5.19)

and

$$r_{ij} = - \begin{vmatrix} r_{i-2,1} & r_{i-2,j+1} \\ \\ r_{i-1,1} & r_{i-1,j+1} \end{vmatrix} / r_{i-1,1}, \quad i = 2, 3, \ldots, n. \quad (5.20)$$

Thus each row in (5.18) is formed by taking all the 2×2 minors involving the first column of the preceding two rows. This is shown by the elements within dashed lines in (5.18). The computational effort involved is clearly much less than for Hurwitz's method.

As mentioned earlier, the Hurwitz and Routh theorems can be useful for determining stability of (3.42) and (5.10) in certain cases. However, it should be noted that a practical disadvantage of application to (5.10) is that it is very difficult to calculate accurately the a_i in (5.13). This is important because small errors in the a_i can lead to large errors in the roots of $a(\lambda)$.

Example 5.10. Investigate the stability of the linear system whose characteristic equation is

$$\lambda^4 + 2\lambda^3 + 9\lambda^2 + \lambda + 4.$$

The Routh array (5.18) is constructed from (5.19) and (5.20) to be

$r_0 j$	1	9	4
$r_1 j$	2	1	
$r_2 j$	$(18-1)/2$ $= 17/2$	$(8-0)/2$ $= 4$	
$r_3 j$	$[(17/2) - 8]/(17/2)$ $= 1/17$		
$r_4 j$	$[(4/17) - 0]/(1/17)$ $= 4$		

Since all r_{i1} are positive the system is asymptotically stable.

Alternatively, from (5.14) $H_1 = 2, H_2 = 17, H_3 = 1, H_4 = 4$ and it is easy to see that (5.17) is satisfied.

Incidentally, if $a(\lambda)$ arises from a system in the form (3.42) having leading coefficient a_0 (>0) then the Hurwitz and Routh conditions still hold but with the unit elements preceding the coefficient a_2 in (5.14) and (5.19) replaced by a_0. Notice also that if any H_i or r_{i1} is nonpositive then the computational procedures of Theorems 5.3 and 5.4 need not be continued since the system is not asymptotically stable. In fact it is then possible to determine the numbers of roots of $a(\lambda)$ with positive and negative real parts. For example, if no r_{i1} is zero then these numbers are respectively V and $n - V$, where V is the number of variations in sign in the first column of the Routh array. For further details, including cases when some r_{i1} are zero, see Gantmacher (1959, 2 p. 180).

Since we have assumed that the a_i are real it is easy to derive a simple *necessary* condition for asymptotic stability:

THEOREM 5.5. If the a_i in (5.13) are real and $a(\lambda)$ corresponds to an asymptotically stable system, then

$$a_i > 0, \ i = 1, 2, \ldots, n \tag{5.21}$$

Proof. Any complex roots of $a(\lambda)$ will occur in conjugate pairs $\alpha \pm i\beta$, the corresponding factor of $a(\lambda)$ being

$$(\lambda - \alpha - i\beta)(\lambda - \alpha + i\beta) = \lambda^2 - 2\alpha\lambda + \alpha^2 + \beta^2.$$

By Theorem 5.1, $\alpha < 0$, and similarly any real factor of $a(\lambda)$ can be written $(\lambda + \gamma)$ with $\gamma < 0$. Thus

$$a(\lambda) = \prod(\lambda + \gamma)\prod(\lambda^2 - 2\alpha\lambda + \alpha^2 + \beta^2) \tag{5.22}$$

and since all the coefficients in (5.22) are positive the a_i must also all be positive.

Of course (5.21) is not a sufficient condition, but it provides a useful initial check: if any a_i are negative or zero then $a(\lambda)$ cannot be asymptotically stable. Furthermore, if (5.21) does hold then it turns out that only about half the Hurwitz determinants in Theorem 5.3 need to be calculated:

THEOREM 5.6. (*Liénard and Chipart*). A necessary and sufficient condition for $a(\lambda)$ to be a Hurwitz polynomial is that *one* of the following conditions holds:

$$a_n > 0, \ a_{n-2} > 0, \ldots; \ H_1 > 0, H_3 > 0, \ldots \tag{5.23}$$

$$a_n > 0, \quad a_{n-2} > 0, \ldots; \quad H_2 > 0, H_4 > 0, \ldots \tag{5.24}$$

$$a_n > 0, \quad a_{n-1} > 0, \quad a_{n-3} > 0, \ldots; \quad H_1 > 0, H_3 > 0, \ldots \tag{5.25}$$

$$a_n > 0, \quad a_{n-1} > 0, \quad a_{n-3} > 0, \ldots; \quad H_2 > 0, H_4 > 0, \ldots \tag{5.26}$$

For a proof see Gantmacher (1959, 2 p. 221). Notice that of course any one of eqns (5.23)–(5.26) implies (5.21). Thus the Lienard-Chipart criterion shows that if (5.21) holds then only $\frac{1}{2}(n-1)$ or $\frac{1}{2}n$ of the H_i in Theorem 5.3 need to be evaluated according as n is odd or even. In fact it has been found recently that a reduction by half in the orders of the determinants is also possible, and the development is interesting since it involves companion matrices and is linked with the ideas of Section 4.3. We have no room here to give details and refer the reader to Barnett (1971, Chapter 2). We have mentioned earlier that for numerical calculations the Routh array is preferable to the Hurwitz determinants. However, if some of the a_i depend upon parameters and the system is asymptotically stable it is often required to determine for what values of the parameters $a(\lambda)$ first becomes non-Hurwitzian. It can be shown (Lehnigk 1966, p. 199) that these values are obtained by solving the 'critical' equations.

$$a_n = 0, \qquad H_{n-1} = 0. \tag{5.27}$$

Although encountered far less often in practice we also give a result for the case when the a_i in (5.13) are complex.

THEOREM 5.7. Let the real and imaginary parts of a_i in (5.13) be denoted by $a_i{}'$ and $a_i{}''$ respectively. Then $a(\lambda)$ is a Hurwitz polynomial if and only if in the Routh array (5.18) with initial two rows

$$
\begin{aligned}
r_{0j} &= \left\{ 1, -a_1{}'', -a_2{}', a_3{}'', a_4{}', -a_5{}'', -a_6{}', \ldots \right\} \\
r_{1j} &= \left\{ a_1{}', -a_2{}'', -a_3{}', a_4{}'', a_5{}', -a_6{}'', -a_7{}', \ldots \right\},
\end{aligned}
\tag{5.28}
$$

all the products

$$r_{11}, r_{11} r_{21} r_{31}, r_{11} r_{21} r_{31} r_{41} r_{51}, \ldots \tag{5.29}$$

are positive.

For a proof and other results on complex polynomials see Marden (1966, p. 179).

5.2.2. Discrete-time

We now turn our attention to discrete-time linear systems in the usual form

$$x(k+1) = A_1 x(k). \tag{5.30}$$

The definitions of Section 5.1 carry over virtually without alteration. We have seen in (3.33) that the general solution of (5.30) subject to $x(0) = x_0$ is

$$x(k) = A_1{}^k x_0 .$$

In addition, we demonstrated in Section 2.7 that $A_1^k \to 0$ as $k \to \infty$ if and only if all the characteristic roots μ_i of A have modulus less than unity, and $A_1^k \to \infty$ if any $|\mu_i| > 1$. It therefore follows that the result corresponding to Theorem 5.1 is:

THEOREM 5.8. The origin of (5.30) is asymptotically stable if and only if A_1 is a *convergent* matrix, i.e. all its characteristic roots satisfy $|\mu_i| < 1$. If any $|\mu_i|$ is greater than unity then the origin is unstable; and completely unstable if all $|\mu_i| > 1$.

Example 5.11. Consider the buffalo population model in Exercise 1.13. Following (3.69) introduce the coordinates

$$x_1(k) = F_k, x_2(k) = F_{k+1}, x_3(k) = M_k, x_4(k) = M_{k+1}$$

so that (1.33) and (1.34) take the form (5.30) with

$$A_1 = \begin{bmatrix} 0 & 1 & 0 & 0 \\ 0.12 & 0.95 & 0 & 0 \\ 0 & 0 & 0 & 1 \\ 0.14 & 0 & 0 & 0.95 \end{bmatrix}$$

It is easy to obtain

$$\det(\lambda I - A_1) = \lambda(\lambda - 0.95)(\lambda^2 - 0.95\lambda - 0.12)$$

$$= \lambda(\lambda - 0.95)(\lambda - 1.063)(\lambda + 0.113)$$

so the system is unstable since A_1 has a root greater than unity.

Just as in Theorem 5.2, if any of the characteristic roots of A_1 have unit modulus then the corresponding elementary divisors must be linear for (5.30) to be stable.

In fact we can establish a direct relationship between Theorems 5.1 and 5.8 by taking

$$A = (A_1 - I)(A_1 + I)^{-1} \qquad (5.31)$$

assuming $A_1 + I$ is nonsingular, i.e. that A_1 has no $\mu_i = -1$. Then the roots λ of A in (5.31) satisfy

$$\lambda = \frac{\mu - 1}{\mu + 1} \qquad (5.32)$$

and it is left as an easy exercise for the reader to show using (5.32) that $\text{Re}\,(\lambda) < 0$ if and only if $|\mu| < 1$, so A in (5.31) is the matrix in Theorem 5.1. In other words, A is a stability matrix if and only if A_1 is a convergent matrix.

If we write the characteristic polynomial of A_1 in the form

$$a_1(\mu) = \alpha_0 \mu^n + \alpha_1 \mu^{n-1} + \cdots + \alpha_n, \qquad \alpha_0 > 0, \qquad (5.33)$$

then $a_1(\mu)$ is also termed *convergent* if all its roots have modulus less than unity. A convenient scheme for determining whether $a_1(\mu)$ is convergent, corresponding to the Routh array of Theorem 5.4, is as follows:

THEOREM 5.9. A necessary and sufficient condition for $a_1(\mu)$ to be a convergent polynomial is that

$$d_{21} > 0, d_{i1} < 0, \quad i = 3, \ldots, n+1, \qquad (5.34)$$

where the d_{i1} are first column elements in the array

$$
\left.
\begin{array}{cccccccc}
\alpha_0 & \alpha_1 & \cdot & \cdot & & \cdot & \alpha_{n-1} & \alpha_n \\
\alpha_n & \alpha_{n-1} & \cdot & \cdot & & \cdot & \alpha_1 & \alpha_0
\end{array}
\right\}
$$

$$
\left.
\begin{array}{cccccccc}
c_{21} & c_{22} & \cdot & \cdot & & \cdot & & c_{2n} \\
d_{21} & d_{22} & \cdot & \cdot & & \cdot & & d_{2n}
\end{array}
\right\}
$$

$$
\left.
\begin{array}{cccccc}
c_{31} & c_{32} & \cdot & \cdot & c_{3,\,n-1} & \\
d_{31} & d_{32} & \cdot & \cdot & d_{3,\,n-1} &
\end{array}
\right\} \qquad (5.35)
$$

$$
\left.
\begin{array}{cccccc}
\boxed{c_{i-1,\,1}} & \cdot & \cdot & \boxed{c_{i-1,\,j+1}} & \cdot & c_{i-1,\,n-i+3} \\
\boxed{d_{i-1,\,1}} & \cdot & \cdot & \boxed{d_{i-1,\,j+1}} & \cdot & d_{i-1,\,n-i+3}
\end{array}
\right\}
$$

$$
\begin{array}{cccc}
\cdot & \cdot & c_{ij} & c_{i,\,j+1} & \cdot \\
\cdot & \cdot & d_{ij} & c_{i,\,j+1} & \cdot \\
\cdot & \cdot & \cdot & \cdot & \cdot
\end{array}
$$

and

$$c_{ij} = \begin{vmatrix} c_{i-1,\,1} & c_{i-1,\,j+1} \\ d_{i-1,\,1} & d_{i-1,\,j+1} \end{vmatrix}, \quad i = 2, 3, \ldots, n+1 \quad (5.36)$$

$$d_{ij} = c_{i,\,n-j-i+3}, \tag{5.37}$$

with

$$c_{1j} = \alpha_{j-1}, \; j = 1, 2, \ldots, n+1. \tag{5.38}$$

For a proof of the theorem see Jury (1964, p. 121). The scheme above for constructing the array has been modified slightly from Jury's form so as to expose the similarity with the Routh array (5.18). The rows in (5.35) are formed in pairs, the second row in each pair being given by (5.37) as merely the first in reverse order. The elements in the first row in each pair are formed by taking all the 2×2 minors (5.36) involving the first column of the preceding two rows, as in (5.20).

The reader will notice the similarity between the tabular schemes of Theorems 5.4 and 5.9, and may wonder why divisions are necessary in (5.20) but not in (5.36). In fact, although this is very seldom pointed out in the literature, either method may be formulated with or without divisions (see Exercise 5.16).

Again a generalization is possible to find the number of zeros of $a_1 (\mu)$ outside the unit disc $|\mu| < 1$ (excluding the boundary). If no $d_{i1} = 0$, let

$$P_k = (-1)^k d_{21} \, d_{31} \ldots d_{k+1,\,1}, \, k = 1, 2, \ldots, n. \tag{5.39}$$

Then the numbers of roots of $a_1 (\lambda)$ inside and outside the unit disc are N and $n - N$, where N is the number of negative products P_k defined in (5.39). For further details and other results, including a determinantal criterion corresponding to that of Hurwitz in Theorem 5.3, the book by Jury (1964, Chapter 3) should be consulted.

Example 5.12. Determine the distribution of the roots of

$$2\mu^3 + 4\mu^2 - 5\mu + 3 \tag{5.40}$$

with respect to the unit disc.

This array (5.35) is constructed using (5.36), (5.37) and (5.38) as

c_{1j}	2	4	−5	3 ⎫
d_{1j}	3	−5	4	2 ⎭
c_{2j}	−22	23	−5 ⎫	
d_{2j}	−5	23	−22 ⎭	
c_{3j}	−391	459 ⎫		
d_{3j}	459	−391 ⎭		
c_{41}	−57800			
$= d_{41}$				

Thus in (5.39), $P_1 > 0, P_2 < 0, P_3 < 0$ so (5.40) has two roots inside the unit disc and one outside, and is therefore the characteristic equation of an unstable discrete-time system by Theorem 5.8.

When the α_i in (5.33) are complex the only change required is that the second row of each pair in (5.35) is the *complex conjugate* of the preceding row in reverse order.

5.2.3. Time varying

When we turn to linear time varying equations

$$\dot{x}(t) = A(t)x(t) \tag{5.41}$$

the situation is much more complicated. In view of Theorem 5.1 it might be thought that if the characteristic roots of $A(t)$ all have negative real parts for all $t \geqslant t_0$ then the origin of (5.41) would be asymptotically stable. Unfortunately this conjecture is not true (see Exercise 5.15). However, if $A(t)$ is *almost constant*, i.e.

$$\lim_{t \to \infty} A(t) = A_\infty, \tag{5.42}$$

where A_∞ is a constant matrix, then the following result can be established.

THEOREM 5.10. If the origin as an asymptotically stable equilibrium point for the system

$$\dot{x}(t) = A_\infty x, \tag{5.43}$$

then it also is for

$$\dot{x}(t) = (A_\infty + B(t))x \qquad (5.44)$$

provided

$$\lim_{t \to \infty} \|B(t)\| = 0. \qquad (5.45)$$

Generally, asymptotic stability of (5.43) does not ensure that of (5.44) unless an additional condition like (5.45) holds. For a proof of the theorem see Willems (1970, p.113), and this book together with that by D'Angelo (1970) should be consulted for further results.

Exercise 5.5.
Analyse the problem in Exercise 5.2 using Theorems 5.1 and 5.2.

Exercise 5.6.
Determine whether the following polynomials are Hurwitzian:

(a) $\lambda^3 + 17\lambda^2 + 2\lambda + 1$ (b) $\lambda^4 + \lambda^3 + 4\lambda^2 + 4\lambda + 3$

(c) $\lambda^4 + 6\lambda^3 + 2\lambda^2 + \lambda + 3$ (d) $4\lambda^5 + 5\lambda^4 + 26\lambda^3 + 30\lambda^2 + 7\lambda + 2.$

Exercise 5.7.
Determine the solution $\hat{x}(t)$ of the linear system

$$\dot{x}(t) = Ax(t) - b, \; x(0) = x_o,$$

where b is a constant column n-vector, by using (3.22). Hence deduce that if A is a stability matrix then the vector $\lim_{t \to \infty} \hat{x}(t)$ is the solution of the system of algebraic equations $Ax = b$.

Exercise 5.8.
Determine the location of the roots of

$$\mu^4 + 2\mu^3 + \mu^2 + 3\mu + 2$$

with respect to the unit disc.

Exercise 5.9.
Show that necessary and sufficient conditions for the real polynomial $a(\lambda)$ to be Hurwitzian are (a) when $n = 2$: $a_1 > 0, a_2 > 0$ (b) when $n = 3$: $a_1 > 0, a_3 > 0, a_1 a_2 - a_3 > 0$.

Exercise 5.10.
Show that necessary and sufficient conditions for the real polynomial
$a_1(\mu)$ to be convergent when $n = 2$ are $\alpha_2 - \alpha_0 < 0, a_1(1) > 0,$
$a_1(-1) > 0$.

Exercise 5.11.
Determine for what range of values of k the polynomial

$$(3 - k)\lambda^3 + 2\lambda^2 + (5 - 2k)\lambda + 2$$

is Hurwitzian.

Exercise 5.12.
Test the polynomial

$$\lambda^3 + (1 + i)\lambda^2 + (2 - 3i)\lambda + 7,$$

where $i = \sqrt{(-1)}$, using Theorem 5.7.

Exercise 5.13.
The characteristic equation

$$\lambda^2 + 2k\omega\lambda + (\omega^2 - 2k\omega\Omega i) = 0,$$

where $i = \sqrt{(-1)}$ arises in the theory of vibrating shafts, Ω being the rotational speed, ω the undamped natural frequency and k a damping coefficient. Use Theorem 5.7 to show that the system is asymptotically stable if and only if $\Omega < \omega$.

Exercise 5.14.
Determine for what range of values of k the real system

$$\dot{x} = \begin{bmatrix} 0 & 1 & 0 \\ 0 & 0 & 1 \\ -k & -1 & -2 \end{bmatrix} x$$

is asymptotically stable. If $k = -1$, and a control term

$$\begin{bmatrix} 0 \\ 1 \\ 0 \end{bmatrix} u$$

is added, find a linear feedback control which makes all the characteristic roots of the closed loop system equal to -1.

Exercise 5.15.

Verify that the characteristic roots of

$$A(t) = \begin{bmatrix} -4 & 3e^{-8t} \\ -e^{8t} & 0 \end{bmatrix}$$

are both constant and negative, but that the solution of (5.41) diverges as $t \to \infty$.

Exercise 5.16.

Define a Routh array (s_{ij}) without divisions by $s_{0j} = r_{0j}$, $s_{1j} = r_{1j}$

$$s_{ij} = - \begin{vmatrix} s_{i-2,1} & s_{i-2,j+1} \\ s_{i-1,1}, & s_{i-1,j+1} \end{vmatrix}, \qquad i = 2, 3, \ldots$$

where the r_{ij} are given by (5.19) and (5.20). Show that this corresponds to taking $s_{2j} = r_{11}r_{2j}$, $s_{3j} = r_{11}r_{21}r_{3j}$, $s_{ij} = k_i r_{ij}$, $i \geqslant 2$ where $k_i = k_{i-1}k_{i-2}r_{i-1, 1}$, $i \geqslant 4$. Hence deduce that the Hurwitz determinants are given by $H_1 = s_{11}$, $H_2 = s_{21}$, $H_3 = s_{31}$, $H_i = s_{i1}/\ell_i$, $i \geqslant 4$ where

$$\ell_i = \ell_{i-1} s_{i-3, 1} s_{i-5, 1} \cdots \begin{cases} s_{11} & (i \text{ even}) \\ s_{21} & (i \text{ odd}). \end{cases}$$

5.3. Nyquist criterion for linear systems

We now consider a general closed loop single-input single-output system with unity feedback, represented in Fig. 1.10. The closed loop transfer function in (1.15) becomes

$$g_c(s) = \frac{g(s)}{1 + g(s)}, \tag{5.46}$$

where $g(s)$ is the open loop transfer function defined in (1.14) by

$$g(s) = \beta(s)/k(s). \tag{5.47}$$

Substitution of (5.47) into (5.46) gives

$$g_c(s) = \frac{\beta(s)}{\beta(s) + k(s)}. \tag{5.48}$$

The characteristic equation of the closed loop system is the denominator in (5.48) (see Exercise 5.17), so stability can be tested by applying, for example, the Routh criterion of Section 5.2 to the polynomial $\beta(s) + k(s)$. In practical applications, however, the coefficients of β and k may not be known precisely and in such cases the criterion due to Nyquist is useful. It involves drawing a diagram in the complex plane of $g(i\omega)$, the open loop frequency transfer function (defined in Section 1.2), which can usually be measured experimentally over a required range of values of ω.

We shall assume to begin with that the open loop system is asymptotically stable, i.e. that all the zeros of $k(s)$ in (5.47) have negative real parts, so $g(s)$ has no poles in the right half of the s-plane (including the imaginary axis) $\Gamma_r : \Re e(s) \geqslant 0$. We can then regard $g(s)$ as a conformal mapping from Γ_r onto the $g(s)$-plane. That is, for each point $z = \sigma + i\omega$ in the complex s-plane with $\sigma \geqslant 0$ we have a corresponding point $U + iV = g(z)$ in the $g(s)$-plane.

Example 5.13. Consider the simple transfer function

$$g(s) = \frac{1}{s + 1} \tag{5.49}$$

The mapping of the imaginary axis $s = i\omega, -\infty < \omega < \infty$ is given by

$$U + iV = \frac{1}{i\omega + 1}$$

so

$$U = (1 + \omega^2)^{-1}, \qquad V = -\omega(1 + \omega^2)^{-1}$$

and it is easy to verify that

$$(U - \tfrac{1}{2})^2 + V^2 = \tfrac{1}{4} .$$

This shows that the mapping of the imaginary axis in the s-plane is a circle in the $g(s)$-plane, centre $\tfrac{1}{2} + i0$, radius $\tfrac{1}{2}$ (see Fig. 5.5). As ω goes from zero to ∞ the semicircle from A to B is traversed. Since

$$g(-i\omega) = \overline{g(i\omega)}$$

it follows that as ω goes from $-\infty$ to zero the path is simply the complex conjugate of BA, shown by the dashed curve in Fig. 5.5.

We do not have space in this book to devote to the theory of conformal mapping, for which the reader is referred to standard texts on complex variables (e.g. Levinson and Redheffer 1970).

Suppose that the half-plane Γ_r is mapped by $g(s)$ into some region R. If any zero μ_i of $\beta(s) + k(s)$ lies in Γ_r then $g(\mu_i)$ will be contained within R, and the closed-loop system is not asymptotically stable (Theorem 5.1).

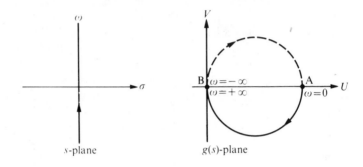

FIG. 5.5

From (5.47) it follows that $\beta(s) + k(s) = 0$ is equivalent to $g(s) = -1$, so μ_i satisfies $g(\mu_i) = -1$. It therefore follows that for the closed loop system to be asymptotically stable, the point $-1 + i0$ must lie outside R. The half-plane Γ_r can be represented by the interior of the semi-circular region shown in Fig. 5.6 where the radius r tends to infinity.

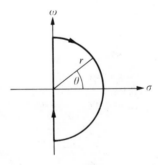

FIG. 5.6

Any point on the curved part of the contour can be written in polar form as $s = r \exp(i\theta)$ and substitution into (5.47) gives

$$g(s) = \beta(re^{i\theta})/k(re^{i\theta}). \tag{5.50}$$

If we assume, as usually happens in practice, that $g(s)$ is proper, then $\delta\beta < \delta k$ and in (5.50) $|g(s)| \to 0$ as $r \to \infty$. Thus the semicircle of infinite radius is mapped into the origin of the $g(s)$-plane. We need therefore only consider the imaginary axis in Fig. 5.6, and the *Nyquist locus* (or *diagram*) of $g(s)$ is defined as the curve

$$U = \Re\{g(i\omega)\}, \qquad V = \mathrm{Im}\{g(i\omega)\} \tag{5.51}$$

for $-\infty < \omega < \infty$. If $g(s)$ has real coefficients then as in Example 5.13, $g(-i\omega) = \overline{g(i\omega)}$ and the part of the mapping corresponding to the negative imaginary axis $(-\infty < \omega \leqslant 0)$ is the complex conjugate of the curve for $0 \leqslant \omega < \infty$. We have therefore established, albeit informally, *the Nyquist criterion:*

THEOREM 5.11. If $g(s)$ has no poles in $\Re e(s) \geqslant 0$ then the closed loop system (5.46) is asymptotically stable if and only if as ω passes from $-\infty$ to ∞ the Nyquist locus of $g(s)$ does not encircle the point $-1 + i0$.

As a simple application of Theorem 5.11 we can see that there is no encirclement of $-1 + i0$ in Fig. 5.5, so the corresponding closed loop system is asymptotically stable. In fact this is very easily verified since from (5.46) and (5.49), $g_c(s) = 1/(s + 2)$.

If $g(s)$ has one or more poles on the imaginary axis then the contour in Fig. 5.6 must be modified as shown in Fig. 5.7, the circles on the ω-axis having radius $\rho \to 0$.

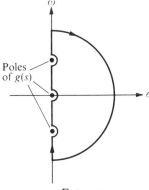

FIG. 5.7

The Nyquist locus is now the path traced out by $g(s)$ as s traverses the indented imaginary axis.

Example 5.14. Consider

$$g(s) = \frac{1}{s(s+1)}$$

which has a pole at $s = 0$.

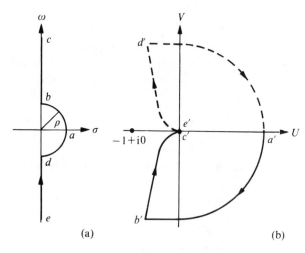

(a)   (b)

FIG. 5.8

On bc, $s = i\omega$ so that

$$g(s) = \frac{1}{i\omega(i\omega + 1)}$$

giving

$$U = -(1 + \omega^2)^{-1}, \qquad V = -\{\omega(1 + \omega^2)\}^{-1}$$

which is the path $b'c'$ in Fig. 5.8(b), On ab, $s = \rho\exp(i\theta)$ with $\rho \to 0$, so

$$g(s) = \lim_{\rho \to 0} \frac{1}{\rho e^{i\theta}(1 + \rho e^{i\theta})}$$

$$= \lim_{\rho \to 0} \frac{1}{\rho e^{i\theta}}$$

Thus as $\rho \to 0$, $g(s)$ has modulus $1/\rho$, argument $-\theta$ with $0 \leqslant \theta \leqslant \pi/2$. It follows that $a'b'$ is the mapping of ab. The reflection in the U axis, corresponding to the path eda, is shown in dashed lines. The point $-1 + i0$ is not encircled so the system is asymptotically stable. Again it is easy to verify that

$$g_c(s) = \frac{1}{s^2 + s + 1} .$$

and the characteristic polynomial is asymptotically stable (see Exercise 5.9(a)).

Clearly it is sufficient to sketch only the salient features of the Nyquist locus, a time-consuming detailed diagram usually not being necessary.

A result more general than Theorem 5.11 for the case when the open-loop system is not asymptotically stable can also be proved. The argument is based on Cauchy's residue theorem and can be found in most textbooks on classical linear control theory.

THEOREM 5.12. The closed loop system with transfer function (5.46) is asymptotically stable if and only if

$$N = -P \leqslant 0$$

where N = total number of clockwise encirclements of $-1 + i0$ by the Nyquist locus of $g(s)$;

P = number of poles of $g(s)$ in Γ_r': $\Re e(s) > 0$.

Furthermore, if $N > 0$, the number of zeros of $1 + g(s)$ (i.e. the number of closed loop poles) in Γ_r' is equal to $N + P$.

It should be remarked that if $P \neq 0$ then it would not be feasible to measure $g(i\omega)$ experimentally, since any open loop characteristic roots with positive real parts would lead to the open loop output growing without limit as $t \to \infty$.

Care must be taken in interpreting the term 'encircle' in Theorems 5.11 and 5.12. Precisely, a closed contour C is said to make n *clockwise encirclements* of a point D if a radial line drawn from D to a point on C rotates in a clockwise direction through $2\pi n$ radians in going completely round C.

Example 5.15. Consider a Nyquist diagram of the form below, shown for simplicity only for ω going from zero to infinity (Fig. 5.9). The reader should sketch the complete Nyquist locus and convince himself that the number of encirclements of the point $-1 + i0$ is zero.

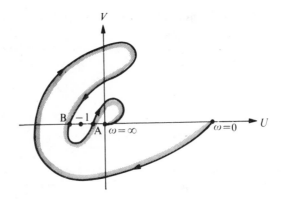

FIG. 5.9

When applying Theorem 5.11 it is only necessary to know whether $-1 + i0$ is enclosed by the contour, and a convenient way of determining this is to hatch the region to the right of the locus as it is traversed in the prescribed direction (see Fig. 5.9). All points within the hatched region are enclosed by the curve.

In practical problems it is often not sufficient to know merely that a linear system is asymptotically stable. This certainly ensures that the effect of perturbations from equilibrium eventually dies away, but it is usually required in addition that this should not take 'too long'. More precisely, the real parts of the closed loop system characteristic roots should be less than some given negative number σ, so that the exponential terms in the solution decay at least as fast as $\exp(\sigma t)$. The Routh array and other methods of Section 5.2 can be adapted to deal with such problems of *relative* stability, but the Nyquist diagram provides a convenient approach.

Example 5.16. Suppose that $g(s)$ in (5.46) is replaced by $kg(s)$ and that for $k = 1$ the Nyquist locus for a given system is as shown in Fig. 5.10. If $g(s)$ has no poles in Γ_r then by Theorem 5.11 the closed loop system is asymptotically stable for $k = 1$. Since the locus for any value of k is given by (5.51) as

$$U = k \, \Re\{g(i\omega)\}, \qquad V = k \, \Im\{g(i\omega)\},$$

then as k increases, the point where the locus meets the negative U-axis moves from $-\frac{1}{4} + i0$ when $k = 1$ to $-1 + i0$ when $k = 4$. Thus the system is asymptotically stable for $k < 4$.

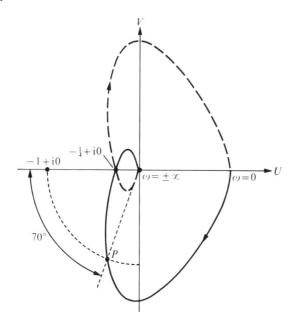

FIG. 5.10

If a circle with unit radius and centre the origin cuts the locus at the point P, then the whole Nyquist locus for $k = 1$ can be rotated clockwise through $70°$ before the point $-1 + i0$ is reached and the system is no longer asymptotically stable.

The quantities $1/(\frac{1}{4}) = 4$ and $70°$ are called the *gain* and *phase margins*, and thus provide a measure of how far the system is from instability (in this case when $k = 1$). In practice a gain margin of at least two and a phase margin of at least $30°$ are desirable as 'safety factors'.

The Bode plot (mentioned in Section 1.2.1) can also be used to determine gain and phase margins, since it presents essentially the same information as the Nyquist diagram in a different form.

In general, if $g(s)$ is replaced by $kg(s)$ in (5.46) the point $-1 + i0$ in the $g(s)$-plane in Theorems 5.11 and 5.12 is replaced by $-1/k + i0$.

It is worth mentioning that in Fig. 5.9 the ideas of gain and phase margins are not very meaningful. For example, the system becomes unstable if the gain is increased so that the point A is to the left of -1, or if the gain is decreased so that B is to the right of -1. Such a system is called *conditionally* stable.

Nyquist diagrams can be developed for discrete-time linear systems (Saucedo and Schiring, 1968, p. 466) and also under certain conditions for systems whose transfer function is not rational (Willems 1970, p. 79).

To summarize, the Nyquist criterion enables the closed loop stability to be determined from the open loop frequency transfer function, even if this is not known analytically and can only be determined experimentally. The technique is also useful if stability is to be investigated as a system parameter varies. For these and other reasons the Nyquist method is a widely used practical tool for both analysis and design of systems, and complements the algebraic criteria of the preceding section. We shall also see in Section 5.7 that Nyquist-type loci can be applied to certain cases of nonlinear feedback.

We close this section by mentioning briefly some recent extensions to deal with systems having vector inputs and outputs. If

$$F(s) = I_r + G(s)H(s) \qquad (5.52)$$

denotes the return-difference matrix in (4.40) with $r = m$, and the Nyquist path is in Fig. 5.7, then the closed loop system is asymptotically stable if and only if $N_1 = -P_1$, where N_1 is the number of clockwise encirclements of the origin by the Nyquist locus of $\det F(s)$ and P_1 is the number of zeros of the open loop characteristic polynomial $\det (sI - A))$ in Γ_r'. The characteristic roots $t_k(s)$ of the $m \times m$ matrix $T(s) = G(s)H(s)$, defined in the usual way by $\det (\lambda I - T) = 0$, will themselves be functions of s. Thus by (2.29) and Exercise 2.9(c)

$$\det F(s) = \prod_{k=1}^{m} (1 + t_k(s))$$

and the Nyquist contours of $t_k(s)$ are called the *characteristic loci.* It can be shown that the necessary and sufficient condition for closed loop asymptotic stability becomes

$$\sum_{k=1}^{m} n_k = -P_1$$

where n_k is the number of clockwise encirclements of $-1 + i0$ by the Nyquist locus of $t_k(s)$.

When $H(s) = I_m$ in (4.40) the closed loop transfer function matrix is

$$G_c(s) = [I_m + G(s)]^{-1} G(s)$$

so that

$$[G_c(s)]^{-1} = [G(s)]^{-1} + I_m.$$

A sufficient condition for closed-loop stability can be inferred from the *inverse Nyquist array,* which is the name given to the set of m^2 Nyquist loci corresponding to the elements of $[G(s)]^{-1}$.

These ideas have been developed into design techniques for multi-variable systems, and the comprehensive survey by MacFarlane (1972) should be consulted for further details, which are outside the scope of this book.

Exercise 5.17.
Verify by substituting (5.47) into (4.41) that the characteristic equation of the closed loop system is $\beta(s) + k(s)$.

Exercise 5.18.
Determine the number of clockwise encirclements by the contour shown below of the points (*a*) the origin (*b*) $-1 + i0$.

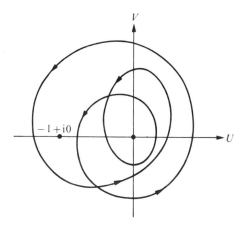

FIG. 5.11

Exercise 5.19.
Sketch the Nyquist diagram for

$$g(s) = \frac{1}{s(s-1)}$$

and hence determine the number of closed loop poles in Γ_r'.

Exercise 5.20.
Sketch the Nyquist locus for the open loop transfer function

$$g(s) = \frac{1}{s^2(s+1)},$$

and determine the stability of the closed loop system.

Exercise 5.21.
Draw the Nyquist locus for

$$g(s) = \frac{k}{(s+10)^3}.$$

Hence calculate the gain and phase margins when $k = 800/3$.

Verify that your result for the gain margin is correct by applying the Routh criterion to the closed loop characteristic polynomial.

5.4. Liapunov theory.

We shall develop the so-called 'second' or 'direct' method of the Russian mathematician Liapunov[†] in relation to the autonomous system of non-linear equations

$$\dot{x} = f(x), \qquad f(0) = 0, \tag{5.53}$$

subject to $x(t_0) = x_0$, but modifications needed to deal with (5.1) are straightforward. The aim is to determine the stability nature of the equilibrium point at the origin of (5.53) without obtaining the solution $x(t)$. This of course has been done algebraically for linear time invariant systems in Section 5.2. The essential idea is to generalize the concept of energy V for a conservative system in mechanics, where a well-known result states that an equilibrium point is stable if the energy is a minimum. Thus V is a positive function which has $\dot{V}$ negative in the neighbourhood of a stable equilibrium point. More generally, we define a *Liapunov function* $V(x)$ as follows:

(*i*) $V(x)$ and all its partial derivatives $\partial V/\partial x_i$ are continuous.
(*ii*) $V(x)$ is *positive definite*, i.e. $V(0) = 0$ and $V(x) > 0$ for $x \neq 0$ in some neighbourhood $\| x \| \leqslant k$ of the origin.
(*iii*) the derivative of V with respect to (5.48), namely

[†] Also transliterated in the literature as Lyapunov or Liapounoff.

$$\dot{V} = \frac{\partial V}{\partial x_1} \dot{x}_1 + \frac{\partial V}{\partial x_2} \dot{x}_2 + \cdots + \frac{\partial V}{\partial x_n} \dot{x}_n$$

$$= \frac{\partial V}{\partial x_1} f_1 + \frac{\partial V}{\partial x_2} f_2 + \cdots + \frac{\partial V}{\partial x_n} f_n \tag{5.54}$$

is negative semidefinite (i.e. $\dot{V}(0) = 0$, and for all x in $\| x \| \leqslant k$, $\dot{V}(x) \leqslant 0$.

Notice that in (5.54) the f_i are the components of f in (5.53), so $\dot{V}$ can be determined directly from the system equations. The definitions of positive or negative definiteness or semidefiniteness are generalizations of those for quadratic forms (see Section 2.8). The statements of the two basic theorems of Liapunov are remarkably simple:

THEOREM 5.13. The origin of (5.53) is stable if there exists a Liapunov function defined as above.

THEOREM 5.14. The origin of (5.53) is asymptotically stable if there exists a Liapunov function whose derivative (5.54) is negative definite.

Proof of Theorem 5.13. This relies on the fact that because of the sign property of V there exists a continuous scalar function $\phi(r)$ of r which vanishes at $r = 0$ and increases strictly monotonically[†] in $0 \leqslant r \leqslant k$ such that

$$V(x) \geqslant \phi(\| x \|). \tag{5.55}$$

Let $\epsilon > 0$ be given and suppose x_0 can be chosen so that the inequalities

$$\| x_0 \| < \epsilon, \quad V(x_0) < \phi(\epsilon) \tag{5.56}$$

are simultaneously satisfied. Since $\phi(\epsilon) > 0$, $V(0) = 0$ and $V(x)$ is continuous, a suitable vector satisfying (5.56) can in fact always be found by taking x_0 sufficiently close to the origin. Also, since $\dot{V} \leqslant 0$,

$$V[x(t_1)] \leqslant V[x(t_0)], t_1 \geqslant t_0$$

$$< \phi(\epsilon), \text{ by (5.56).} \tag{5.57}$$

If there exists some $t_1 > t_0$ such that $\| x(t_1) \| \geqslant \epsilon$ then by (5.55)

$$V[x(t_1)] \geqslant \phi(\| x(t_1) \|$$

$$\geqslant \phi(\epsilon)$$

[†] i.e. $\phi(r_2) > \phi(r_1)$ if $r_2 > r_1$

which contradicts (5.57). Hence for all $t_1 > t_0$ we have $\| x(t_1) \| < \epsilon$, so the origin is stable since $\delta = \epsilon$ in the definition in Section 5.1.

The proof of Theorem 5.14 is similar (see Hahn 1963, p. 15). It is worth noting that if the conditions on V in Theorem 5.14 hold everywhere in state space it does not necessarily follow that the origin is asymptotically stable in the large. For this to be the case $V(x)$ must have the additional property that it is *radially unbounded,* which means that $V(x) \to \infty$ for all x such that $\| x \| \to \infty$. For instance, $V = x_1^2 + x_2^2$ is radially unbounded, but $V = x_1^2 /(1 + x_1^2) + x_2^2$ is not since, for example, $V \to 1$ as $x_1 \to \infty, x_2 \to 0$. A similar line of reasoning shows that if Ω is the set of points *outside* a bounded region containing the origin, and if throughout Ω, $V > 0$, $\dot{V} \leqslant 0$, and V is radially unbounded then the origin is Lagrange stable (Willems 1970, p.34).

It may be helpful to consider a geometrical interpretation of Theorem 5.14 when $n = 2$.

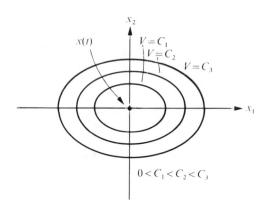

FIG. 5.12

Since V is positive definite the curves $V =$ constant must enclose the origin. They can be thought of as contours of a cup-shaped surface. Since $\dot{V} < 0$ on any trajectory, each trajectory must tend towards the origin as $t \to \infty$ (V 'falls to the bottom of the cup').

Example 5.17. Consider a unit mass suspended from a fixed support by a spring as shown in Fig. 5.13, z being the displacement from equilibrium.

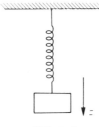

FIG. 5.13

If first the spring is assumed to obey Hooke's law then the equation of motion is

$$\ddot{z} + kz = 0, \tag{5.58}$$

where k is the spring constant. Taking $x_1 = z$, $x_2 = \dot{z}$, (5.58) becomes

$$\dot{x}_1 = x_2, \quad \dot{x}_2 = -kx_1. \tag{5.59}$$

Since the system is conservative the total energy

$$E = \tfrac{1}{2} kx_1^2 + \tfrac{1}{2} x_2^2 \tag{5.60}$$

is a Liapunov function and it is very easy to see from (5.59) that

$$\dot{E} = kx_1(x_2) + x_2(-kx_1) = 0,$$

so by Theorem 5.13 the origin is stable (of course this is trivial since (5.58) represents simple harmonic motion). Suppose now that the force exerted by the spring, instead of being linear is some function $k(x_1)$ satisfying $k(0) = 0$, $k(x_1) \neq 0$ if $x_1 \neq 0$, so that the second equation in (5.59) becomes $\dot{x}_2 = -k$. The total energy is now

$$E = \tfrac{1}{2} x_2^2 + \int_0^{x_1} k(\sigma)\, d\sigma \tag{5.61}$$

and

$$\dot{E} = x_2(-k) + k\dot{x}_1 = 0,$$

so again by Theorem 5.13 the origin is stable for any nonlinear spring satisfying the above conditions.

Example 5.18. Consider now the system of the previous example but with a damping force $d\dot{z}$ added, so that the equation of motion is

$$\ddot{z} + d\dot{z} + kz = 0 \tag{5.62}$$

instead of (5.58). Equation (5.62) can also be used to describe an LCR series electric circuit, motion of a gyroscope, and many other problems.

Assume first that both d and k are constant, and for simplicity let $d = 1, k = 2$. The system equations in state space form are

$$\dot{x}_1 = x_2, \quad \dot{x}_2 = -2x_1 - x_2 \tag{5.63}$$

and the total energy is still E in (5.60), so that using (5.63)

$$\dot{E} = 2x_1(x_2) + x_2(-2x_1 - x_2)$$
$$= -x_2^2$$

which is negative semidefinite, so by Theorem 5.13 the origin of (5.63) is stable. However, now consider the function

$$V = 7x_1^2 + 2x_1x_2 + 3x_2^2. \tag{5.64}$$

From (5.63)

$$\dot{V} = 14x_1(x_2) + 2[x_2(x_2) + x_1(-2x_1 - x_2)]$$
$$+ 6x_2(-2x_1 - x_2)$$
$$= -4x_1^2 - 4x_2^2.$$

Clearly $\dot{V}$ is negative definite and it is easy to verify that the quadratic form in (5.64) is positive definite (see Section 2.8), so by Theorem 5.14 the origin of (5.63) is asymptotically stable (in fact, in the large).

This example illustrates that a suitably-chosen Liapunov function can provide more information than the energy function. However, when $\dot{V}$ is only negative semidefinite the following result is often useful.

THEOREM 5.15. (*Barbashin*). If in Theorem 5.13 there exists a Liapunov function such that $\dot{V}$ does not vanish identically on any nontrivial trajectory of (5.53), then the origin is asymptotically stable.

Example 5.19. Consider again the damped mass-spring system described by (5.62), but now suppose that both d and k are not constant. Let $k(x_1)$ be as defined in the second part of Example 5.17, and let $d(x_2)$ have the property $d(x_2) > 0, x_2 \neq 0, d(0) = 0$. The state-space equations are

$$\dot{x}_1 = x_2, \quad \dot{x}_2 = -k - x_2 d \tag{5.65}$$

so if E is defined as in (5.61),

$$\dot{E} = x_2(-k - dx_2) + kx_2$$
$$= -x_2^2 \, d \leqslant 0.$$

Now E is positive definite and $\dot{E}$ vanishes only when $x_2(t) \equiv 0$, which by the second equation in (5.65) implies $k(x_1) \equiv 0$, which in turn implies $x_1(t) \equiv 0$. Thus $\dot{E}$ vanishes only on the trivial solution of (5.62), and so by Theorem 5.15 the origin is asymptotically stable.

Example 5.20. The *Van der Pol* equation

$$\ddot{z} + \epsilon(z^2 - 1)\dot{z} + z = 0, \tag{5.66}$$

where ϵ is a negative constant, arises in a number of engineering problems. In a control context it can be thought of as application of nonlinear feedback

$$u = -z + \epsilon(1 - z^2)\dot{z}$$

to the system described by $\ddot{z} = u$.

As usual take $x_1 = z, x_2 = \dot{z}$ to transform (5.66) into

$$\dot{x}_1 = x_2, \dot{x}_2 = -x_1 - \epsilon(x_1^2 - 1)x_2. \tag{5.67}$$

Try as a potential Liapunov function $V = x_1^2 + x_2^2$ which is obviously positive definite. Then

$$\dot{V} = 2x_1\dot{x}_1 + 2x_2\dot{x}_2$$
$$= 2\epsilon x_2^2 (1 - x_1^2).$$

Thus $\dot{V} \leqslant 0$ if $x_1^2 < 1$, and then by Theorem 5.15 the origin is asymptotically stable. It follows that all trajectories starting inside the region $\Gamma: x_1^2 + x_2^2 < 1$ converge to the origin as $t \to \infty$, and Γ is therefore called a *region of asymptotic stability*. The reader may be tempted to think that the infinite strip $x_1^2 < 1$ is a region of asymptotic stability. This is not in fact true, since a trajectory starting outside Γ can move outside this strip whilst continuing in the direction of decreasing V circles, and hence lead to divergence (see Fig. 5.14).

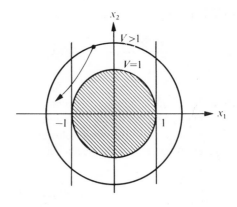

FIG. 5.14

In general if a closed region R defined by $V(x) \leqslant$ constant is *bounded* and has $\dot{V}$ negative definite throughout then R is a region of asymptotic stability.

Suppose that we now take as state variables

$$x_1 = z, \quad x_3 = \int_0^t z \, dt.$$

The corresponding state equations are $\dot{x}_3 = x_1$ and

$$\dot{x}_1 = \dot{z}$$

$$= - \int_0^t z \, dt - \epsilon \int_0^t (z^2 - 1)\dot{z} \, dt \quad \text{(integrating (5.66))}$$

$$= -x_3 - \epsilon \left(\tfrac{1}{3} z^3 - z \right)$$

$$= -x_3 - \epsilon \left(\tfrac{1}{3} x_1^3 - x_1 \right).$$

Hence using $V = x_1^2 + x_3^2$,

$$\dot{V} = 2x_1 \left(-x_3 - \tfrac{1}{3} \epsilon x_1^3 + \epsilon x_1 \right) + 2x_3 x_1$$

$$= 2\epsilon x_1^2 \left(1 - \tfrac{1}{3} x_1^2 \right)$$

$$< 0 \text{ if } x_1^2 < 3,$$

so the region of asymptotic stability obtained by this different set of state variables is $x_1^2 + x_3^2 < 3$, larger than before.

In general if the origin is an asymptotically stable equilibrium point then the total set of initial points from which trajectories converge to the origin as $t \to \infty$ is called the *domain of attraction*. Knowledge of this domain is of great value in practical problems since it enables permissible deviations from equilibrium to be determined. However, Example 5.20 illustrates the fact that since a particular Liapunov function gives only sufficient conditions for stability, the region of asymptotic stability obtained can be expected to be only part of the domain of attraction. Different Liapunov functions or different sets of state variables may well yield different stability regions. We shall discuss methods of constructing Liapunov functions for nonlinear systems in Section 5.6, but the general problem of finding 'optimum' Liapunov functions, which give best possible estimates for the domain of attraction, is a difficult one.

It may be a waste of effort trying to determine the stability properties of an equilibrium point, since the point may be unstable. The following theorem is then useful:

THEOREM 5.16. Let a function $V(x)$ with $V(0) = 0$ have continuous first partial derivatives. If there is some neighbourhood containing the origin in which V takes negative values, and if in addition $\dot{V}$ in (5.54) is negative semidefinite, then the origin of (5.53) is not asymptotically stable. If $\dot{V}$ is negative definite the origin is unstable, and if both V and $\dot{V}$ are negative definite the origin is completely unstable.

The proof follows along similar lines to those of Theorems 5.13 and 5.14. Notice that in the first two parts of Theorem 5.16 we do not need V itself to be negative throughout the neighbourhood, only at *some* points arbitrarily close to the origin. Also, as in Theorem 5.15, if $\dot{V}$ is negative semidefinite but $\dot{V} \not\equiv 0$ on any non-trivial trajectory then the origin is unstable. It is perhaps worth mentioning here that in all the Liapunov theorems the terms 'positive' and 'negative' can be interchanged simply by using $(-V)$ instead of V. It is only the relative signs of the Liapunov function and its derivative which matter.

To close this section we point out that all the theorems in it are applicable to discrete-time systems

$$x(k + 1) = f\{x(k)\}, \tag{5.68}$$

the only difference being that the derivative of V is replaced by its *difference*

$$\Delta V = V[x(k + 1)] - V[x(k)]$$
$$= V\{f[x(k)]\} - V[x(k)]. \tag{5.69}$$

Exercise 5.22.

Write the system

$$\ddot{z} + \dot{z} + z^3 = 0$$

in state space form. Let

$$V = ax_1^4 + bx_1^2 + cx_1x_2 + dx_2^2$$

and choose the constants a, b, c, d such that

$$\dot{V} = -x_1^4 - x_2^2.$$

Hence investigate the stability nature of the equilibrium point at the origin.

Exercise 5.23.

Using the function

$$V = 5x_1^2 + 2x_1x_2 + 2x_2^2$$

show that the origin of

$$\dot{x}_1 = x_2, \dot{x}_2 = -x_1 - x_2 + (x_1 + 2x_2)(x_2^2 - 1)$$

is asymptotically stable by considering the region $|x_2| < 1$. State the region of asymptotic stability thus determined.

Exercise 5.24.

Investigate the stability of the origin for the system

$$\dot{x}_1 = x_1^2 - x_2^2, \dot{x}_2 = -2x_1x_2$$

using the function $V = 3x_1x_2^2 - x_1^3$.

Exercise 5.25.

For the equations in Exercise 5.1, investigate stability of the origin using $V = x_2^2 - x_1^2$.

If in Exercise 5.1 the transformed system variables are y_1 and y_2, use

$$V = y_1 + 2y_2 - 2\ell n \left(1 + \tfrac{1}{2} y_1\right) - \ell n \left(1 + 2y_2\right)$$

to investigate the stability of the second equilibrium point.

Exercise 5.26.
Use the function $V = x_1^2 + x_2^2$ to show that the origin of the system

$$\dot{x}_1 = -x_1 + 2x_2, \qquad \dot{x}_2 = -2x_1 - x_2$$

is asymptotically stable in the large. If a term $-x_2 q$ is added to the right hand side of the second equation, find conditions on $q(x_1, x_2)$ such that the stability nature of the origin is unaffected.

Exercise 5.27.
Find the domain of attraction for the origin of the system described by the scalar equation

$$\dot{z} = \tfrac{1}{2} z(z - 2).$$

Exercise 5.28.
The equations of motion of a gyroscope without external forces are

$$A\dot{\omega}_1 + (C - B)\,\omega_2\omega_3 = 0$$
$$B\dot{\omega}_2 + (A - C)\,\omega_3\omega_1 = 0$$
$$C\dot{\omega}_3 + (B - A)\,\omega_1\omega_2 = 0$$

where A, B, C are the principal moments of inertia and ω_1, ω_2, ω_3 are the angular rates about the principal axes. Put $\omega_1 = \omega_0 + x_1$, $\omega_2 = x_2$, $\omega_3 = x_3$ (where ω_0 is a constant) and show that the origin of coordinates is then stable if $A < B < C$ by using the function

$$V = B(B - A)x_2^2 + C(C - A)x_3^2 + [Bx_2^2 + Cx_3^2 + A\,(x_1^2 + 2x_1\,\omega_0)]^2$$

(For further study of stability of gyroscopes see Leipholz (1970, p. 155); see also Exercise 5.54.)

Exercise 5.29.
Show that if the origin is an asymptotically stable equilibrium point for (5.53) with Liapunov function $V(x)$, then it also is for

$$\dot{x} = f(x) + [S(x) - Q(x)]\,\phi(x)$$

where $\phi(x) = \nabla V$, $Q(x)$ is any positive semidefinite $n \times n$ matrix and $S(x)$ is any skew symmetric $n \times n$ matrix, assuming that conditions for existence and uniqueness of solution still hold.

Apply this result to the system in Exercise 5.23 by choosing $S \equiv 0$ and a suitable matrix $Q(x)$ to show that the second equation can be replaced by

$$\dot{x}_2 = -x_1 - x_2 + (x_1 + 2x_2)[h(x_1, x_2) + x_2^2 - 1]$$

where $h(x_1, x_2)$ is any continuous function satisfying $h(x_1, x_2) \leqslant 0$.

5.5. Application of Liapunov theory to linear systems

We now return to the real linear time invariant system

$$\dot{x} = Ax . \tag{5.70}$$

In Section 5.2 we gave criteria for determining asymptotic stability via the characteristic equation of A. We now show how Liapunov theory can be used to deal directly with (5.70) by taking as a potential Liapunov function the quadratic form

$$V = x^T P x \tag{5.71}$$

where P is a real symmetric matrix. The time derivative of V with respect to (5.70) is

$$\dot{V} = \dot{x}^T P x + x^T P \dot{x}$$
$$= x^T A^T P x + x^T P A x$$
$$= -x^T Q x,$$

where

$$A^T P + P A = -Q, \tag{5.72}$$

and it is easy to see that Q is also symmetric. If P and Q are both positive definite then by Theorem 5.14 the (origin of) system (5.70) is asymptotically stable. If Q is positive definite and P is negative definite or indefinite then in both cases V can take negative values in the neighbourhood of the origin so by Theorem 5.16, (5.70) is unstable. We have therefore proved:

THEOREM 5.17. The real matrix A is a stability matrix if and only if for any given real symmetric positive definite (r.s.p.d.) matrix Q the solution P of the *continuous Liapunov matrix* equation (5.72) is also positive definite.

Notice that it would be no use choosing P to be positive definite and calculating Q from (5.72). For unless Q turned out to be definite or semidefinite (which is unlikely) nothing could be inferred about asymptotic stability from the Liapunov theorems. If A has complex elements then Theorem 5.17 still holds but with P and Q in (5.72) Hermitian, A^T replaced by A^*. A direct algebraic proof of Theorem 5.17, without relying on Liapunov theory, has also been given including an extension to the numbers of characteristic roots of A with positive and negative real parts. Furthermore, by a suitable choice of P and Q in (5.72) it is possible to deduce the Hurwitz stability criterion of Theorem 5.3 (Lancaster 1969, p. 272), so that a completely algebraic proof of this result can be achieved. In fact the sufficiency part of Theorem 5.17 is very easily shown. Let A be complex, and let λ and w be any corresponding characteristic root and vector. Then from (2.30)

$$Aw = \lambda w, \quad w^*A^* = \bar{\lambda} w^*, \tag{5.73}$$

and using (5.73) and the complex form of (5.72) we obtain

$$w^*Qw = -w^*(A^*P + PA)w$$

$$= -(\bar{\lambda} + \lambda)w^*Pw.$$

Hence if P and Q are both positive definite,

$$\Re(\lambda) = \tfrac{1}{2}(\bar{\lambda} + \lambda) = -\tfrac{1}{2}\, w^*Qw/w^*Pw < 0,$$

showing A is a stability matrix.

Eqn (5.72) is a special case of (2.37) with $B = A^T$. Since the characteristic roots of A^T are the same as those of A (see Exercise 2.9), by the result obtained in Section 2.4 it follows that the solution of (5.72) for P will be unique (given arbitrary Q) if and only if the characteristic roots λ_i of A are such that $\lambda_i + \lambda_j \neq 0$, all i, j. When A is complex, B in (2.37) is set equal to A^* and by again appealing to Exercise 2.9 the condition for uniqueness is seen to be $\bar{\lambda}_i + \lambda_j \neq 0$, all i, j.

Assuming the appropriate uniqueness condition is satisfied it is convenient to set Q equal to I_n. Although (5.72) can be expressed in the form of n^2 linear equations for the unknown elements of P as in (2.68), it follows since P and Q are symmetric that only $\tfrac{1}{2} n(n + 1)$ of the equations and unknowns are independent. However, when n is larger than about ten, direct solution of (5.72) in this form becomes unwieldy and a solution method involving an infinite matrix series is to be preferred (Barnett and Storey 1970, p. 100; see also Exercise 5.35). Equations similar in form to (5.72) also arise in other areas of control theory (see for example Section 6.1). However, it must be admitted that since a digital computer will be required to solve (5.72) except for small values of n, so far as stability determination of (5.70) is concerned it will be preferable instead to find the characteristic roots of A. The true value and importance of Theorem 5.17 lies in its use as a theoretical tool, and we shall see some applications of this later. Also Liapunov theory, unlike the classical methods of Section 5.2, is applicable to both linear and non linear systems and therefore provides a unified approach.

We now return to the discrete-time system described by (5.30). Again take V to be the quadratic form in (5.71) and from (5.69)

$$\Delta V = x^{\mathrm{T}}(k+1)Px(k+1) - x(k)Px(k)$$
$$= x^{\mathrm{T}}(k)A_1^{\mathrm{T}}PA_1 x(k) - x(k)Px(k)$$
$$= -x^{\mathrm{T}}(k) Q_1 x(k)$$

where now

$$A_1^{\mathrm{T}}PA_1 - P = -Q_1. \tag{5.74}$$

Otherwise the argument used to establish Theorem 5.17 is unchanged, so its discrete analogue is:

THEOREM 5.18. The real matrix A_1 is convergent if and only if for any given r.s.p.d. matrix Q_1 the solution P of the *discrete Liapunov matrix equation* (5.74) is also positive definite.

The condition for uniqueness of the solution of (5.74) is that the roots μ of A_1 are such that $\mu_i \mu_j \neq 1$. When A_1 is complex, transpose in (5.74) is replaced by conjugate transpose, and the uniqueness condition is $\bar{\mu}_i \mu_j \neq 1$ (see Exercise 2.17).

It is interesting to realize that the two Liapunov matrix equations are closely related. If we apply the transformation (5.31), which sends a stability matrix into a convergent matrix, to eqn (5.72) then we obtain

$$(A_1^{\mathrm{T}} + I)^{-1}(A_1^{\mathrm{T}} - I)P + P(A_1 - I)(A_1 + I)^{-1} = -Q$$

which can be simplified to

$$A_1^{\mathrm{T}}PA_1 - P = -\tfrac{1}{2}(A_1^{\mathrm{T}} + I)Q(A_1 + I). \tag{5.75}$$

Provided no $\mu_i = -1$, the matrix on the right in (5.75) is positive definite, so this equation is equivalent to (5.74). The matrices P in (5.72) and (5.75) are identical, so solution of either of the two types of Liapunov matrix equation can be achieved in terms of the other.

The usefulness of linear theory can be extended by use of the idea of linearization. Suppose the components of f in (5.53) are such that we can apply Taylor's theorem to obtain

$$f(x) = A'x + g(x), \tag{5.76}$$

using $f(0) = 0$. In (5.76) A' denotes the $n \times n$ constant matrix having elements $(\partial f_i / \partial x_j)_{x=0}$, $g(0) = 0$ and the components of g have power series expansions in $x_1, \ldots, x_n$ beginning with terms of at least second degree. The system

$$\dot{x} = A'x \tag{5.77}$$

is called the *first approximation* to (5.53). We then have:

THEOREM 5.19. (*Liapunov's linearization theorem*). If (5.77) is asymptotically stable so is (5.76); if (5.77) is unstable so is (5.76).

Proof. Consider the function $V = x^T P x$ where P satisfies

$$(A')^T P + PA' = -Q,$$

Q being an arbitrary r.s.p.d. matrix. If (5.77) is asymptotically stable then by Theorem 5.17 P is positive definite. The derivative of V with respect to (5.76) is

$$\dot{V} = -x^T Q x + 2g^T P x. \tag{5.78}$$

Because of the nature of g, the second term in (5.78) has degree three at least, and so for x sufficiently close to the origin, $\dot{V} < 0$. Hence by Theorem 5.14 the origin of (5.76) is asymptotically stable.

Conversely, if (5.77) is unstable, $\dot{V}$ remains negative definite but P is indefinite so V can take negative values and therefore satisfies the conditions of Theorem 5.16 for instability.

In fact the condition on g can be relaxed to $\| g(x) \| < \lambda \| x \|$ for sufficiently small $\lambda > 0$ (Lehnigk 1966, p. 55). Notice that if (5.77) is stable but not asymptotically stable, Theorem 5.19 provides no information about the stability of the origin of (5.76), and other methods must be used.

Furthermore, it is clear that linearization cannot provide any information about regions of asymptotic stability for the nonlinear system (5.53), since if the first approximation (5.77) is asymptotically stable then it is so in the large. Thus the extent of asymptotic stability for (5.53) is determined by the nonlinear terms in (5.76).

The following example illustrates the simplicity of Theorem 5.19 when it is applicable.

Example 5.21. Consider the scalar equation

$$\ddot{z} + a\dot{z} + bz + g(z, \dot{z}) = 0$$

or

$$\dot{x}_1 = x_2, \quad \dot{x}_2 = -bx_1 - ax_2 - g(x_1, x_2). \qquad (5.79)$$

The linear part of (5.79) is asymptotically stable if and only if $a > 0$, $b > 0$ (see Exercise 5.9), so if g is *any* function of x_1 and x_2 satisfying the conditions of Theorem 5.19, the origin of (5.79) is also asymptotically stable.

Exercise 5.30.
Using the matrix A in Exercise 3.1(a) and taking

$$P = \begin{bmatrix} p_1 & p_2 \\ p_2 & p_3 \end{bmatrix}$$

solve the equation (5.72) with $Q = I$. Hence determine the stability nature of A.

Exercise 5.31.
Integrate both sides of the matrix differential equation in Exercise 3.12 with respect to t from $t = 0$ to $t = \infty$. Hence deduce that if A is a stability matrix the solution of (5.72) can be written as

$$P = \int_0^\infty \exp(A^T t) Q \exp(At) \, dt.$$

Exercise 5.32.
Convert the second order equation

$$\ddot{z} + a_1 \dot{z} + a_2 z = 0$$

into state space form. Using V in (5.71) with $\dot{V} = -x_2^2$ obtain the necessary and sufficient conditions $a_1 > 0$, $a_2 > 0$ for asymptotic stability (see Exercise 5.9).

Exercise 5.33.
By using the quadratic Liapunov function $V(x)$ which has derivative $-2(x_1^2 + x_2^2)$, determine the stability of the system

$$\dot{x}_1 = -kx_1 - 3x_2, \quad \dot{x}_2 = kx_1 - 2x_2$$

when $k = 1$. Using the *same* function $V(x)$ obtain sufficient conditions on k for the system to be asymptotically stable. What is the necessary and sufficient condition?

Exercise 5.34.
Write (5.72) in the form

$$(PA + \tfrac{1}{2}Q) + (PA + \tfrac{1}{2}Q)^T = 0$$

and hence deduce that $P = (S - \tfrac{1}{2}Q)A^{-1}$, assuming A is nonsingular, where S is the real skew symmetric matrix satisfying

$$A^T S + SA = \tfrac{1}{2}(A^T Q - QA).$$

This represents a reduction to $\tfrac{1}{2}n(n-1)$ of the number of unknowns and equations when (2.38) is used.

Exercise 5.35.
Verify that the matrix equation (5.74) has solution

$$P = Q_1 + A_1^T Q_1 A_1 + (A_1^T)^2 Q_1 A_1^2 + (A_1^T)^3 Q_1 A_1^3 + \ldots$$

Assume that A_1 is similar to a diagonal matrix, and hence show that the series for P converges provided A_1 is a convergent matrix.

Exercise 5.36.
Replace A by $A + \sigma I$ in Theorem 5.17, where σ is a real number. Hence deduce the relative stability condition that the real parts of the roots of A are less than $-\sigma$ if and only if the solution P of

$$A^T P + PA + 2\sigma P = -Q$$

is positive definite.

Exercise 5.37.
Use Theorem 5.17 to show that the matrix $A = P_0(S_0 - Q_0)$ is a stability matrix, where P_0 and Q_0 are arbitrary r.s.p.d. matrices, and S_0 is an arbitrary real skew symmetric matrix.

Exercise 5.38.
If for a given real stability matrix A the solution of (5.72) is P, show that $A + (S_1 - Q_1)P$ is also a stability matrix, S_1 and Q_1 being arbitrary real skew and positive semidefinite $n \times n$ matrices respectively. (Compare with Exercise 5.29).

Exercise 5.39.
If $n = 2$, show that eqn (5.30) is asymptotically stable if and only if $|\det A_1| < 1$ and $1 + \det A_1 > |\operatorname{tr} A_1|$. (Hint: use the result in Exercise 5.10).
    What is the corresponding result for eqn (5.70)?

Exercise 5.40.
The equations describing a time varying LCR series electric circuit are

$$\dot{x}_1 = x_2/L(t), \quad \dot{x}_2 = -x_1/C(t) - x_2 R(t)/L(t),$$

where x_1 is the charge on the capacitor, x_2 is the flux in the inductor and $L(t), C(t), R(t) > 0, t \geqslant 0$.
    Use the Liapunov function $V = x^T P(t)x$, where

$$P(t) = \begin{bmatrix} R + 2L/RC & 1 \\ 1 & 2/R \end{bmatrix}$$

to show that $\dot{V} = -x^T Q(t)x$, where

$$Q(t) = \begin{bmatrix} 2/C & 0 \\ 0 & 2/L \end{bmatrix} - \dot{P},$$

and hence deduce that sufficient conditions for the origin to be asymptotically stable are

$$1 + \dot{R}(L/R^2 - \tfrac{1}{2}C) + \dot{C}L/RC - \dot{L}/R > 0,$$
$$1 + \dot{R}L/R^2 > 0$$

(it can be assumed that Theorem 5.14 still holds even though the system is non-autonomous).
    Notice that it would be difficult to obtain 'sharp' (i.e. almost necessary) conditions without considering the nature of the functions $L(t), C(t), R(t)$ in detail.

Exercise 5.41.
Investigate the stability nature of the equilibrium points at the origin for
the systems

$$(a) \quad \dot{x}_1 = 7x_1 + 2 \sin x_2 - x_2^4$$
$$\dot{x}_2 = \exp(x_1) - 3x_2 - 1 + 5x_1^2$$
$$(b) \quad \dot{x}_1 = (3/4) \sin x_1 - 7x_2 (1 - x_2)^{\frac{1}{3}} + x_1^3$$
$$\dot{x}_2 = (2/3)x_1 - 3x_2 \cos x_2 - 11x_2^5.$$

Exercise 5.42.
In the inverted pendulum problem of Exercise 1.3 assume that motions
about equilibrium are so small that second and higher degree terms in
the Taylor series expansion of $f(x, \dot{x})$ can be neglected, and hence obtain
the linearized form of the state equations. By finding the characteristic
equation, use Theorem 5.19 to determine the stability nature of the
origin (see Example 1.4 and Exercise 5.4).

Exercise 5.43.
Solve the scalar equation

$$\dot{z} = z - e^t z^3$$

by using the substitution $z = e^t w$. Hence verify that $z(t) \to 0$ as $t \to \infty$,
although the linear part is unstable.

This illustrates that Theorem 5.19 does not carry over to linear time
varying systems.

5.6. Construction of Liapunov functions.

We have seen in the previous section how a quadratic form can always be
used as a potential Liapunov function for a constant linear system. Before
seeking Liapunov functions for the nonlinear system (5.53) we must be
certain that we are not wasting our time, and this is ensured by a number
of results which are the converse of the stability theorems in Section 5.4.
We quote one of these as an example, and refer the reader to Hahn (1963,
Chapter 4) for further details.

THEOREM 5.20. If the origin of (5.53) is asymptotically stable, and
all the components of f and their first partial derivatives with respect to
the x_i are continuous in some region, then there exists in this region a
Liapunov function for (5.53) having $\dot{V}$ negative definite.

This theorem is of only theoretical interest since it does not help in construction of Liapunov functions. We now briefly describe two out of the many methods which are available for this purpose (for further details see Schultz 1965).

5.6.1.   *Variable gradient method.*

In both the asymptotic stability and instability theorems of Section 5.4 we require $\dot{V}$ to be negative definite, and as in (5.54)

$$\dot{V} = \frac{\partial V}{\partial x_1} f_1 + \frac{\partial V}{\partial x_2} f_2 + \cdots + \frac{\partial V}{\partial x_n} f_n$$

$$= (\nabla V)^{\mathrm{T}} f \tag{5.80}$$

where

$$\nabla V = \left[\frac{\partial V}{\partial x_1} , \frac{\partial V}{\partial x_2} , \ldots , \frac{\partial V}{\partial x_n} \right]^{\mathrm{T}} \tag{5.81}$$

is the *gradient* of V. The idea of the method is to let the gradient have the form

$$\nabla V = \begin{bmatrix} \alpha_{11} x_1 + \alpha_{12} x_2 + \cdots + \alpha_{1n} x_n \\ \alpha_{21} x_1 + \quad \cdots \cdots + \alpha_{2n} x_n \\ \cdot \\ \cdot \\ \alpha_{n1} x_1 + \quad \cdot \quad \cdots \cdots + \alpha_{nn} x_n \end{bmatrix} \tag{5.82}$$

the α_{ij} being functions of the xs and chosen so as to satisfy the conditions
(1) $\dot{V}$ in (5.80) is negative definite
(2) ∇V in (5.82) is indeed the gradient of a scalar function.
From vector theory this requires that the n-dimensional curl of ∇V be identically zero, i.e.

$$\frac{\partial G_i}{\partial x_j} = \frac{\partial G_j}{\partial x_i}, \quad i,j = 1, 2, \ldots, n, \tag{5.83}$$

$$(i \neq j),$$

where G_i is the ith component in (5.82).
After the conditions (5.83) have been satisfied, a check is then needed

to ensure that $\dot{V}$ is still negative definite – if not, the procedure will have to be repeated. Finally, V is obtained from the line integral

$$\int_{(0, 0, \ldots, 0)}^{(x_1, x_2 \ldots, x_n)} (G_1 dx_1 + \cdots + G_n dx_n)$$

for which a convenient expression is

$$\int_0^{x_1} G_1(x_1, 0, 0, \ldots, 0)dx_1 + \int_0^{x_2} G_2(x_1, x_2, 0, \ldots, 0)dx_2$$

$$+ \cdots + \int_0^{x_n} G_n(x_1, x_2, \ldots, x_n)dx_n. \qquad (5.84)$$

Of course the n^2 functions α_{ij} are not determined uniquely by the above conditions so to that extent the method is one of 'trial and error'. Note also that failure to find a suitable function using the variable gradient method does not imply anything about the stability nature of the equilibrium point.

Example 5.22. Consider the system described by

$$\dot{x}_1 = -3x_2 - x_1^5$$
$$\dot{x}_2 = -2x_2 + x_1^5.$$

The first approximation (5.77) has matrix

$$\begin{bmatrix} 0 & -3 \\ 0 & -2 \end{bmatrix}$$

which has characteristic roots 0 and -2, and so is only stable (Theorem 5.2). Hence the linearization Theorem 5.19 does not apply.

From (5.80) and (5.82)

$$\dot{V} = -(3x_2 + x_1^5)(\alpha_{11}x_1 + \alpha_{12}x_2) - (2x_2 - x_1^5)(\alpha_{21}x_1 + \alpha_{22}x_2)$$
$$= -x_1^2(\alpha_{11}x_1^4 - \alpha_{21}x_1^4) + x_1x_2(-3\alpha_{11} - \alpha_{12}x_1^4 - 2\alpha_{21} + \alpha_{22}x_1^4)$$
$$- x_2^2(3\alpha_{12} + 2\alpha_{22}). \qquad (5.85)$$

A simple way of obtaining $\dot{V} < 0$, although of course not the only one, is to make the x_1x_2 term in (5.85) vanish by taking

$$\alpha_{12} = 0, \quad \alpha_{21} = 0, \quad \alpha_{11} = \tfrac{1}{3}\alpha_{22}x_1^4.$$

This gives

$$\dot{V} = -\alpha_{11}x_1^6 - 2\alpha_{22}x_2^2$$
$$= -\alpha_{22}\left(\tfrac{1}{3}x_1^{10} + 2x_2^2\right)$$

which is negative definite provided $\alpha_{22} > 0$. In this case

$$\nabla V = \begin{bmatrix} \tfrac{1}{3}\alpha_{22}x_1^5 \\ \\ \alpha_{22}x_2 \end{bmatrix} = \begin{bmatrix} G_1 \\ \\ G_2 \end{bmatrix}$$

so the curl condition (5.83) is just

$$\frac{\partial(\tfrac{1}{3}\alpha_{22}x_1^5)}{\partial x_2} = \frac{\partial(\alpha_{22}x_2)}{\partial x_1}$$

which will be satisfied if α_{22} is a constant. There is no need to check $\dot{V}$, so from (5.84)

$$V = \int_0^{x_1} \tfrac{1}{3}\alpha_{22}x_1^5 \ dx_1 + \int_0^{x_2} \alpha_{22}x_2 dx_2$$

$$= \alpha_{22}(x_1^6 + 9x_2^2)/18$$

which is positive definite, so the origin is asymptotically stable in the large by Theorem 5.14.

5.6.2. Zubov's method

The aim is again to try and find a Liapunov function by starting with a negative definite function $\phi(x)$ as its derivative, so we now wish to solve for $V(x_1, x_2, \dots, x_n)$ the partial differential equation

$$\frac{\partial V}{\partial x_1} f_1 + \frac{\partial V}{\partial x_2} f_2 + \cdots + \frac{\partial V}{\partial x_n} f_n = \phi, \qquad (5.86)$$

subject to the boundary condition $V(0) = 0$. Equation (5.86) can be written

$$dV/dt = \phi$$

which on integration with respect to t gives

$$V[x(T)] - V(x_0) = \int_{t_0}^{T} \phi[x(t)] dt, \qquad (5.87)$$

where $x_0 = x(t_0)$. If the origin of (5.53) is asymptotically stable, and x_0 lies within its domain of attraction then letting $T \to \infty$ in (5.87) produces

$$V(x_0) = - \int_{t_0}^{\infty} \phi \, dt$$

which is positive, so we can expect the solution of (5.86) to be positive definite. As x_0 approaches the boundary of the domain of attraction then in (5.87) $V(x_0)$ tends to infinity since $V\{x(T)\} \to \infty$ as $T \to \infty$. To avoid this difficulty the procedure can be altered by defining a function

$$W(x) = 1 - \exp\,[- V(x)]. \tag{5.88}$$

The differential equation (5.86) then becomes

$$\frac{\partial W}{\partial x_1} f_1 + \frac{\partial W}{\partial x_2} f_2 + \cdots + \frac{\partial W}{\partial x_n} f_n = (1 - W)\phi. \tag{5.89}$$

The boundary of the domain of attraction is now given by $W(x) = 1$.

Example 5.23. Consider the system described by

$$\dot{x}_1 = - 2x_1 + 2x_2^4, \dot{x}_2 = -x_2.$$

With $\phi = - 24(x_1^2 + x_2^2)$ equation (5.86) becomes

$$\frac{\partial V}{\partial x_1} (- 2x_1 + 2x_2^4) + \frac{\partial V}{\partial x_2}(- x_2) = - 24(x_1^2 + x_2^2)$$

and this has solution

$$V = 6x_1^2 + 12x_2^2 + 4x_1 x_2^4 + x_2^8,$$
$$= 2x_1^2 + 12x_2^2 + (2x_1 + x_2^4)^2$$

which is positive definite, showing the origin is asymptotically stable in the large.

Exercise 5.44.
Consider the equilibrium point at the origin for the system

$$. \, \dot{x}_1 = -x_1 + 2x_1^2 x_2, \dot{x}_2 = -x_2.$$

Construct a Liapunov function using the variable gradient method by taking $\alpha_{11} = 1, \alpha_{22} = 2, \alpha_{12} = \alpha_{21} = 0$ in (5.82), and determine the corresponding region of asymptotic stability.

Exercise 5.45.
In Exercise 5.22 deduce the stated expression for V using the variable gradient method.

Exercise 5.46.
The equations describing a homogeneous atomic reactor with constant power extraction can be written

$$\dot{x}_1 = -\alpha x_2/\tau,$$
$$\dot{x}_2 = \{\exp(x_1) - 1\}/\epsilon$$

where $P(t) = \exp x_1(t)$ is the instantaneous reactor power, $x_2(t)$ is the temperature, $\alpha > 0$ is the temperature coefficient, $\epsilon > 0$ is the heat capacity and $\tau > 0$ the average life of a neutron. Use the variable gradient method with $\alpha_{22} = 1$, $\alpha_{12} = \alpha_{21} = 0$ in (5.82) to determine the stability nature of the equilibrium point at the origin. (Hint: set $\dot{V} = 0$).

Exercise 5.47.
Consider the first order system

$$\dot{x}_1 = x_1^3 - x_1.$$

Use Zubov's method with $\phi = -2x_1^2$ to determine the stability nature of the origin.

5.7. Stability and control

Apart from Section 5.3, where we developed the Nyquist criterion for closed loop linear systems, our discussions in this chapter have so far not directly involved the control terms in the system equations. We now consider some stability problems associated explicitly with the control variables.

5.7.1. Input–output stability

Our definitions in Section 5.1 referred to stability with respect to perturbations from an equilibrium state. When a system is subject to inputs it is useful to define a new type of stability. The nonlinear system

$$\dot{x} = f(x, u, t), \quad f(0, 0, t) = 0$$

with output $y = g(x, u, t)$ is said to be *bounded input – bounded output* (*b.i.b.o.*) *stable* if any bounded input produces a bounded output. That is, given

$$\| u(t) \| < \ell_1, t \geqslant t_0 \tag{5.90}$$

where ℓ_1 is any positive constant, then there exists a number $\ell_2 > 0$ such that $\| y(t) \| < \ell_2$ for $t \geqslant t_0$, regardless of initial state $x(t_0)$. The problem of studying b.i.b.o. stability for nonlinear systems is a difficult one, but we can give some results for the usual linear system

$$\dot{x} = Ax + Bu \tag{5.91}$$

$$y = Cx. \tag{5.92}$$

Using (3.22) and the properties of norms (see Section 2.7) we have

$$\| y(t) \| \leqslant \| C \| \, \| x \|$$

$$\leqslant \| C \| \, [\, \| \exp (At)x_0 \| \,] + \| C \| \int_0^t \| \exp [A(t - \tau)] \| \, \| Bu \| \, \mathrm{d}\tau. \tag{5.93}$$

If A is a stability matrix then

$$\| \exp (At) \| \leqslant K \exp (-at) \leqslant K, t \geqslant 0 \tag{5.94}$$

for some positive constants K and a (see (5.12)). Thus (5.90), (5.93), and (5.94) imply

$$\| y \| \leqslant \| C \| \, [K \| x_0 \| + \ell_1 K \| B \| \, \{1 - \exp (-at)\}/a]$$

$$\leqslant \| C \| \, [K \| x_0 \| + \ell_1 K \| B \| \, /a], t \geqslant 0,$$

showing that the input is bounded, since $\| C \|$ and $\| B \|$ are positive numbers. We have therefore established:

THEOREM 5.21. If $\dot{x} = Ax$ is asymptotically stable, then the system described by (5.91) and (5.92) is b.i.b.o. stable.

An interesting link with the ideas of Chapter 4 is provided by the fact that the converse of Theorem 5.21 holds only if $\{A, B, C\}$ is a minimal realization. In other words, by Theorem 4.23:

THEOREM 5.22. If the system (5.91) and (5.92) is c.c. and c.o. and b.i.b.o. stable, then $\dot{x} = Ax$ is asymptotically stable.

For a proof see the book by Willems (1970, p. 53). Similar results for discrete-time systems also hold (see Exercise 5.51). However, for linear time varying systems Theorem 5.21 is not true (see Exercise 5.52) unless for all t the norms of $B(t)$ and $C(t)$ are bounded and the norm of the transition matrix $\Phi(t, t_0)$ in (3.27) is bounded and tends to zero as $t \to \infty$ independently of t_0 (Willems 1970, p. 105).

In the definition of complete controllability in Section 4.1 no restrictions were applied to $u(t)$, but in practical situations there will clearly always be finite bounds on the magnitudes of the control variables and on the duration of their application. It is then intuitively obvious that this will imply that not all states are attainable. As a trivial example, if a finite thrust is applied to a rocket for a finite time then there will be a limit to the final velocity which can be achieved. We give here one formal result for linear systems due to Mohler (1973).

THEOREM 5.23. The linear system (5.91), with A a stability matrix and u bounded by (5.90), is not c.c.

Proof. Let V be a quadratic form Liapunov function (5.71) for the unforced system. Then with respect to (5.91)

$$\dot{V} = -x^{\mathrm{T}}Qx + u^{\mathrm{T}}B^{\mathrm{T}}(\nabla V), \qquad (5.95)$$

where P and Q satisfy (5.72) and ∇V is defined in (5.81). The second term on the right hand side of eqn (5.95) is linear in x and since u is bounded it follows that for $\| x \|$ sufficiently large, $\dot{V} = \dot{x}^{\mathrm{T}}(\nabla V)$ is negative. This shows that $\dot{x}$ points into the interior of the region $V(x) = M$ for some M sufficiently large. Hence points outside this region cannot be reached, so by definition the system is not c.c.

It is most interesting that bilinear systems, which contain product terms $u_i x_j$, can still be c.c. even when the inputs are bounded. An example given by Mohler is that the linear system

$$\dot{x}_1 = x_2, \dot{x}_2 = -2x_1 - x_2 + u$$

with $|u| \leqslant 1$ is not c.c. by Theorem 5.23, but if the second equation is

$$\dot{x}_2 = -2x_1 - x_2 + u + ux_1 + 2ux_2$$

then the resulting bilinear system is c.c. Bilinear mathematical models of control systems are being increasingly studied, and a number of practical applications are described in Mohler's book (see also Example 1.5 and Exercise 6.13).

5.7.2. Linear feedback.

Consider again the linear system (5.91). If the open loop system is unstable (i.e. by Theorem 5.1 one or more of the characteristic roots of

A has a positive real part) then an essential practical objective would be to apply control so as to *stabilize* the system – that is, make the closed loop system asymptotically stable. If (5.91) is c.c. then we saw in Section 4.4 (Theorem 4.17) that stabilization can always be achieved by linear feedback $u = Kx$, since there are an infinity of matrices K which will make $A + BK$ a stability matrix. If the pair $[A, B]$ is not c.c. then we can define the weaker property that $[A, B]$ is *stabilizable* if and only if there exists a constant matrix K such that $A + BK$ is asymptotically stable. We can see at once from the canonical form of (5.91) displayed in Theorem 4.9 that the system is stabilizable if and only if A_3 in (4.21) is a stability matrix. In this case the feedback is $u = K_1 x^{(1)}$, where K_1 can be chosen to make $A_1 + B_1 K_1$ asymptotically stable since the pair $[A_1, B_1]$ is c.c. By duality (see Theorem 4.11) we define the pair $[A, C]$, where C is the output matrix in (5.92), to be *detectable* if and only if $[A^T, C^T]$ is stabilizable.

Methods for constructing feedback matrices K were discussed in Section 4.4, where the disadvantages of the method of prespecifying closed loop poles were indicated. Two simple illustrations of the application of stabilizing linear feedback have been provided by the rabbit–fox problem (Exercise 4.33), in which a disease lethal to rabbits keeps the animal population finite; and by the buffalo model (Exercise 4.53) in which slaughtering animals for food fulfils the same function. Another method of constructing matrices K will be developed in Chapter 6 using the ideas of optimal control. It is interesting to consider here a simple application of the Liapunov methods of Section 5.5. First notice that if (5.70) is asymptotically stable with Liapunov function $V = x^T P x$, where P satisfies (5.72), then

$$\dot{V}/V = -x^T Q x / x^T P x$$
$$\leqslant -\sigma \qquad (5.96)$$

where σ is the minimum value of the ratio $x^T Q x / x^T P x$ (in fact this is equal to the smallest characteristic root of QP^{-1}). Integrating (5.96) with respect to t gives

$$V[x(t)] \leqslant \exp(-\sigma t) V[x(0)]. \qquad (5.97)$$

Since $V[x(t)] \to 0$ as $t \to \infty$, (5.97) can be regarded as a measure of the way in which trajectories approach the origin, so the larger σ the 'faster' does $x(t) \to 0$. Suppose now we apply the control

$$u = (S - Q_1) B^T P x \qquad (5.98)$$

to (5.91), where P is the solution of (5.72) and S and Q_1 are arbitrary skew-symmetric and positive definite symmetric matrices respectively. The closed loop system is thus

$$\dot{x} = [A + B(S - Q_1)B^\mathrm{T}P]x \qquad (5.99)$$

and it is easy to verify that if $V = x^\mathrm{T}Px$ then the derivative with respect to (5.99) is

$$\dot{V} = -x^\mathrm{T}Qx - 2x^\mathrm{T}PBQ_1B^\mathrm{T}Px$$
$$< -x^\mathrm{T}Qx$$

since $PBQ_1B^\mathrm{T}P = (PB)Q_1(PB)^\mathrm{T}$ is positive definite. Hence by the argument just developed it follows that (5.99) is 'more stable' than the open loop system (5.70), in the sense that trajectories will approach the origin more quickly. Of course (5.98) is of rather limited practical value because it requires asymptotic stability of the open loop system, but nevertheless the power of Liapunov theory is apparent by the ease with which the asymptotic stability of (5.99) can be established. This would be impossible using the classical methods of Section 5.2, requiring calculation of the characteristic equation of (5.99). Furthermore, the Liapunov approach often enables extensions to nonlinear problems to be made (see for example Exercise 5.53).

†5.7.3. Nonlinear feedback.

We now consider the system with a single control variable

$$\dot{x} = Ax - bu \qquad (5.100)$$

subject to nonlinear feedback

$$u = f(y) \qquad (5.101)$$

where

$$y = cx. \qquad (5.102)$$

In (5.101) $f(y)$ is a continuous function of the scalar output y, and A, b, and c in (5.100) and (5.102) are such that the triple $\{A, b, c\}$ is a minimal realization of a scalar transfer function $g(s)$. It is assumed that $f(0) = 0$ so the origin $x = 0$ is an equilibrium point for (5.100) and (5.101).

The stability theorems to be quoted in this section involve the notion of a *positive real* function $r(s)$, which we define to be a rational function

$p(s)/q(s)$ with real coefficients such that $p(s)$ and $q(s)$ are relatively prime and

(a) $r(s)$ has no poles in $\Re e(s) > 0$

(b)   any purely imaginary poles of $r(s)$ are simple and have real positive residues

(c) $\Re e\{r(i\omega)\} \geqslant 0$ for all real $\omega \geqslant 0$.

We can now state a recent result which gives a sufficient stability condition.

THEOREM 5.24. (*Popov*). The origin of the system described by (5.100), (5.101) and (5.102) is asymptotically stable in the large if

(i)
$$0 < \frac{f(y)}{y} < k_1, \text{ all } y \neq 0, \tag{5.103}$$

where k_1 is a positive constant, and

(ii)   there exists a real number α such that

$$(1 + \alpha s)g(s) + 1/k_1 \tag{5.104}$$

is positive real.

Proofs of the theorem are too complicated to give in this book. One (Siljak 1969, p. 330) relies on using a Liapunov function of the form

$$x^{\mathrm{T}}Px + \alpha \int_0^y f(\sigma)\,\mathrm{d}\sigma$$

where P is the solution of the Liapunov matrix equation (5.72) (note that positive-realness of (5.104) ensures that A has no characteristic roots with positive real parts). Another approach to the proof uses functional analysis (see Willems 1970, p. 152).

Notice that (5.103) means that provided condition (ii) of Theorem 5.24 is satisfied, the origin is asymptotically stable in the large for any continuous function $f(y)$ lying within the sector bounded by the line $z = k_1 y$ and the y axis, as shown in Fig. 5.15. In this case the system is said to be *absolutely* stable in the sector $[0, k_1]$.

An interesting and useful aspect of the Popov criterion is that it has a simple graphical interpretation. Positive realness of (5.104) requires that $g(s)$ must have no poles in $\Re e(s) > 0$, and that any imaginary poles of $g(s)$ are simple and the corresponding residues of (5.104) are real and positive. In particular, if A is a stability matrix (i.e. the open loop system is asymptotically stable) these conditions will certainly be satisfied.

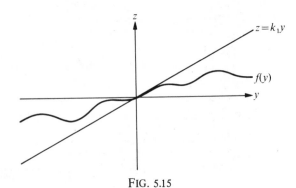

FIG. 5.15

Condition (*c*) of the positive realness definition applied to (5.104) gives

$$\mathfrak{Re}\{(1 + i\alpha\omega)g(i\omega) + 1/k_1\} \geqslant 0 \qquad (5.105)$$

for $\omega \geqslant 0$. We define a curve in the complex plane by means of

$$U_1 = \mathfrak{Re}\{g(i\omega)\}, \quad V_1 = \omega\mathrm{Im}\{g(i\omega)\}, \quad \omega \geqslant 0, \qquad (5.106)$$

which differs from the Nyquist locus (5.51) only in that the imaginary part has an extra factor ω. Substitution of (5.106) into (5.105) produces

$$\alpha V_1 - U_1 \leqslant 1/k_1.$$

It follows that for (5.105) to be satisfied it must be possible to draw a straight line through the point $-1/k_1 + i0$ such that the locus has no points to the left of the line, as shown in Fig. 5.16.

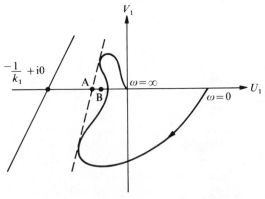

FIG. 5.16

The value of α is given by the slope of the straight line $\alpha V_1 - U_1 = 1/k_1$ (the *Popov line*). The largest value of k_1 would be when $-1/k_1 + i0$ is at the point A in Fig. 5.16. If k_1 is increased further so that the point B is reached (5.105) cannot be satisfied (although this does not mean the origin is unstable, as Theorem 5.24 is only sufficient).

When f is a linear function then we simply have linear feedback, so $u = \kappa y$ and the Nyquist criterion of Theorem 5.11 (in the modified form of p. 171) applies. The necessary and sufficient condition for absolute stability in the sector $[0, k_1]$ (i.e. $0 < \kappa < k_1$) is that the Nyquist locus of $g(s)$ should not intersect the real axis to the left of $-1/k_1 + i0$ (including the point itself), for if it did there would be some point $-1/k_0 + i0$ with $k_0 < k_1$ enclosed by the locus. If the system with u given by (5.101) is to be absolutely stable, it clearly must be stable for the particular case when f is linear, so the condition on the Nyquist locus is a necessary one for absolute stability of the nonlinear system in the sector $[0, k_1]$.

Example 5.24. Consider the transfer function

$$g(s) = \frac{1}{s(s^2 + s + 2)} .$$

By Exercise 5.9, $s^2 + s + 2$ is a Hurwitz polynomial, and for the simple pole at the origin the residue is $\frac{1}{2}$, so it remains to satisfy (5.105). From (5.106)

$$U_1 = -\frac{1}{\omega^2 + (\omega^2 - 2)^2} , \quad V_1 = \frac{\omega^2 - 2}{\omega^2 + (\omega^2 - 2)^2}$$

and the locus is shown below.

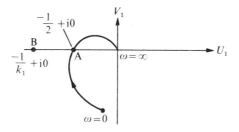

FIG. 5.17

A tangent can be drawn from $-1/k_1 + i0$ to the curve provided B is to the left of A, i.e. $k_1 < 2$. Thus (5.104) is positive real, so by Theorem 5.24 the system is absolutely stable in the sector $[0, 2]$.

We now consider (5.100) with feedback of the form

$$u = h(x)cx \tag{5.107}$$

where $h(x)$ is a scalar function of x. A sufficient condition for stability is then the following:

THEOREM 5.25. The origin of the system described by (5.100) and (5.107) is asymptotically stable in the large if

$$k_3 < h(x) < k_2, \text{ all } x, \tag{5.108}$$

and the function

$$\frac{1 + k_2 g(s)}{1 + k_3 g(s)} \tag{5.109}$$

is positive real.

We also omit this proof, which can be developed either by Liapunov theory (Willems 1970, p. 161) or using functional analysis. Instead we shall again develop a graphical interpretation using the frequency transfer function.

The positive realness condition (c) on p. 201 applied to (5.109) require that

$$\Re \left[\frac{k_2 g(i\omega) + 1}{k_3 g(i\omega) + 1} \right] \geqslant 0 \tag{5.110}$$

for $\omega \geqslant 0$, and this time the standard Nyquist locus (5.51) is used. Substituting $g(i\omega) = U + iV$ into (5.110) reduces it to

$$k_2 k_3 (U^2 + V^2) + (k_2 + k_3)U + 1 \geqslant 0. \tag{5.111}$$

When equality occurs in (5.111) the expression represents a circle in the $g(s) -$ plane,

$$\text{centre} - \frac{(k_2 + k_3)}{2 k_2 k_3} + i0, \quad \text{radius} \ \frac{k_2 - k_3}{2 k_2 k_3} \ .$$

This circle $\mathscr{C}$ has the points $-1/k_3 + i0$, $-1/k_2 + i0$ at opposite ends of a diameter, as shown in Fig. 5.18.

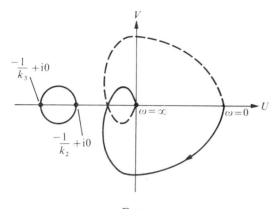

FIG. 5.18

The condition (5.111) is equivalent to requiring that the Nyquist locus of $g(s)$ does not enter $\mathscr{C}$ if k_2 and k_3 have the same sign, and must not have any point outside $\mathscr{C}$ if $k_2 k_3 < 0$. For (5.109) to be positive real the conditions (a) and (b) of the definition on p. 201 must also be satisfied. It can be shown that these can be replaced by the requirement that $p(s) + q(s)$ be a Hurwitz polynomial. Since k_2 and k_3 are constants, positive realness of (5.109) is equivalent to that of

$$\frac{k_3}{k_2} \cdot \frac{1 + k_2 g(s)}{1 + k_3 g(s)} = \frac{k(s)/k_2 + \beta(s)}{k(s)/k_3 + \beta(s)}$$

when $k_2 k_3 > 0$, using the expression for $g(s)$ in (5.47). Hence the polynomial

$$2\beta(s) + \left(\frac{1}{k_2} + \frac{1}{k_3}\right) k(s) \tag{5.112}$$

must be of Hurwitz type. The zeros of (5.112) are the poles of

$$\frac{\beta(s)}{\frac{1}{2}\left(\frac{1}{k_2} + \frac{1}{k_3}\right) k(s) + \beta(s)} = \frac{g(s)}{\frac{1}{2}\left(\frac{1}{k_2} + \frac{1}{k_3}\right) + g(s)},$$

and the condition that they should all be in $\Re e(s) < 0$ is (by Theorem 5.12) that the complete Nyquist locus of $g(s)$ for $-\infty \leqslant \omega \leqslant \infty$ should encircle the point $-\frac{1}{2}(1/k_2 + 1/k_3) + i0$ in an anticlockwise direction P times, where P is the number of poles of $g(s)$ in $\Re e(s) > 0$. This point is just the centre of the circle $\mathscr{C}$, so when k_2 and k_3 have the same sign

Theorem 5.25 is equivalent to requiring that the complete Nyquist locus of $g(s)$ does not enter $\mathscr{C}$, and encircles it P times in an anticlockwise direction. When $k_2 k_3 < 0$ the condition is simply that the entire Nyquist locus must lie inside $\mathscr{C}$.

An instability result when $k_2 k_3 > 0$ is that at least one solution of (5.100) and (5.107) is unbounded as $t \to \infty$ if the Nyquist locus of $g(s)$ does not intersect $\mathscr{C}$ and encircles it fewer than P times in an anticlockwise direction.

Because of the graphical interpretation Theorem 5.25, and variants of it in which h can also be a function of t, are called *circle criteria*. The theorem is applied to find values of k_2 and k_3 by drawing circles, if possible, in the $g(s)$ −plane satisfying the above requirements with respect to the Nyquist locus. When $k_2 \to k_3$ the circle criterion tends to the Nyquist stability criterion ($\mathscr{C}$ shrinks to the point $-1/k + i0$).

An extension of circle theorems to multivariable systems has recently been given by Rosenbrock and Cook (1973).

Exercise 5.48.
Consider the mass-spring system in Example 5.17, which is stable but not asymptotically stable. If a vertical control force is applied to the mass, determine whether the system is b.i.b.o. stable.

Exercise 5.49.
Consider again the inverted pendulum of Example 1.4 and Exercise 1.3, and use the linearized model developed in Exercise 5.42 in the following. It is required to keep the rod as nearly vertical as possible by means of the horizontal control force $u(t)$ applied to the platform. Determine the control terms in the linearized system equations (see Fig. 1.5). Show that stabilization cannot be achieved by linear feedback $u = k\theta$, but that if $k > (m + M)g$ then the rod can be given an oscillatory motion about the vertical position.

What would be the implications of Theorem 4.17 for this problem?

Exercise 5.50.
Show that the system described by

$$\dot{x} = \begin{bmatrix} 0 & -1 & 0 \\ 1 & 0 & 0 \\ 0 & 0 & -1 \end{bmatrix} x + \begin{bmatrix} 0 \\ 0 \\ 1 \end{bmatrix} u, \quad y = x$$

is stable i.s.L. and b.i.b.o. stable, but not asymptotically stable. (It is easy to verify that the system is not c.c., so Theorem 5.22 does not apply).

Exercise 5.51.
Prove the analogue of Theorem 5.21 for the discrete-time system

$$x(k + 1) = Ax(k) + Bu(k), \ y(k) = Cx(k).$$

(Hint: use (3.38)).

Exercise 5.52.
Consider the system described by the scalar equation

$$\dot{x}_1(t) = -x_1(t)/(t + 3) + u(t), \ x_1(0) = \dot{x}_0.$$

Show that if $u(t) \equiv 0$, $t \geqslant 0$ then the origin is asymptotically stable, but that if $u(t)$ is the unit step function (defined in (1.16)) then $\lim_{t \to \infty} x(t) = \infty$.

Exercise 5.53.
If the origin of the system described by $\dot{x} = f(x)$ is stable, with Liapunov function $V(x)$, show that the system $\dot{x} = f(x) + u$ is made asymptotically stable by taking

$$u = [S(x) - Q(x)] \ \phi(x),$$

where $\phi(x) = \nabla V$, $S(x)$ is an arbitrary skew symmetric matrix and $Q(x)$ is an arbitrary positive definite matrix.

Exercise 5.54.
Consider the equilibrium point at the origin for the gyroscope system of Exercise 5.28 with external forces, so that the equations of motion are

$$A\dot{\omega}_1 + (C - B)\omega_2\omega_3 = Au_1$$

$$B\dot{\omega}_2 + (A - C)\omega_3\omega_1 = Bu_2$$

$$C\dot{\omega}_3 + (B - A)\omega_1\omega_2 = Cu_3.$$

Verify that the total rotational energy $V = \frac{1}{2}(A\omega_1^2 + B\omega_2^2 + C\omega_3^2)$ is a Liapunov function for the unforced system, and use the result of Exercise 5.53 with $S \equiv 0$ and Q diagonal to obtain a stabilizing control vector.

Exercise 5.55.
If in Theorem 5.24 $g(s) = 1/(s^3 + as^2 + bs)$ where $a > 0, b > 0$, show that
the sector of absolute stability is $[0, ab]$.

Exercise 5.56.
By considering the Nyquist locus of $r(s) = p(s)/q(s)$ deduce from Theorem
5.11 that if $r(s)$ is positive real and has no purely imaginary poles then
$p(s) + q(s)$ is a Hurwitz polynomial.

Exercise 5.57.
Sketch the Nyquist locus for $g(s) = 1/(s^2 + 2s)$. By finding the largest
circle centred on $-1 + i0$ in the $g(s)$ plane which satisfies the conditions
of Theorem 5.25, show that the resulting bounds (5.108) are
$2(2 - \sqrt{3}) < h(x) < 2(2 + \sqrt{3})$.

6 Optimal control

This chapter deals with the problem of compelling a system to behave in some 'best possible' way. Of course, the precise control strategy will depend upon the criterion used to decide what is meant by 'best', and we first discuss some choices for measures of system performance. This is followed by a description of some mathematical techniques for determining optimal control policies, including the special case of linear systems with quadratic performance index when a complete analytical solution is possible. Optimal control theory also has an extremely large literature so our treatment is of necessity very concise.

6.1. Performance indices

6.1.1. Measures of performance.

We consider systems described by a general set of n nonlinear differential equations

$$\dot{x}(t) = f(x_1, \ldots, x_n, u_1, \ldots, u_m, t) \qquad (6.1)$$

subject to

$$x(t_0) = x_0, \qquad (6.2)$$

where the components of f satisfy the same conditions as for (5.1). A *performance index* is a scalar which provides a measure by which the performance of the system can be judged.

Minimum-time problems. Here $u(t)$ is to be chosen so as to transfer the system from an initial state x_0 to a specified state in the shortest possible time. This is equivalent to minimizing the performance index

$$J = t_1 - t_0$$

$$= \int_{t_0}^{t_1} dt \qquad (6.3)$$

where t_1 is the first instant of time at which the desired state is reached.

Example 6.1. An aircraft pursues a ballistic missile and wishes to intercept it as quickly as possible. For simplicity neglect gravitational and aerodynamic forces and suppose that the trajectories are horizontal. At $t = 0$ the aircraft is a distance a from the missile, whose motion is known to be described by $x(t) = a + bt^2$, where b is a positive constant. The motion of the aircraft is given by $\ddot{x}_a = u$, where the thrust $u(t)$ is subject to $|u| \leqslant 1$, with suitably chosen units. Clearly the optimal strategy for the aircraft is to accelerate with maximum thrust $u(t) = +1$. After a time t the aircraft has then travelled a distance $ct + \frac{1}{2}t^2$, where $\dot{x}_a(0) = c$, so interception will occur at time T where

$$cT + \tfrac{1}{2}T^2 = a + bT^2.$$

This equation may not have any real positive solution; in other words, this minimum-time problem may have no solution for certain initial conditions.

Terminal control. In this case the final state $x_f = x(t_1)$ is to be brought as near as possible to some desired state $r(t_1)$. A suitable performance measure to be minimized is

$$e^{\mathrm{T}}(t_1)\,Me\,(t_1), \tag{6.4}$$

where $e(t) = x(t) - r(t)$ and M is a real symmetric positive definite (r.s.p.d.) $n \times n$ matrix. A special case is when M is the unit matrix and (6.4) reduces to $\| x_f - r(t_1) \|_{\mathrm{e}}^2$. More generally, if $M = \mathrm{diag}\,[m_1, \ldots, m_n]$ then the m_i are chosen so as to weight the relative importance of the deviations $[x_i(t_1) - r_i(t_1)]^2$. If some of the $r_i(t_1)$ are not specified then the corresponding elements of M will be zero and M will be only positive semidefinite (r.s.p.s.d.).

Minimum effort. The desired final state is now to be attained with minimum total expenditure of control effort. Suitable performance indices to be minimized are

$$\int_{t_0}^{t_1} \sum \beta_i \,|u_i|\, \mathrm{d}t, \tag{6.5}$$

or

$$\int_{t_0}^{t_1} u^{\mathrm{T}} Ru \, \mathrm{d}t \tag{6.6}$$

where R is r.s.p.d. and the β_i and r_{ij} are weighting factors. We have already encountered expressions of the type (6.6) in Chapter 4 (Theorem 4.4 and Exercise 4.13).

Tracking problems. The aim here is to follow or 'track' as closely as possible some desired state $r(t)$ throughout the interval $t_0 \leqslant t \leqslant t_1$. Following (6.4) and (6.6) a suitable index is

$$\int_{t_0}^{t_1} e^{\mathrm{T}} Q e \, \mathrm{d}t \tag{6.7}$$

where Q is r.s.p.s.d. We introduced the term *servomechanism* for such systems in Section 1.2, a *regulator* being the special case when $r(t)$ is constant or zero. If the $u_i(t)$ are unbounded then minimization of (6.7) can lead to a control vector having infinite components. This is unacceptable for real life problems, so to restrict the total control effort a combination of (6.6) and (6.7) can be used, giving

$$\int_{t_0}^{t_1} (e^{\mathrm{T}} Q e + u^{\mathrm{T}} R u) \, \mathrm{d}t \tag{6.8}$$

Expressions of the form (6.6), (6.7), and (6.8) are termed *quadratic* performance indices.

Example 6.2. A landing vehicle separates from a spacecraft at time $t = 0$ at an altitude h from the surface of a planet, with initial downward velocity v. For simplicity assume that gravitational forces can be neglected and that the mass of the vehicle is constant. Consider vertical motion only, with upwards regarded as the positive direction. Let x_1 denote altitude, x_2 velocity and $u(t)$ the thrust exerted by the rocket motor, subject to $|u(t)| \leqslant 1$ with suitable scaling. The equations of motion are

$$\dot{x}_1 = x_2, \quad \dot{x}_2 = u, \tag{6.9}$$

and the initial conditions are

$$x_1(0) = h, \quad x_2(0) = -v. \tag{6.10}$$

For a 'soft landing' at some time T we require

$$x_1(T) = 0, \quad x_2(T) = 0. \tag{6.11}$$

A suitable performance index might be

$$\int_0^T (|u| + k) \, \mathrm{d}t, \tag{6.12}$$

which is a combination of (6.3) and (6.5). The expression (6.12) represents a sum of total fuel consumption and time to landing, k being a factor which weights the relative importance of these two quantities.

The expression for the optimal control which minimizes (6.12) subject to (6.9), (6.10), and (6.11) will be developed in Section 6.3. Of course the simple equations (6.9) arise in a variety of situations (e.g. take angular displacement and velocity as state variables in Example 4.1).

The performance indices given above are termed *functionals,* since they assign a unique real number to a set of functions $x_i(t)$, $u_j(t)$. In the classical optimization literature more general functionals are used, for instance the problem of *Bolza* is to choose $u(t)$ so as to minimize

$$J(u) = \phi\,[x(t_1), t_1] + \int_{t_0}^{t_1} F(x, u, t)\,\mathrm{d}t \qquad (6.13)$$

subject to (6.1), the scalar functions ϕ and F being continuous and having continuous first partial derivatives.

6.1.2. Evaluation of quadratic indices.

Before dealing with problems of determining optimal controls we return to the constant linear system

$$\dot{x}(t) = Ax(t), \quad x(0) = x_0 \qquad (6.14)$$

and show how to evaluate associated quadratic indices

$$J_r = \int_0^\infty t^r x^{\mathrm{T}} Qx\,\mathrm{d}t, \quad r = 0, 1, 2, \ldots, \qquad (6.15)$$

where Q is r.s.p.d. If (6.14) represents a regulator, with $x(t)$ being the deviation from some desired constant state, then minimizing J_r with respect to system parameters is equivalent to making the system approach its desired state in an 'optimal' way. Increasing the value of r in (6.15) corresponds to penalizing large values of t in this process.

To evaluate J_0 we use the techniques of linear Liapunov theory in Section 5.5. It was shown that

$$\frac{\mathrm{d}}{\mathrm{d}t}(x^{\mathrm{T}} Px) = -x^{\mathrm{T}} Qx \qquad (6.16)$$

where P and Q satisfy the Liapunov matrix equation (5.72), namely

$$A^{\mathrm{T}} P + PA = -Q. \qquad (6.17)$$

Integrating both sides of (6.16) with respect to t gives

$$J_0 = - [x^T (t)Px(t)]_{t=0}^{t=\infty}$$

$$= x_0^T P x_0, \qquad (6.18)$$

provided A is a stability matrix, since in this case $x(t) \to 0$ as $t \to \infty$ (Theorem 5.1). Furthermore, by virtue of Theorem 5.17, P is positive definite so $J_0 > 0$ for all $x_0 \neq 0$. A repetition of the argument leads to a similar expression for $J_r, r > 0$. For example,

$$\frac{d}{dt} (tx^T Px) = x^T Px - tx^T Qx,$$

and integrating we have

$$J_1 = \int_0^\infty tx^T Qx \, dt$$

$$= \oint_0^\infty x^T Px \, dt - [tx^T Px]_{t=0}^{t=\infty}$$

$$= x_0^T P_1 x_0 - 0,$$

where by comparison with (6.17)

$$A^T P_1 + P_1 A = -P.$$

It is left as an easy exercise for the reader to verify that

$$J_r = r! x_0^T P_r x_0 \qquad (6.19)$$

where

$$A^T P_{r+1} + P_{r+1} A = -P_r, \quad r = 0, 1, 2, \ldots \qquad (6.20)$$

with $P_0 = P$. Thus evaluation of (6.15) involves merely successive solution of the linear matrix equations (6.20); there is no need to calculate the solution $x(t)$ of (6.14). Some remarks on solving equations of the form (6.20) were made in Section 5.5.

Example 6.3. A general second order linear system can be written as

$$\ddot{z} + 2\omega\zeta\dot{z} + \omega^2 z = 0$$

where ω is the natural frequency of the undamped system and ζ is a damping coefficient (compare with eqn (5.62)). With the usual choice of state variables $x_1 = z, x_2 = \dot{z}$, and taking $Q = \text{diag}\,[1, q]$ in (6.17), it is easy to obtain the corresponding solution P with elements

$$p_{11} = \zeta/\omega + (1 + q\omega^2)/4\zeta\omega,\ p_{12} = 1/2\omega^2,\ p_{22} = (1 + q\omega^2)/4\zeta\omega^3.$$

In particular if $x(0) = [1, 0]^T$ then (6.18) gives $J_0 = p_{11}$. Regarding ζ as a parameter, optimal damping could be defined as that which minimizes J_0. By setting $dJ_0/d\zeta = 0$ this gives

$$\zeta^2 = (1 + q\omega^2)/4.$$

For example, if $q = 1/\omega^2$ then the 'optimal' value of ζ is $1/\sqrt{2}$. In fact by determining $x(t)$ it can be deduced that this value does indeed give desirable system transient behaviour. However, there is no *a priori* way of deciding on a suitable value for the factor q, which weights the relative importance of reducing $z(t)$ and $\dot{z}(t)$ to zero.

This illustrates a disadvantage of the performance index approach, although in some applications it is possible to use physical arguments to choose values for weighting factors.

Equivalent results for the discrete-time system

$$x_{k+1} = A_1 x_k,\ k = 0, 1, 2, \ldots \qquad (6.21)$$

can be derived using the associated matrix equation (5.74). The performance index corresponding to (6.15) is

$$K_r = \sum_{k=0}^{\infty} k^r x_k^T Q_1 x_k,\ r = 0, 1, 2, \ldots, \qquad (6.22)$$

where Q_1 is r.s.p.d. To find the expression for K_0 corresponding to (6.18), from eqn. (5.74) we have

$$x_k^T Q_1 x_k = -x_k^T (A_1^T P A_1 - P) x_k$$
$$= x_k^T P x_k - x_{k+1}^T P x_{k+1}, \qquad (6.23)$$

the second step following by virtue of (6.21). Summing both sides of (6.23) from $k = 0$ to $k = \infty$ produces

$$K_0 = x_0^T P x_0,$$

provided A_1 is a convergent matrix so that $x_k \to 0$ as $k \to \infty$ (Theorem 5.8). Similarly, multiplying both sides of (6.23) by k and summing leads to

$$K_1 = \sum_{k=0}^{\infty} k x_k^T Q_1 x_k$$

$$= \sum_{0}^{\infty} x_k^T P x_k - x_0^T P x_0$$

$$= x_0^T (P_1 - P) x_0$$

where by comparison with (5.74)

$$A_1^T P_1 A_1 - P_1 = -P.$$

Generally it can be shown that for $r > 0$

$$K_r = x_0^T \left[\sum_{i=1}^{r+1} b_{ri} P_{i-1} \right] x_0, \qquad (6.24)$$

where

$$A_1^T P_{i+1} A_1 - P_{i+1} = -P_i, \quad i = 0, 1, 2, \ldots$$

with $P_0 = P$, and general expressions for the constants b_{ri} can be derived.

Exercise 6.1.
In Example 6.1 show that if $b > \frac{1}{2}$ and the missile is initially a distance greater than $c^2/2(2b - 1)$ from the aircraft then it cannot be caught.

Exercise 6.2.
If $x(t)$ is the solution of (6.14), show by considering $d[x(t) \otimes x(t)]/dt$ that if A is a stability matrix then

$$\int_0^{\infty} (x \otimes x) dt = -B^{-1} x_0 \otimes x_0,$$

where $B = A \otimes I + I \otimes A$.

Similarly differentiate $tx \otimes x$ to show that

$$\int_0^\infty tx \otimes x \, \mathrm{d}t = B^{-2} x_0 \otimes x_0.$$

Exercise 6.3.
Determine K_2 in the form (6.24).

Exercise 6.4.
Show that if x_k is the solution of (6.21) and A_1 is a convergent matrix then

$$\sum_{k=0}^\infty x_k \otimes x_k = \beta^{-1} (x_0 \otimes x_0), \quad \sum_1^\infty k x_k \otimes x_k = \beta^{-2} (x_1 \otimes x_1),$$

where $\beta = I - A_1 \otimes A_1$.

6.2. Calculus of variations.

This subject dates back to Newton, and we have room for only a brief treatment. In particular we shall not mention the well known Euler equation approach which can be found in standard texts (e.g. Kirk 1970).

We consider the problem of minimizing $J(u)$ in (6.13) subject to the differential equations (6.1) and initial conditions (6.2). We assume that there are no constraints on the control functions $u_i(t)$, and that $J(u)$ is *differentiable*, i.e., if u and $u + \delta u$ are two controls for which J is defined then

$$\Delta J = J(u + \delta u) - J(u)$$
$$= \delta J(u, \delta u) + j(u, \delta u) \, \| \delta u \| \tag{6.25}$$

where δJ is linear in δu and $j(u, \delta u) \to 0$ as $\| \delta u \| \to 0$ (using any suitable norm). In (6.25) δJ is termed the *variation* in J corresponding to a variation δu in u. The control u^* is an *extremal*, and J has a relative minimum, if there exists an $\epsilon > 0$ such that for all functions u satisfying $\| u - u^* \| < \epsilon$ the difference $J(u) - J(u^*)$ is nonnegative. A fundamental result is the following.

THEOREM 6.1. A necessary condition for u^* to be an extremal is that $\delta J(u^*, \delta u) = 0$ for all δu.

For a proof see the book by Kirk (1970, p. 121).

We now apply Theorem 6.1 to (6.13). Introduce a vector of Lagrange multipliers $p = [p_1, \ldots, p_n]^T$ so as to form an augmented functional incorporating the constraints:

$$J_a = \phi[x(t_1), t_1] + \int_{t_0}^{t_1} [F(x, u, t) + p^T(f - \dot{x})] \, dt \qquad (6.26)$$

Integrating the last term on the right hand side of (6.26) by parts gives

$$J_a = \phi[x(t_1), t_1] + \int_{t_0}^{t_1} [F + p^T f + (\dot{p})^T x] \, dt - [p^T x]_{t_0}^{t_1}$$

$$= \phi[x(t_1), t_1] - [p^T x]_{t_0}^{t_1} + \int_{t_0}^{t_1} [H + (\dot{p})^T x] \, dt \qquad (6.27)$$

where the *Hamiltonian* function is defined by

$$H(x, u, t) = F(x, u, t) + p^T f. \qquad (6.28)$$

Assume that u is continuous and differentiable on $t_0 \leqslant t \leqslant t_1$ and that t_0 and t_1 are fixed. The variation in J_a corresponding to a variation δu in u is

$$\delta J_a = \left[\left(\frac{\partial \phi}{\partial x} - p^T\right)\delta x\right]_{t=t_1} + \int_{t_0}^{t_1}\left[\frac{\partial H}{\partial x}\delta x + \frac{\partial H}{\partial u}\delta u + (\dot{p})^T \delta x\right]dt, \quad (6.29)$$

where δx is the variation in x in the differential equations (6.1) due to δu, using the notation

$$\frac{\partial H}{\partial x} = \left[\frac{\partial H}{\partial x_1}, \ldots, \frac{\partial H}{\partial x_n}\right]$$

and similarly for $\partial \phi/\partial x$ and $\partial H/\partial u$. Notice that since $x(t_0)$ is specified, $(\delta x)_{t=t_0} = 0$. It is convenient to remove the term in (6.29) involving δx by suitably choosing p, i.e. by taking

$$\dot{p}_i = -\frac{\partial H}{\partial x_i}, \quad i = 1, 2, \ldots, n, \qquad (6.30)$$

and

$$p_i(t_1) = \left(\frac{\partial \phi}{\partial x_i}\right)_{t=t_1} \qquad (6.31)$$

Eqn (6.29) then reduces to

$$\delta J_a = \int_{t_0}^{t_1} \left(\frac{\partial H}{\partial u} \delta u \right) dt \qquad (6.32)$$

so by Theorem 6.1 a necessary condition for u^* to be an extremal is that

$$\left(\frac{\partial H}{\partial u_i} \right)_{u=u^*} = 0, \ t_0 \leqslant t \leqslant t_1, i = 1, \ldots, m. \qquad (6.33)$$

We have therefore established:

THEOREM 6.2. Necessary conditions for u^* to be an extremal for (6.13) subject to (6.1) and (6.2) are that (6.30), (6.31), and (6.33) hold.

The state equations (6.1) and the *adjoint* equations (6.30) give a total of $2n$ nonlinear differential equations with mixed boundary conditions $x(t_0)$ and $p(t_1)$. In general analytical solution is not possible and numerical techniques have to be used.

Example 6.4. Choose $u(t)$ so as to minimize

$$\int_0^T (x_1^2 + u^2) \, dt \qquad (6.34)$$

subject to

$$\dot{x}_1 = -ax_1 + u, \ x_1(0) = x_0 \qquad (6.35)$$

where a and T are positive constants.

From (6.28)

$$H = x_1^2 + u^2 + p_1(-ax_1 + u)$$

and (6.30) and (6.33) give respectively

$$\dot{p}_1^* = -2x_1^* + ap_1^* \qquad (6.36)$$

and

$$2u^* + p_1^* = 0, \qquad (6.37)$$

where x_1^* and p_1^* denote the state and adjoint variables for an optimal solution. Substituting (6.37) into (6.35) produces

$$\dot{x}_1^* = -ax_1^* - \tfrac{1}{2}p_1^*, \qquad (6.38)$$

and since $\phi \equiv 0$ the boundary condition (6.31) is just $p_1(T) = 0$. The equations (6.36) and (6.38) are linear and so can be solved using the methods of Chapter 3. It is easy to verify that x_1^* and p_1^* take the form $c \exp(\lambda t) + d \exp(-\lambda t)$ where $\lambda = \sqrt{(1 + a^2)}$, and the constants c and d are found using the conditions at $t = 0$ and $t = T$. From (6.37) the optimal control is $u_1^*(t) = -\frac{1}{2} p_1^*(t)$ (although of course we have only found necessary conditions for optimality; further discussion of this point is outside the scope of this book, and will not be referred to in subsequent examples).

Notice that (6.34) is a simple case of the quadratic index (6.8), and that together with the linear system equation (6.35) this leads to the adjoint equation (6.30) being linear, so that an analytical solution to the problem is possible. We shall generalize this in Section 6.4.

If the functions f and F do not *explicitly* depend upon t then from (6.28)

$$\frac{dH}{dt} = \frac{\partial F}{\partial u}\dot{u} + \frac{\partial F}{\partial x}\dot{x} + p^T\left(\frac{\partial f}{\partial u}\dot{u} + \frac{\partial f}{\partial x}\dot{x}\right) + (\dot{p})^T f$$

$$= \left(\frac{\partial F}{\partial u} + p^T\frac{\partial f}{\partial u}\right)\dot{u} + \left(\frac{\partial F}{\partial x} + p^T\frac{\partial f}{\partial x}\right)\dot{x} + (\dot{p})^T f$$

$$= \frac{\partial H}{\partial u}\dot{u} + \frac{\partial H}{\partial x}\dot{x} + (\dot{p})^T f$$

$$= \frac{\partial H}{\partial u}\dot{u} + \left(\frac{\partial H}{\partial x} + (\dot{p})^T\right)f,$$

using (6.1). Since on an optimal trajectory (6.30) and (6.33) hold it follows that $dH/dt = 0$ when $u = u^*$, so that

$$(H)_{u=u^*} = \text{constant}, \quad t_0 \leqslant t \leqslant t_1. \tag{6.39}$$

We have so far assumed that t_1 is fixed and $x(t_1)$ is free. If this is not necessarily the case, then by considering (6.27) the terms in δJ_a in (6.29) outside the integral are obtained to be

$$\left[\left(\frac{\partial\phi}{\partial x} - p^T\right)\delta x + \left(H + \frac{\partial\phi}{\partial t}\right)\delta t\right]_{\substack{u=u^* \\ t=t_1}}. \tag{6.40}$$

The expression in (6.40) must be zero by virtue of Theorem 6.1, since (6.30) and (6.33) still hold, making the integral in (6.29) zero. The implications of this for some important special cases are now listed. The initial conditions (6.2) hold throughout.

Final time t_1 specified.

   (*i*) $x(t_1)$ *free*
      In (6.40) we have $\delta t_1 = 0$ but $\delta x(t_1)$ is arbitrary, so the conditions
(6.31) must hold (with (6.39) when appropriate), as before.
   (*ii*) $x(t_1)$ *specified*
      In this case $\delta t_1 = 0$, $\delta x(t_1) = 0$ so (6.40) is automatically zero.
The conditions are thus

$$x^*(t_1) = x_f \qquad (6.41)$$

and (6.41) replaces (6.31).

Final time t_1 free
   (*iii*) $x(t_1)$ *free*
      Both δt_1 and $\delta x(t_1)$ are now arbitrary so for the expression in
(6.40) to vanish, (6.31) must hold together with

$$\left(H + \frac{\partial \phi}{\partial t}\right)_{\substack{u=u^* \\ t=t_1}} = 0. \qquad (6.42)$$

      In particular if ϕ, F, and f do not explicitly depend upon t then (6.39)
and (6.42) imply

$$(H)_{u=u^*} = 0, \quad t_0 \leqslant t \leqslant t_1. \qquad (6.43)$$

   (*iv*) $x(t_1)$ *specified*
      Only δt_1 is now arbitrary in (6.40) so the conditions are (6.41)
and (6.42) (or (6.43)).
      If the preceding conditions on $x(t_1)$ apply to only some of its compon-
ents, then since the $\delta x_i(t_1)$ in (6.40) are independent it follows that the
appropriate conditions hold only for these components.

   Example 6.5. A ship moves through a region of strong currents. For
simplicity, and by a suitable choice of coordinates, assume that the current
is parallel to the x_1 axis and has velocity $c = -Vx_2/a$, where a is a positive
constant, and V is the magnitude (assumed constant) of the ship's velocity
relative to the water. The problem is to steer the ship so as to minimize
the time of travel from some given point A to the origin.

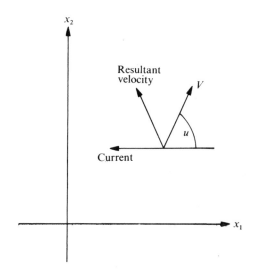

FIG. 6.1

We see in Fig. 6.1 that the control variable is the angle u. The equations of motion are

$$\dot{x}_1 = V \cos u + c$$

$$= V(\cos u - x_2/a) \qquad (6.44)$$

$$\dot{x}_2 = V \sin u, \qquad (6.45)$$

where $(x_1(t), x_2(t))$ denotes the position of the ship at time t. The performance index is (6.3) with $t_0 = 0$, so from (6.28)

$$H = 1 + p_1 V(\cos u - x_2/a) + p_2 V \sin u. \qquad (6.46)$$

The condition (6.33) gives

$$-p_1^* V \sin u^* + p_2^* V \cos u^* = 0$$

so that

$$\tan u^* = p_2^*/p_1^* . \qquad (6.47)$$

The adjoint equations (6.30) are

$$\dot{p}_1^* = 0, \quad \dot{p}_2^* = p_1^* V/a, \qquad (6.48)$$

which imply that $p_1^* = c_1$, a constant. Since t_1 is not specified we have case (*iv*) on p.220, so that (6.43) holds. From (6.46) this gives

$$0 = 1 + p_1^* V(\cos u^* - x_2^*/a) + p_2^* V \sin u^*$$

$$= 1 + c_1 V(\cos u^* - x_2^*/a) + c_1 V \sin^2 u^*/\cos u^*, \qquad (6.49)$$

using the expression for p_2^* in (6.47). Substituting $x_2^*(t_1) = 0$ into (6.49) leads to

$$c_1 = -\cos u_1/V, \qquad (6.50)$$

where $u_1 = u^*(t_1)$. Eqn (6.50) reduces (6.49), after some rearrangement, to

$$x_2^*/a = \sec u^* - \sec u_1. \qquad (6.51)$$

Differentiating (6.51) with respect to t gives

$$(\mathrm{d}u^*/\mathrm{d}t) \sec u^* \tan u^* = \dot{x}_2^*/a$$

$$= V \sin u^*/a, \text{ by (6.45).}$$

Hence

$$(V/a)(\mathrm{d}t/\mathrm{d}u^*) = \sec^2 u^*$$

which on integration produces

$$\tan u^* - \tan u_1 = (V/a)(t - t_1). \qquad (6.52)$$

Use of (6.44), (6.51), and (6.52) and some straightforward manipulation leads to an expression for x_1^* in terms of u^* and u_1, which enables the optimal path to be computed. Further details can be found in the book by Bryson and Ho (1969, p. 77), and a typical minimum-time path is shown in Fig. 6.2.

If the state at final time t_1 (assumed fixed) is to lie on a surface defined by some function $m[x(t)] = 0$, where m may in general be a k-vector, then it can be shown (Kirk 1970, p. 189) that in addition to the k conditions

$$m[x^*(t_1)] = 0 \qquad (6.53)$$

there are a further n conditions which can be written as

$$\frac{\partial \phi}{\partial x} - p^{\mathrm{T}} = d_1 \left(\frac{\partial m_1}{\partial x}\right) + d_2 \left(\frac{\partial m_2}{\partial x}\right) + \cdots + d_k \left(\frac{\partial m_k}{\partial x}\right) \qquad (6.54)$$

both sides being evaluated at $t = t_1$, $u = u^*$, $x = x^*$, $p = p^*$. The d_i in (6.54) are constants to be determined. Together with the $2n$ constants of

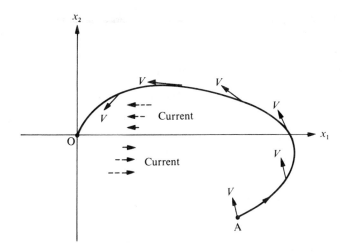

FIG. 6.2

integration there are thus a total of $2n + k$ unknowns and $2n + k$ conditions (6.53), (6.54), and (6.2). If t_1 is free then in addition (6.42) holds.

The conditions which hold at $t = t_1$ for the various cases we have covered are summarized in Table 6.1.

TABLE 6.1

	t_1 fixed	t_1 free
$x(t_1)$ free	(6.31)	(6.31) and (6.42)
$x(t_1)$ fixed	(6.41)	(6.41) and (6.42)
$x(t_1)$ lies on $m[x(t_1)] = 0$	(6.53) and (6.54)	(6.42), (6.53), and (6.54)

Example 6.6. If a second order system is to be transferred from the origin to a circle of unit radius, centre the origin, at some time T then we must have

$$[x_1^*(T)]^2 + [x_2^*(T)]^2 = 1. \tag{6.55}$$

Since

$$m(x) = x_1^2 + x_2^2 - 1$$

(6.54) gives

$$-[p_1^*(T), p_2^*(T)] = d_1 [2x_1^*(T), 2x_2^*(T)],$$

assuming $\phi \equiv 0$, and hence

$$p_1^*(T)/p_2^*(T) = x_1^*(T)/x_2^*(T). \qquad (6.56)$$

Eqns (6.55) and (6.56) are the conditions to be satisfied at $t = T$.

Example 6.7. A system described by

$$\dot{x}_1 = x_2, \quad \dot{x}_2 = -x_2 + u \qquad (6.57)$$

is to be transferred from $x(0) = 0$ to the line

$$ax_1 + bx_2 = c$$

at time T so as to minimize

$$\int_0^T u^2 \, dt,$$

which is of the form (6.6). The values of a, b, c, and T are given.
   From (6.28)

$$H = u^2 + p_1 x_2 - p_2 x_2 + p_2 u,$$

and (6.33) gives

$$u^* = -\tfrac{1}{2} p_2^* . \qquad (6.58)$$

The adjoint equations (6.30) are

$$\dot{p}_1^* = 0, \quad \dot{p}_2^* = -p_1^* + p_2^*$$

so that

$$p_1^* = c_1, \quad p_2^* = c_2 e^t + c_1 \qquad (6.59)$$

where c_1 and c_2 are constants. Substituting (6.58) and (6.59) into (6.57) leads to

$$x_1^* = c_3 e^{-t} - \tfrac{1}{4} c_2 e^t - \tfrac{1}{2} c_1 t + c_4, \quad x_2^* = -c_3 e^{-t} - \tfrac{1}{4} c_2 e^t - \tfrac{1}{2} c_1,$$

and the conditions

$$x_1^*(0) = 0, x_2^*(0) = 0, ax_1^*(T) + bx_2^*(T) = c, \qquad (6.60)$$

must hold.
   It is easy to verify that (6.54) produces

$$p_1^*(T)/p_2^*(T) = a/b, \qquad (6.61)$$

and (6.60) and (6.61) give four equations for the four unknown constants c_i. The optimal control $u^*(t)$ is then obtained from (6.58) and (6.59).

In some problems the restriction on the total amount of control effort which can be expended to carry out a required task may be expressed in the form

$$\int_{t_0}^{t_1} g(x, u, t) \, dt = c, \tag{6.62}$$

where c is a given constant, such a constraint being termed *isoperimetric*. A convenient way of dealing with (6.62) is to define a new variable

$$x_{n+1}(t) = \int_{t_0}^{t} g(x, u, t) \, dt$$

so that

$$\dot{x}_{n+1}(t) = g(x, u, t). \tag{6.63}$$

The differential equation (6.63) is simply added to the original set (6.1) together with the conditions

$$x_{n+1}(t_0) = 0, \quad x_{n+1}(t_1) = c$$

and the procedure then continues as before, ignoring (6.62).

Exercise 6.5.
A system is described by

$$\dot{x}_1 = -2x_1 + u,$$

and the control $u(t)$ is to be chosen so as to minimize

$$\int_0^1 u^2 \, dt.$$

Show that the optimal control which transfers the system from $x_1(0) = 1$ to $x_1(1) = 0$ is $u^* = -4e^{2t}/(e^4 - 1)$.

Exercise 6.6.
The equations describing a production scheduling problem are

$$\frac{dI}{dt} = -S + P, \quad \frac{dS}{dt} = -\alpha P$$

where $I(t)$ is the level of inventory (or stock), $S(t)$ is the rate of sales and α is a positive constant. The production rate $P(t)$ can be controlled and is assumed unbounded. It is also assumed that the rate of production costs is proportional to P^2. It is required to choose the production rate which will change $I(0) = I_0$, $S(0) = S_0$ into $I(T) = I_1$, $S(T) = S_1$ in a fixed time T whilst minimizing the total production cost. Show that the optimal production rate has the form $P^* = k_1 + k_2 t$ and indicate how the constants k_1 and k_2 can be determined.

Exercise 6.7.

A particle of mass m moves on a smooth horizontal plane with rectangular cartesian coordinates x and y. Initially the particle is at rest at the origin, and a force of constant magnitude ma is applied to it so as to ensure that after a fixed time T the particle is moving along a given fixed line parallel to the x-axis with maximum speed. The angle $u(t)$ made by the force with the positive x direction is the control variable, and is unbounded. Show that the optimal control is given by

$$\tan u^* = \tan u_0 + ct$$

where c is a constant and $u_0 = u^*(0)$. Hence deduce that

$$\dot{y}^*(t) = (a/c)(\sec u^* - \sec u_0)$$

and obtain a similar expression for $\dot{x}^*(t)$ (hint: change the independent variable from t to u).

Exercise 6.8.

For the system in Example 6.7 described by eqn (6.57), determine the control which transfers it from $x(0) = 0$ to the line $x_1 + 5x_2 = 15$ and minimizes

$$\tfrac{1}{2} [x_1(2) - 5]^2 + \tfrac{1}{2} [x_2(2) - 2]^2 + \tfrac{1}{2} \int_0^2 u^2 \, dt.$$

6.3. Pontryagin's principle

In real life problems the control variables are usually subject to constraints on their magnitudes, typically of the form $| u_i(t) | \leqslant k_i$. This implies that the set of final states which can be achieved is restricted (see Section 5.7.1). Our aim here is to derive the necessary conditions for optimality corresponding to Theorem 6.2 for the unbounded case. An *admissible* control is one which satisfies the constraints, and we consider variations such that $u^* + \delta u$ is admissible and $\| \delta u \|$ is sufficiently small so that the sign of

$$\Delta J = J(u^* + \delta u) - J(u^*),$$

where J is defined in (6.13), is determined by δJ in (6.25). Because of the restriction on δu, Theorem 6.1 no longer applies, and instead a necessary condition for u^* to minimize J is

$$\delta J(u^*, \delta u) \geqslant 0. \tag{6.64}$$

The development then proceeds as in Section 6.2; Lagrange multipliers are introduced to define J_a in (6.26) and are chosen so as to satisfy (6.30) and (6.31). The only difference is that the expression for δJ_a in (6.32) is replaced by

$$\delta J_a(u, \delta u) = \int_{t_0}^{t_1} [H(x, u + \delta u, p, t) - H(x, u, p, t)] \, dt. \tag{6.65}$$

It therefore follows by (6.64) that a necessary condition for $u = u^*$ to be a minimizing control is that $\delta J_a(u^*, \delta u)$ in (6.65) be nonnegative for all admissible δu. This in turn implies that

$$H(x^*, u^* + \delta u, p^*, t) \geqslant H(x^*, u^*, p^*, t), \tag{6.66}$$

for all admissible δu and all t in $t_0 \leqslant t \leqslant t_1$; for if (6.66) did not hold in some interval $t_2 \leqslant t \leqslant t_3$, say, with $t_3 - t_2$ arbitrarily small, then by choosing $\delta u = 0$ for t outside this interval $\delta J_a(u^*, \delta u)$ would be made negative. Eqn (6.66) states that u^* minimizes H, so we have established:

THEOREM 6.3. (*Pontryagin's minimum principle*) Necessary conditions for u^* to minimize (6.13) are (6.30), (6.31), and (6.66).

With a slightly different definition of H the principle becomes one of maximizing H, and is then referred to in the literature as the maximum principle. Note that u^* is now allowed to be piecewise continuous.

Our derivation assumed that t_1 was fixed and $x(t_1)$ free; the boundary conditions for other situations are precisely the same as those given in the preceding section and summarized in Table 6.1. It can also be shown that when H does not explicitly depend upon t then (6.39) and (6.43) still hold for the respective cases when the final time t_1 is fixed or free.

Example 6.8. (Takahashi *et al.* 1970, p. 637). Consider again the 'soft landing' problem described in Example 6.2, where (6.12) is to be minimized subject to the system equations (6.9). The Hamiltonian (6.28) is

$$H = |u| + k + p_1 x_2 + p_2 u. \qquad (6.67)$$

Since the admissible range of control is $-1 \leqslant u(t) \leqslant 1$, it follows that H will be minimized by the following:

$$\left. \begin{array}{l} u^*(t) = -1 \text{ if } p_2^*(t) > 1 \\ = 0 \text{ if } 1 > p_2^*(t) > -1 \\ = +1 \text{ if } p_2^*(t) < -1. \end{array} \right\} \qquad (6.68)$$

Such a control is referred to in the literature by the graphic term *bang–zero–bang,* since only maximum thrust is applied in a forward or reverse direction; no intermediate nonzero values are used. If there is no period in which u^* is zero the control is called bang–bang. For example, a racing-car driver approximates to bang–bang operation, since he tends to use either full throttle or maximum braking when attempting to circuit a track as quickly as possible.

In (6.68) u^* switches in value according to the magnitude of $p_2^*(t)$, which is therefore termed the *switching function.* We must however use physical considerations to determine an actual optimal control. Since the landing vehicle begins with a downwards velocity at an altitude h, logical sequences of control would seem to either

$$u^* = 0, \text{ followed by } u^* = +1$$

(upwards is regarded as positive), or

$$u^* = -1, \text{ then } u^* = 0, \text{ then } u^* = +1. \qquad (6.69)$$

Consider the first possibility and suppose that u^* switches from zero to one at time t_1. By virtue of (6.68) this sequence of control is possible if p_2^* decreases with time. It is easy to verify that the solution of (6.9) subject to the initial conditions (6.10) is

$$\left. \begin{array}{l} x_1^* = h - vt, x_2^* = -v, \ 0 \leqslant t \leqslant t_1 \\ x_1^* = h - vt + \tfrac{1}{2}(t - t_1)^2, x_2^* = -v + (t - t_1), t_1 \leqslant t \leqslant T. \end{array} \right\} \qquad (6.70)$$

Substituting the soft landing requirements (6.11) into (6.70) gives

$$T = h/v + \tfrac{1}{2}v, \ t_1 = h/v - \tfrac{1}{2}v. \qquad (6.71)$$

Because the final time is not specified and because of the form of H in (6.67), eqn (6.43) holds, so in particular $(H)_{u=u^*} = 0$ at $t = 0$, i.e. with $t = 0$ in (6.67)

$$k + p_1^*(0)x_2^*(0) = 0$$

or

$$p_1^*(0) = k/v.$$

The adjoint equations (6.30) are

$$\dot{p}_1^* = 0, \quad \dot{p}_2^* = -p_1^*.$$

Hence

$$p_1^*(t) = k/v, \, t \geqslant 0$$

and

$$p_2^*(t) = -kt/v - 1 + kt_1/v. \qquad (6.72)$$

using the assumption that $p_2^*(t_1) = -1$. Thus the assumed optimal control will be valid if $t_1 > 0$ and $p_2^*(0) < 1$ (the latter conditions being necessary since $u^*(0) = 0$), and using (6.71) and (6.72) these conditions imply that

$$h > \tfrac{1}{2}v^2, k < 2v^2/(h - \tfrac{1}{2}v^2). \qquad (6.73)$$

If these inequalities do not hold then some different control strategy, such as (6.69), becomes optimal. For example, if k is increased so that the second inequality in (6.73) is violated then this means that more emphasis is placed on the time to landing in the performance index (6.12). It is therefore reasonable to expect this time would be reduced by first accelerating downwards with $u^* = -1$ before coasting with $u^* = 0$, as in (6.69). It is interesting to note that provided (6.73) holds then the total time T to landing in (6.71) is independent of k.

Example 6.9. Suppose that in the preceding example it is now required to determine a control which achieves a soft landing in the least possible time, starting with an arbitrary given initial state $x(0) = x_0$. The performance index is just (6.3) with $t_0 = 0, t_1 = T$. The Hamiltonian (6.28) is now

$$H = 1 + p_1 x_2 + p_2 u$$

and Theorem 6.3 gives the optimal control:

$$u^* = +1, p_2^* < 0; u^* = -1, p_2 > 0,$$

or more succinctly,

$$u^*(t) = \text{sgn}(-p_2^*) \tag{6.74}$$

where the *signum function* is defined by

$$\text{sgn}(z) = +1, z > 0$$
$$= -1, z < 0.$$

The optimal control thus has bang–bang form, and we must determine the switching function $p_2^*(t)$. Using (6.30) we again obtain

$$\dot{p}_1^* = 0, \dot{p}_2^* = -p_1^*$$

so

$$p_1^* = c_1, p_2^* = -c_1 t + c_2$$

where c_1 and c_2 are constants. Since p_2^* is a linear function of t it can change sign at most once in $0 \leqslant t \leqslant T$, so the optimal control (6.74) must take *one* of the following forms:

$$u^*(t) = \begin{cases} +1, 0 \leqslant t \leqslant T \\ -1, 0 \leqslant t \leqslant T \\ +1, 0 \leqslant t < t_1; -1, t_1 \leqslant t \leqslant T \\ -1, 0 \leqslant t < t_2; +1, t_2 \leqslant t \leqslant T. \end{cases} \tag{6.75}$$

Integrating the state equations (6.9) with $u = \pm 1$ gives

$$x_1 = \pm \tfrac{1}{2} t^2 + c_3 t + c_4, x_2 = \pm t + c_3. \tag{6.76}$$

Eliminating t in (6.76) produces

$$x_1(t) = \tfrac{1}{2} x_2^2(t) + c_5, \text{ when } u^* = +1, \tag{6.77}$$

$$x_1(t) = -\tfrac{1}{2} x_2^2(t) + c_6, \text{ when } u^* = -1. \tag{6.78}$$

The trajectories (6.77) and (6.78) represent two families of parabolas, shown in Fig. 6.3(a) and Fig. 6.3(b) respectively. The direction of the arrows represents t increasing.

We can now investigate the various cases in (6.75):

(i) $u^* = +1, 0 \leqslant t \leqslant T$. The initial state x_0 must lie on the lower part of the curve PO corresponding to $c_5 = 0$ in Fig. 6.3(a).

(ii) Similarly, if $u^* = -1, 0 \leqslant t \leqslant T$, then x_0 must lie on the upper part of the curve QO corresponding to $c_6 = 0$ in Fig. 6.3(b).

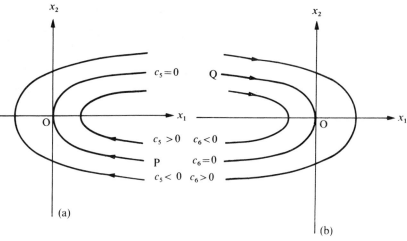

FIG. 6.3

(iii)   With the third case in (6.75), since $u^* = -1$ for $t_1 \leqslant t \leqslant T$ it
          follows that $x^*(t_1)$ must lie on the curve QO. The point $x^*(t_1)$
          is reached using $u^* = +1$ for $0 \leqslant t < t_1$, so the initial part of
          the optimal trajectory must belong to the curves in Fig. 6.3(a).
          The optimal trajectory will thus be as shown in Fig. 6.4. The
          point R corresponds to $t = t_1$, and is where u^* switches from
          $+1$ to -1; QO is therefore termed the *switching curve*. By
          considering Fig. 6.3 it is clear that the situation just described
          holds for any initial state lying to the left of both PO and QO.

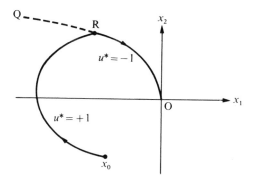

FIG. 6.4

(*iv*)   A similar argument shows that the last case in (6.75) applies for any initial state lying to the right of PO and QO, a typical optimal trajectory being shown in Fig. 6.5. The switching now takes place on PO, so the complete switching curve is QOP, shown in Fig. 6.6.

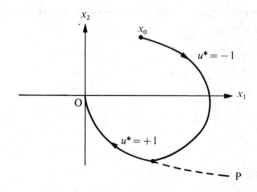

FIG. 6.5

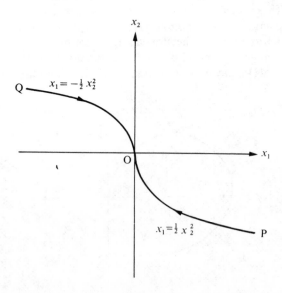

FIG. 6.6

To summarize, if x_0 lies on the switching curve then $u^* = \pm 1$ according as $x_1(0)$ is positive or negative. If x_0 does not lie on the switching curve then u^* must initially be chosen so as to move $x^*(t)$ towards the switching curve.

We can now discuss a general linear regulator problem in our usual form

$$\dot{x} = Ax + Bu, \tag{6.79}$$

where $x(t)$ is the deviation from some desired constant state. The aim is to transfer the system from some initial state to the origin in minimum time, subject to $|u_i(t)| \leqslant k_i$. The Hamiltonian (6.28) is

$$H = 1 + p^T(Ax + Bu)$$
$$= 1 + p^TAx + (p^Tb_1, \ldots, p^Tb_m)u$$
$$= 1 + p^TAx + \sum_{i=1}^{m} (p^Tb_i)u_i, \tag{6.80}$$

where the b_i are the columns of B. Application of Theorem 6.3 to (6.80) gives the necessary condition for optimality that

$$u_i^*(t) = -k_i \, \text{sgn}\,[s_i(t)], i = 1, \ldots, m, \tag{6.81}$$

where

$$s_i(t) = [p^*(t)]^T b_i \tag{6.82}$$

is the switching function for the ith variable. The adjoint equations (6.30) are

$$p_i^* = -\frac{\partial}{\partial x_i} \, [(p^*)^T Ax]$$

or

$$\dot{p}^* = -A^T p^*. \tag{6.83}$$

The solution of (6.83) can be written as in (3.7) in the form

$$p^*(t) = \exp{(-A^Tt)}p(0)$$

so the switching function in (6.82) becomes

$$s_i(t) = p^T(0) \exp{(-At)}b_i.$$

If $s_i(t) \equiv 0$ in some time interval then $u_i^*(t)$ is indeterminate in this interval. We now therefore investigate whether the expression in (6.82) can vanish. Firstly, we can assume that $b_i \neq 0$. Next, since the final time is free the condition (6.43) holds, which for (6.80) gives

$$1 + [p^*(t)]^T (Ax^* + Bu^*) = 0, \text{ all } t,$$

so clearly $p^*(t)$ cannot be zero for any value of t. Finally, if the product $(p^*)^T b_i$ in (6.82) is zero, then $s_i = 0$ implies together with (6.83) that

$$\dot{s}_i (t) = - [p^*(t)]^T A b_i = 0,$$

and similarly for higher derivatives of s_i. This leads to

$$[p^*(t)]^T [b_i, A b_i, A^2 b_i, \ldots, A^{n-1} b_i] = 0. \qquad (6.84)$$

If the system (6.79) is completely controllable by the ith input acting alone (i.e. $u_j \equiv 0, j \neq i$) then by Theorem 4.1 the matrix in (6.84) is nonsingular, and eqn (6.84) then has only the trivial solution $p^*(t) = 0$. However, we have already ruled out this possibility, so s_i cannot be zero. Thus provided the controllability condition holds there is no time interval in which u_i^* is indeterminate. The optimal control for the ith variable then has the bang–bang form $u_i^* = \pm k_i$ in (6.81). The following more general result has also been proved (Boltyanskii 1971, Chapter 3):

THEOREM 6.4. If A is a stability matrix then there exists a unique optimal control u^* which transfers the system (6.79) from an arbitrary initial state to the origin in minimum time. Furthermore if all the characteristic roots of A are real then each $u_i^*(t)$ can switch at most $n - 1$ times.

The second part of Theorem 6.4 states that each $u_i^*(t)$ consists of at most n periods with constant values $\pm k_i$. In general the switchings will not occur simultaneously for each variable, so $u^*(t)$ will switch more than $n - 1$ times.

Exercise 6.9.

A system is described by

$$\frac{d^3 z}{dt^3} = u(t)$$

where $z(t)$ denotes displacement. Starting from some given initial position with given velocity and acceleration it is required to choose $u(t)$, which is constrained by $| u(t) | \leqslant k$, so as to make displacement, velocity, and acceleration equal to zero in the least possible time. Show using Theorem 6.3 that the optimal control consists of $u^* = \pm k$ with zero, one, or two switchings.

Exercise 6.10.
A linear system is described by

$$\ddot{z}(t) + a\dot{z}(t) + bz(t) = u(t)$$

where $a > 0$ and $a^2 < 4b$. The control variable is subject to $|u(t)| \leqslant k$ and is to be chosen so that the system reaches the state $z(T) = 0$, $\dot{z}(T) = 0$ in minimum possible time. Show that the optimal control is $u^* = k \operatorname{sgn} p(t)$, where $p(t)$ is a periodic function of t.

Exercise 6.11.
A rocket is ascending vertically above the earth, which is assumed flat. It is also assumed that aerodynamic forces can be neglected, that the gravitational attraction is constant, and that the thrust from the motor acts vertically downwards. The equations of motion are

$$\frac{d^2 h}{dt^2} = -g + \frac{cu}{m}, \quad \frac{dm}{dt} = -u(t)$$

where $h(t)$ is the vertical height, $m(t)$ is the rocket mass, and c and g are positive constants. The propellant mass flow can be controlled subject to $0 \leqslant u(t) \leqslant k$. The mass, height, and velocity at time $t = 0$ are all known and it is required to maximize the height subsequently reached. Show that the optimal control has the form

$$u^*(t) = k, s > 0; \quad u^*(t) = 0, \ s < 0$$

where the switching function $s(t)$ satisfies the equation $ds/dt = -c/m$.

If switching occurs at time t_1, show that

$$s(t) = \frac{c}{k} \ln \left\{ \frac{m(t)}{m(t_1)} \right\}, \ 0 \leqslant t \leqslant t_1$$

$$= c(t_1 - t)/m(t_1), \ t_1 \leqslant t \leqslant T.$$

Exercise 6.12.
A reservoir is assumed to have a constant cross-section, and the depth of the water at time t is $x_1(t)$. The net inflow rate of water $u(t)$ can be

controlled subject to $0 \leqslant u(t) \leqslant k$, but the reservoir leaks, the differential equation describing the system being

$$\dot{x}_1 = -0.1x_1 + u.$$

Find the control policy which maximizes the total amount of water in the reservoir over 100 units of time, i.e.

$$\int_0^{100} x_1(t) \, dt.$$

If during the same period the total inflow of water is limited by

$$\int_0^{100} u(t) \, dt = 60k$$

determine the optimal control in this case.

Exercise 6.13.
The following model can be thought of as representing a situation where a cup of hot coffee is to be cooled as quickly as possible using a finite amount of cold milk, but could refer to a more general problem where cold liquid is being added to a container of hot liquid. Suppose that the coffee cup is originally full and at $100°$ C. The flow of milk, assumed to be at a constant temperature, is represented by $u(t)$ and is subject to $0 \leqslant u(t) \leqslant 1$. The total amount of milk is limited by

$$\int_0^T u \, dt = 1.$$

The thermodynamic equation describing the liquid in the cup is bilinear, namely

$$\dot{x}_1 = -x_1 - 25u - \tfrac{1}{4} ux_1,$$

where the first term on the right hand side corresponds to heat loss to the surroundings, the second term is due to the inflow of cold milk and the third term is for the overflow. It is required to reduce the temperature x_1 of the coffee to $0°$ C in minimum time T. Show that the optimal strategy is $u^* = 0, 0 \leqslant t < 0.69; u^* = 1, 0.69 \leqslant t \leqslant 1.69$ (thus, somewhat unexpectedly, there is a delay before the milk is added).

Exercise 6.14.
In Example 6.9 let $x_1(0) = \alpha$, $x_2(0) = \beta$ be an arbitrary initial point to
the right of the switching curve in Fig. 6.5, with $\alpha \geqslant 0$. Show that the
minimum time to the origin is $T^* = \beta + (4\alpha + 2\beta^2)^{\frac{1}{2}}$.

Exercise 6.15.
For the problem in Example 6.8 suppose that the control is now to be
chosen so as to minimize the total fuel consumption, measured by

$$\int_0^{T_1} |u(t)|\, dt$$

where T_1 is fixed. Let the initial state be as in Exercise 6.14. If the
optimal control has the form

$$u^*(t) = \begin{cases} -1, & 0 \leqslant t < t_1 \\ 0, & t_1 \leqslant t < t_2 \\ +1, & t_2 \leqslant t \leqslant T \end{cases}$$

show that

$$t_1, t_2 = \tfrac{1}{2}\,[\,T_1 + \beta \mp \{(T_1 - \beta)^2 - (4\alpha + 2\beta^2)\}^{\frac{1}{2}}\,]$$

and deduce that $T_1 \geqslant T^*$ where T^* is the minimum time in Exercise 6.14.

Exercise 6.16.
Consider again the system described by the equations (6.9) subject to
$|u(t)| \leqslant 1$. It is required to transfer the system to some point lying on
the perimeter of the square in the (x_1, x_2) plane having vertices $(\pm 1, \pm 1)$
in minimum time, starting from an arbitrary point outside the square.
Determine the switching curves.

6.4. Linear regulator.

We have noted that a general closed form solution of the optimal control
problem is possible for a linear regulator with quadratic performance
index. Specifically, consider the time varying system (3.29), i.e.

$$\dot{x}(t) = A(t)\,x(t) + B(t)\,u(t) \qquad (6.85)$$

with a criterion obtained by combining together (6.4) and (6.8):

$$\tfrac{1}{2} x^{\mathrm{T}}(t_1)\, Mx(t_1) + \tfrac{1}{2} \int_0^{t_1} [x^{\mathrm{T}} Q(t)x + u^{\mathrm{T}} R(t)u]\, \mathrm{d}t \qquad (6.86)$$

with M and $R(t)$ r.s.p.d. and $Q(t)$ r.s.p.s.d. for $t \geqslant 0$ (the factors $\tfrac{1}{2}$ enter only for convenience). The quadratic term in $u(t)$ in (6.86) ensures that the total amount of control effort is restricted, so that the control variable can be assumed unbounded.

The Hamiltonian (6.28) is

$$H = \tfrac{1}{2} x^{\mathrm{T}} Qx + \tfrac{1}{2} u^{\mathrm{T}} Ru + p^{\mathrm{T}} (Ax + Bu),$$

and the necessary condition (6.33) for optimality gives

$$\frac{\partial}{\partial u} [\tfrac{1}{2} (u^*)^{\mathrm{T}} Ru^* + (p^*)^{\mathrm{T}} Bu^*] = Ru^* + B^{\mathrm{T}} p^* = 0,$$

so that

$$u^* = -R^{-1} B^{\mathrm{T}} p^*, \qquad (6.87)$$

$R(t)$ being nonsingular since it is positive definite. The adjoint equations (6.30) are

$$\dot{p}^* = -Qx^* - A^{\mathrm{T}} p^*. \qquad (6.88)$$

Substituting (6.87) into (6.85) gives

$$\dot{x}^* = Ax^* - BR^{-1} B^{\mathrm{T}} p^*$$

and combining this equation with (6.88) produces the system of $2n$ linear equations

$$\frac{\mathrm{d}}{\mathrm{d}t} \begin{bmatrix} x^*(t) \\ p^*(t) \end{bmatrix} = \begin{bmatrix} A(t) & -B(t)R^{-1}(t)B^{\mathrm{T}}(t) \\ -Q(t) & -A^{\mathrm{T}}(t) \end{bmatrix} \begin{bmatrix} x^*(t) \\ p^*(t) \end{bmatrix}. \qquad (6.89)$$

Since $x(t_1)$ is not specified we have case (i) on p. 220, so the boundary condition is (6.31) with $\phi = \tfrac{1}{2} x^{\mathrm{T}} Mx$, i.e.

$$p^*(t_1) = Mx^*(t_1). \qquad (6.90)$$

It is convenient to express the solution of (6.89) using eqn (3.28), but in terms of the conditions at time t_1, i.e.

$$\begin{bmatrix} x^*(t) \\ p^*(t) \end{bmatrix} = \Phi(t, t_1) \begin{bmatrix} x^*(t_1) \\ p^*(t_1) \end{bmatrix}$$

$$= \begin{bmatrix} \phi_1 & \phi_2 \\ \phi_3 & \phi_4 \end{bmatrix} \begin{bmatrix} x^*(t_1) \\ p^*(t_1) \end{bmatrix} \qquad (6.91)$$

where Φ is the transition matrix for (6.89). Hence

$$x^*(t) = \phi_1 x^*(t_1) + \phi_2 p^*(t_1)$$
$$= (\phi_1 + \phi_2 M)x^*(t_1) \qquad (6.92)$$

using (6.90). Equations (6.90) and (6.91) also give

$$p^*(t) = (\phi_3 + \phi_4 M)x^*(t_1)$$
$$= (\phi_3 + \phi_4 M)(\phi_1 + \phi_2 M)^{-1} x^*(t)$$
$$= P(t) x^*(t), \text{ say}, \qquad (6.93)$$

using (6.92) (it can be shown that $\phi_1 + \phi_2 M$ is nonsingular for all $t \geqslant 0$). It now follows from (6.87) and (6.93) that the optimal control is of linear feedback form

$$u^*(t) = -R^{-1}(t) B^T(t) P(t) x^*(t). \qquad (6.94)$$

To determine the matrix $P(t)$, differentiating (6.93) gives

$$\dot{P}x^* + P\dot{x}^* - \dot{p}^* = 0,$$

and substituting for $\dot{x}^*$, $\dot{p}^*$ from (6.89) and p^* from (6.93) produces

$$(\dot{P} + PA - PB R^{-1}B^T P + Q + A^T P)x^*(t) = 0.$$

Since this must hold throughout $0 \leqslant t \leqslant t_1$ it follows that $P(t)$ satisfies

$$\dot{P} = P BR^{-1}B^T P - A^T P - PA - Q \qquad (6.95)$$

with boundary condition given by (6.90) and (6.93) as

$$P(t_1) = M. \qquad (6.96)$$

Equation (6.95) is often referred to as a *matrix Riccati differential equation*. This is however rather a misnomer, as Riccati studied only some special cases of the scalar version of (6.95) in the early eighteenth century, before the introduction of matrices. Since M in (6.96) is symmetric it follows that $P(t)$ is symmetric for all t, so (6.95) represents $\frac{1}{2}n(n+1)$ first order quadratic differential equations, which can be integrated numerically.

Example 6.10. A wire is being wound onto a reel which is driven by an electric motor. Let $J(t)$ be the inertia of the reel and wire, and $\omega(t)$ the angular velocity at time t. The equation of motion is

$$\dot{z}(t) = -k_1 z(t)/J(t) + k_2 v(t) \tag{6.97}$$

where $z(t) = J(t)\,\omega(t)$, $v(t)$ is the input voltage, k_1 is a friction coefficient and k_2 a torque coefficient. The speed of winding the wire on the reel is $s(t) = r(t)\,\omega(t)$, where $r(t)$ is the total radius at time t. It is required to regulate the system so that $s(t)$ is kept at a constant value s_0. Since

$$z(t)/s(t) = J(t)/r(t)$$

the corresponding value of $z(t)$ is

$$z_0(t) = s_0\, J(t)/r(t),$$

and from (6.97)

$$v_0(t) = \frac{1}{k_2}\left(\dot{z}_0 + \frac{k_1 z_0}{J}\right).$$

Clearly $J(t)$ and $r(t)$ increase with time, and $\omega(t)$ must be decreased in order to keep $s(t)$ constant.

Define as state variables

$$x_1(t) = z(t) - z_0(t), \quad x_2(t) = s(t) - s_0$$

and as control variable

$$u(t) = v(t) - v_0(t).$$

It is easy to verify that (6.97) becomes

$$\dot{x}_1 = -k_1 x_1/J(t) + k_2 u,$$

which is in the form (6.85), and that

$$x_2 = r(t)x_1/J(t).$$

A suitable index to be minimized could be

$$\int_0^{t_1} (x_2^2 + ku^2)\,dt,$$

where k is a weighting factor, and the Riccati equation (6.95) is a scalar equation:

$$\dot{p}(t) = p^2(t)k_2^2/k + 2k_1 p(t)/J(t) - r^2(t)/J^2(t),$$

subject to (6.96), namely $p(t_1) = 0$. The feedback control (6.94) is

$$u^*(t) = -k_2 p(t)x_1^*(t)/k.$$

For a numerical case see the book by Kwakernaak and Sivan (1972, p. 234).

It should be noted that even when the matrices A, B, Q, and R are all time invariant the solution $P(t)$ of (6.95), and hence the feedback matrix in (6.94), will in general still be time varying. However of particular interest is the case when in addition the final time t_1 in (6.86) tends to infinity. There is then no need to include the terminal expression in (6.86) since the aim is to make $x(t_1) \to 0$ as $t_1 \to \infty$, so we set $M = 0$. Let Q_1 be a matrix having the same rank as Q and such that $Q = Q_1^T Q_1$. It can then be shown (Kwakernaak and Sivan 1972, p. 237) that the solution $P(t)$ of (6.95) does become a constant matrix P, and we have:

THEOREM 6.5. If the constant linear system (6.79) is c.c. and $[A, Q_1]$ is c.o. then the control which minimizes

$$\int_0^\infty (x^T Q x + u^T R u)\, dt \qquad (6.98)$$

is given by

$$u^* = -R^{-1}B^T Px, \qquad (6.99)$$

where P is the unique r.s.p.d. matrix which satisfies the so-called *algebraic* Riccati equation

$$PBR^{-1}B^T P - A^T P - PA - Q = 0. \qquad (6.100)$$

Equation (6.100) represents $\frac{1}{2}n(n + 1)$ quadratic equations for the unknown elements of P, so the solution will not in general be unique. However, it is easy to show that if a positive definite solution of (6.100) exists (which is ensured by the conditions of Theorem 6.5) then there is only one such solution (see Exercise 6.20).

The matrix Q_1 can be interpreted by defining an output vector $y = Q_1 x$ and replacing the quadratic term involving the state in (6.98) by $y^T y (= x^T Q_1^T Q_1 x)$.

The closed loop system obtained by substituting (6.99) into (6.79) is

$$\dot{x} = \mathscr{A} x \qquad (6.101)$$

where $\mathscr{A} = A - BR^{-1}B^T P$. It is easy to verify that

$$\begin{aligned} \mathscr{A}^T P + P\mathscr{A} &= A^T P + PA - 2PBR^{-1}B^T P \\ &= -PBR^{-1}B^T P - Q, \end{aligned} \qquad (6.102)$$

using the fact that P is the solution of (6.100). Since R^{-1} is positive definite and Q is positive semidefinite the matrix on the right in (6.102) is negative definite, so by Theorem 5.17 $\mathscr{A}$ is a stability matrix. It can also be shown (Kucera 1972) that if the triple $[A, B, Q_1]$ is not c.c. and c.o., but is stabilizable and detectable (see Section 5.7.2) then eqn. (6.100) has a unique positive semidefinite solution, and the closed loop system (6.101) is asymptotically stable.

Thus solution of (6.100) leads to a stabilizing linear feedback control (6.99) irrespective of whether or not the open loop system is stable. This provides an alternative to the methods of Section 4.4. For example, in the linearized model of the inverted pendulum problem presented in Exercise 5.49, the system can be stabilized by linear feedback in all the state variables, and this could be generated via (6.99) with a suitable choice of elements of Q and R in (6.98).

If $x^*(t)$ is the solution of (6.101), then as in (6.16) eqn. (6.102) implies

$$\begin{aligned} \frac{\mathrm{d}}{\mathrm{d}t} [(x^*)^T P x^*] &= -(x^*)^T (PBR^{-1}B^T P + Q)x^* \\ &= -(u^*)^T R u^* - (x^*)^T Q x^* \end{aligned} \qquad (6.103)$$

using (6.99). Since $\mathscr{A}$ is a stability matrix, we can integrate both sides of (6.103) with respect to t from zero to infinity to obtain the minimum value of (6.98):

$$\int_0^\infty \{(x^*)^T Q x^* + (u^*)^T R u^*\} \mathrm{d}t = x_0^T P x_0, \qquad (6.104)$$

using the same argument as for (6.18). Of course when $B \equiv 0$, (6.100) and (6.104) reduce simply to (6.17) and (6.18) respectively.

A number of methods for solving (6.100) have been developed. One relies on calculating the right characteristic vectors of the matrix in (6.89), namely

$$L = \begin{bmatrix} A & -BR^{-1}B^{\mathrm{T}} \\ -Q & -A^{\mathrm{T}} \end{bmatrix} \qquad (6.105)$$

in which A, B, Q, and R are now time invariant. Assuming that L has a diagonal Jordan form, if $\alpha_1, \ldots, \alpha_n$ are characteristic vectors of L corresponding to roots having negative real parts and $\alpha_i^{\mathrm{T}} = [\beta_i^{\mathrm{T}}, \gamma_i^{\mathrm{T}}]$, where β_i, γ_i are column n-vectors, then the r.s.p.d. solution of (6.100) is

$$P = [\gamma_1, \gamma_2, \ldots, \gamma_n] \ [\beta_1, \beta_2, \ldots, \beta_n]^{-1}$$

(for a proof see Barnett 1971, p. 122).

The frequency domain interpretation of Theorem 6.5 is interesting. First, suppose $m = 1$ so B is a column vector b, and without loss of generality we can set $R = 1$ in (6.98). It can then be shown (Anderson and Moore 1971, p. 69–73) that a necessary and sufficient condition for optimality is

$$|1 + t(i\omega)| \geqslant 1 \qquad (6.106)$$

where

$$t(s) = k(sI - A)^{-1}b \qquad (6.107)$$

and k is the feedback matrix $b^{\mathrm{T}}P$ obtained from (6.99). It is easy to see that (6.106) implies that the Nyquist locus of $t(s)$ must not enter the disc of unit radius centred on $-1 + i0$. It can be shown that the gain margin (see Section 5.3) of the closed loop system is infinite and that the phase margin is at least $60°$. These are larger than necessary, and this constitutes a practical disadvantage of using Theorem 6.5 for generating linear feedback.

For the multivariable case $m > 1$, eqns. (6.106) and (6.107) have been generalized by MacFarlane (1970). It turns out that

$$|1 + t_r(i\omega)| \geqslant 1, \ r = 1, 2, \ldots, m,$$

where the functions $1 + t_r(s)$ are the characteristic roots of the optimal return difference matrix

$$F(s) = I_m + K(sI - A)^{-1}B$$

with $K = R^{-1}B^{\mathrm{T}}P$, so the characteristic loci (see p. 172) must not enter the unit disc centred on $-1 + i0$.

For linear tracking problems the performance index (6.8) is used, together with the terminal expression (6.4) if t_1 is finite. Because of the quadratic term in u the optimal control is again linear state feedback as in (6.99) but contains an added term which depends upon $r(t)$ (see Exercise 6.22).

Exercise 6.17.
Use Theorem 6.5 to find the feedback control which minimizes

$$\int_0^\infty (x_2^2 + 0.1u^2)\,dt$$

subject to

$$\dot{x}_1 = -x_1 + u, \quad \dot{x}_2 = x_1.$$

Exercise 6.18.
Use the Riccati equation formulation to determine the feedback control for the system

$$\dot{x}_1 = -x_1 + u$$

which minimizes

$$\tfrac{1}{2}\int_0^1 (3x_1^2 + u^2)\,dt.$$

(Hint: in the Riccati equation for the problem put $P(t) = -\dot{w}(t)/w(t)$).
If the system is to be transferred to the origin from an arbitrary initial state with the same performance index, use the calculus of variations to determine the optimal control.

Exercise 6.19.
If the matrices $X(t)$, $Y(t)$ satisfy

$$\frac{d}{dt}\begin{bmatrix} X \\ Y \end{bmatrix} = L \begin{bmatrix} X \\ Y \end{bmatrix},$$

where L is defined in (6.105), show that $P(t) = Y(t)X^{-1}(t)$ is a solution of eqn (6.95) with A, B, Q, R time invariant.

Exercise 6.20.
If P_1 and P_2 are two positive definite solutions of (6.100) show that

$$(P_1 - P_2)(A - BR^{-1}B^T P_1) + (A^T - P_2 BR^{-1}B^T)(P_1 - P_2) = 0.$$

Hence deduce, using the uniqueness condition derived for eqn. (2.37), that $P_1 \equiv P_2$.

Exercise 6.21.
Let $y = Cx$ be an output vector for the system (6.79), where C is a constant matrix. If u is chosen so as to minimize

$$\tfrac{1}{2} \int_0^\infty (y^T Q y + u^T R u)\, dt,$$

where Q and R are both r.s.p.d., write down the appropriate Riccati equation corresponding to (6.100) and denote its positive definite solution by P_1 (the system is assumed c.c. and c.o.).

Consider the dual system (4.25) with A, B, C time invariant, and suppose that for this system u is to be chosen so as to minimize

$$\tfrac{1}{2} \int_0^\infty (y^T R^{-1} y + u^T Q^{-1} u)\, dt.$$

Show that the positive definite solution of the associated Riccati equation is P_1^{-1}.

Exercise 6.22.
Consider the optimal linear tracking problem in which it is required to minimize (one half) the sum of (6.4) and (6.8) subject to (6.85). It can be shown (Kirk 1970, p. 220) that eqn. (6.93) is replaced by

$$p^*(t) = P(t)x^*(t) + s(t).$$

Show that the optimal control has the form $u^*(t) + v(t)$, where $u^*(t)$ is given by (6.94) with $P(t)$ satisfying (6.95) and (6.96), and $v(t) = -R^{-1}B^T s(t)$ where

$$\dot{s}(t) = [PBR^{-1}B^T - A^T]\, s(t) + Qr(t), \quad s(t_1) = -Mr(t_1).$$

6.5. Dynamic programming

The basic idea of dynamic programming can be understood through a simple example.

Example 6.11. Suppose a road map is available on which distances between all junctions are marked. By trial the shortest route between two particular junctions A and B could be found, as indicated by arrows in Fig. 6.7. If C is some intermediate point on this shortest route, then it follows that CDB must be the shortest path between C and B; for if some other path, such as CEB were shorter, then this would provide a shorter route from A to B.

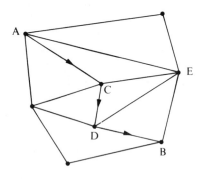

FIG. 6.7

At each road junction a decision has to be made as to which direction to take, and the problem is an example of what is called a *multistage decision process*. The argument we applied to obtain the property of an optimal route is expressed more formally by the *Principle of Optimality* (*P.O.*) (Bellman 1957, p. 83):

An optimal policy has the property that whatever the initial state and initial decision are, the remaining decisions must constitute an optimal policy with regard to the state resulting from the first decision.

Example 6.12. Find the set of numbers $x_1, \ldots, x_n$ satisfying $x_1 + \cdots + x_n = c$, where c is a positive constant, such that the product $x_1 x_2 \ldots x_n$ is a maximum.

To apply dynamic programming, define the function $f_n(c)$ as the maximum attainable value of the product for given values of c and n. Clearly $f_1(c) = c$, and

$$f_2(c) = \max_{0 \leqslant x_1 \leqslant c} \left\{ x_1 (c - x_1) \right\} \qquad (6.108)$$

since $x_2 = c - x_1$. The expression to be optimized in (6.108) is a function of the single variable x_1, and it is easy to verify by elementary calculus that

$$f_2(c) = c^2/4 \qquad (6.109)$$

when $x_1 = \frac{1}{2} c = x_2$. Suppose that we have solved the problem for $n = 2, 3, \ldots, m$, and consider the case $n = m + 1$. The maximum attainable product for $c - x_1$ divided into m parts is by definition $f_m(c - x_1)$. Regarding x_1 as the initial decision, we can conclude from the P.O. that

$$f_{m+1}(c) = \max_{0 \leqslant x_1 \leqslant c} \left\{ x_1 f_m(c - x_1) \right\} \qquad (6.110)$$

and this agrees with (6.108) when $m = 1$. When $m = 2$, (6.110) gives

$$f_3(c) = \max_{0 \leqslant x_1 \leqslant c} \left\{ x_1 (c - x_1)^2 /4 \right\}$$

using the expression for f_2 in (6.109). Again using calculus of one variable it is easy to show that

$$f_3(c) = c^3/27 \qquad (6.111)$$

with $x_1 = c/3$, and since $c - x_1 = 2c/3$ it follows by our result for $n = 2$ that $x_2 = x_3 = c/3$. In view of (6.109) and (6.111) it is reasonable to conjecture that

$$f_n(c) = (c/n)^n \qquad (6.112)$$

with

$$x_1 = x_2 = \cdots = x_n = c/n, \qquad (6.113)$$

and we now prove by induction on n that this is indeed correct. From (6.110) and the induction hypothesis we have

$$f_{m+1}(c) = \max_{0 \leqslant x_1 \leqslant c} \left\{ x_1 \frac{(c - x_1)^m}{m^m} \right\} ,$$

and again by straightforward calculus the optimal value of x_1 is found to be $c/(m + 1)$, so that

$$f_{m+1}(c) = \frac{c}{m+1} \left(c - \frac{c}{m+1}\right)^m / m^m$$

$$= c^{m+1}/(m+1)^{m+1},$$

establishing (6.112). Also $c - x_1 = cm/(m + 1)$ so by the induction assumption $x_2 = x_3 = \cdots = x_m = c/(m + 1)$, and this verifies (6.113)

In general it is not possible to obtain analytical results, as in the preceding example. However, dynamic programming is essentially an ingenious way of reducing a multistage decision process to a sequence of single stage processes, and as such is a useful tool for constructing algorithms for solving optimization problems. We now sketch an application to a simple optimal control problem.

Example 6.13. Consider a two-stage process described by the scalar difference equation

$$x(k + 1) = ax(k) + bu(k), \quad k = 0, 1, \tag{6.114}$$

where a and b are constants. It is required to choose $u(0)$ and $u(1)$ to as to minimize the quadratic performance index

$$q_1 x^2(2) + q_2 u^2(0) + q_3 u^2(1),$$

where the q_i are nonnegative weighting factors, subject to the constraints that $x(k)$ and $u(k)$ take certain discrete values within prescribed finite ranges.

We first find the optimal policy for the *last* stage of the process: put $k = 1$, and for each allowable value of $x(1)$ calculate the cost

$$J_{12} = q_1 x^2(2) + q_3 u^2(1)$$

of going from $x(1)$ to $x(2)$, the latter being evaluated from (6.114). Of course J_{12} is a function of $x(1)$ and $u(1)$, and we can write

$$J_{12}^*[x(1)] = \min_{u(1)} J_{12}.$$

The penultimate stage $k = 0$ is then considered. By the P.O. the minimum cost over the last two stages is

$$\min_{u(0)} \left\{ J_{01}[x(0), u(0)] + J_{12}^*[x(1)] \right\}, \tag{6.115}$$

where $J_{01} = q_2 u^2(0)$ is the cost in the interval $k = 0$ to $k = 1$. The procedure represented by (6.115) can be converted into an algorithm suitable for computer application, and can obviously be extended for processes involving more than two stages. For specific details see the book by Kirk (1970, p. 60). In this same text (p. 78) a development is given for the general discrete linear system (3.31) subject to a quadratic performance index, providing a discrete analogue of the continuous-time regulator problem of Section 6.4.

We now derive a continuous form of dynamic programming by considering again the problem of Section 6.2 of minimizing (6.13) subject to the system equations (6.1). Define

$$J[x(t), t, u(\tau)] = \phi[x(t_1), t_1] + \int_t^{t_1} F[x(\tau), u(\tau), \tau] \, d\tau,$$

with $t \leqslant \tau \leqslant t_1$, and write

$$
\begin{aligned}
J^*[x(t), t] &= \min_{u(\tau)} J[x(t), t, u(\tau)] \\
&= \min_{u(\tau)} \left\{ \int_t^{t+\Delta t} F d\tau + \int_{t+\Delta t}^{t_1} F d\tau + \phi[x(t_1), t_1] \right\} \quad (6.116) \\
&= \min_{u(\tau)} \left\{ \int_t^{t+\Delta t} F d\tau + J^*[x(t + \Delta t), t + \Delta t] \right\}
\end{aligned}
$$

the last step following by the P.O. Assuming that J^* can be expanded in a Taylor series we have

$$J^*[x(t), t] = \min_{u(\tau)} \left\{ \int_t^{t+\Delta t} F d\tau + J^*[x(t), t] + \frac{\partial J^*}{\partial t} \Delta t \right.$$

$$\left. + \frac{\partial J^*}{\partial x} [x(t + \Delta t) - x(t)] + \text{higher order terms} \right\}. \quad (6.117)$$

Since J^* is independent of u, the terms $J^*[x(t), t]$ cancel out in (6.117), and if Δt is small the resulting expression can be written as

$$0 = \min_u \left(F\Delta t + \frac{\partial J^*}{\partial t} \cdot \Delta t + \frac{\partial J^*}{\partial x} f\Delta t + \text{higher terms} \right),$$

using (6.1). Dividing by Δt and letting $\Delta t \to 0$ produces

$$0 = \frac{\partial J^*}{\partial t} + \min_u (H), \quad (6.118)$$

where by analogy with (6.28) the Hamiltonian is

$$H\left(x, u, \frac{\partial J^*}{\partial x}, t\right) = F + \frac{\partial J^*}{\partial x_1} f_1 + \cdots + \frac{\partial J^*}{\partial x_n} f_n. \quad (6.119)$$

Eqn (6.118) is a partial differential equation to be solved for J^*, subject to the boundary condition obtained by putting $t = t_1$ in (6.116), namely

$$J^*[x(t_1), t_1] = \phi[x(t_1), t_1]. \quad (6.120)$$

Example 6.14. Find the control which minimizes

$$x_1^2(T) + \int_0^T u^2 \, dt$$

subject to the scalar equation

$$\dot{x}_1 = x_1 + u.$$

The expression (6.119) gives

$$H = u^2 + \frac{\partial J^*}{\partial x_1} (x_1 + u), \quad (6.121)$$

and assuming that u is unbounded a necessary condition for optimality is (6.33) in Theorem 6.2, namely

$$\frac{\partial H}{\partial u} = 0 = 2u^* + \frac{\partial J^*}{\partial x_1}.$$

Substituting $u^* = -\frac{1}{2} \partial J^*/\partial x_1$ into (6.121) gives

$$\min_u H = \tfrac{1}{4} (J_{x_1}^*)^2 + J_{x_1}^* (x_1 - \tfrac{1}{2} J_{x_1}^*)$$

$$= -\tfrac{1}{4} (J_{x_1}^*)^2 + x_1 J_{x_1}^*,$$

and eqn. (6.118) then becomes

$$0 = \frac{\partial J^*}{\partial t} + x_1 \frac{\partial J^*}{\partial x_1} - \tfrac{1}{4} \left(\frac{\partial J^*}{\partial x_1}\right)^2,$$

subject to (6.120) which is just

$$J^*[x_1(T), T] = x_1^2(T).$$

In general such a partial differential equation must be solved numerically but in fact in this example an analytical solution is possible (see Exercise 6.24).

We close by noting that the Pontryagin principle (Theorem 6.3) can be derived from the dynamic programming equation (6.118) (see Kirk 1970, p. 417).

Exercise 6.23.
Use dynamic programming to find the numbers x_1, x_2, x_3 which minimize the sum $x_1^2 + 2x_2^2 + 3x_3^2$ subject to $x_1 + x_2 + x_3 = c$, where c is a constant.

Exercise 6.24.
In Example 6.14 assume that J^* takes the form $k(t)x_1^2$, and hence obtain the optimal control. Deduce that as $T \to \infty$ this approaches constant linear feedback.

References

ANDERSON, B. D. O. and MOORE, J. B. (1971). *Linear optimal control.* Prentice—Hall, Englewood Cliffs, New Jersey.

BARNETT, S. (1971). *Matrices in control theory.* Van Nostrand Reinhold, London.

    and STOREY, C. (1970). *Matrix methods in stability theory.* Nelson, London.

BELLMAN, R. (1957). *Dynamic programming.* Princeton University Press, Princeton, New Jersey.

    (1970). *Introduction to matrix analysis*, 2nd edn. McGraw—Hill, New York.

BOLTYANSKII, V. G. (1971). *Mathematical methods of optimal control.* Holt, Rinehart and Winston, New York.

BRAUER, F. and NOHEL, J. A. (1969). *The qualitative theory of ordinary differential equations.* Benjamin, New York.

BROCKETT, R. W. (1970). *Finite dimensional linear systems.* Wiley, New York.

BRYSON, A. E. Jr. and HO, Y. —C. (1969). *Applied optimal control.* Blaisdell, Waltham, Massachusetts.

CADZOW, J. A. (1973). *Discrete-time systems.* Prentice—Hall, Englewood Cliffs, New Jersey.

CHEN, C. —T. (1970). *Introduction to linear system theory.* Holt, Rinehart and Winston, New York.

COOK, P. A. (1973). In *Recent mathematical developments in control* (ed. D. J. Bell), p. 367. Academic Press, London.

CULLEN, C. G. (1972). *Matrices and linear transformations*, 2nd edn. Addison—Wesley, Reading, Massachusetts.

D'ANGELO, H. (1970). *Linear time-varying systems.* Allyn and Bacon, Rockleigh, New Jersey.

DESOER, C. A. (1970). *Notes for a second course on linear systems.* Van Nostrand Reinhold, New York.

DIRECTOR, S. W. and ROHRER, R. A. (1972). *Introduction to systems theory.* McGraw—Hill, New York.

ELGERD, O. I. (1967). *Control systems theory.* McGraw—Hill, New York.

EVELEIGH, V. W. (1972). *Introduction to control systems design.* McGraw—Hill, New York.

FULLER, A. T. (Ed.) (1974). *Stability of motion.* Taylor and Francis, London.

GANTMACHER, F. R. (1959). *The theory of matrices*, 1 and 2. Chelsea Publishing Company, New York.

HAHN, W. (1963). *Theory and application of Liapunov's direct method.* Prentice—Hall, Englewood Cliffs, New Jersey.

HOLLAND, J. M. (1972). *Studies in structure.* Macmillan, London.

INTRILIGATOR, M. D. (1971). *Mathematical optimization and economic theory.* Prentice–Hall, Englewood Cliffs, New Jersey.

JURY, E. I. (1964). *Theory and application of the z-transform method.* Wiley, New York.

KALMAN, R. E., FALB, P. L., and ARBIB, M. A. (1969). *Topics in mathematical system theory.* McGraw–Hill, New York.

KIRK, D. E. (1970). *Optimal control theory.* Prentice–Hall, Englewood Cliffs, New Jersey.

KUCERA, V. (1972). *I.E.E.E. Trans. autom. Control,* **17**, 344.

KWAKERNAAK, H. and SIVAN, R. (1972). *Linear optimal control systems.* Wiley–Interscience, New York.

LANCASTER, P. (1969). *The theory of matrices.* Academic Press, New York.

LA SALLE, J. P. and LEFSCHETZ, S. (1961). *Stability by Liapunov's direct method with applications.* Academic Press, New York.

LEHNIGK, S. H. (1966). *Stability theorems for linear motions with an introduction to Liapunov's direct method.* Prentice–Hall, Englewood Cliffs, New Jersey.

LEIPHOLZ, H. (1970). *Stability theory.* Academic Press, New York.

LEVINSON, N. and REDHEFFER, R. M. (1970). *Complex variables.* Holden–Day, San Francisco.

MACFARLANE, A. G. J. (1970). *Proc. Instn. elect. Engrs,* **117**, 2037. (1972). *Automatica,* **8**, 455.

MARDEN, M. (1966). *Geometry of polynomials.* American Mathematical Society, Providence, Rhode Island.

MAYR, O. (1970). *The origins of feedback control.* M.I.T. Press, Cambridge, Massachusetts.

MIRSKY, L. (1963). *An introduction to linear algebra.* Clarendon Press, Oxford.

MOHLER, R. R. (1973). *Bilinear control processes.* Academic Press, New York.

PORTER, B. and CROSSLEY, R. (1972). *Modal control.* Taylor and Francis, London.

ROSENBROCK, H. H. (1970). *State-space and multivariable theory.* Nelson, London. (1973). In *Recent mathematical developments in control* (ed. D. J. Bell) p. 345. Academic Press, London.

RUBIO, J. E. (1971). *The theory of linear systems.* Academic Press, New York.

SAUCEDO, R. and SCHIRING, E. E. (1968). *Introduction to continuous and digital control systems.* Macmillan, New York.

SCHULTZ, D. G. (1965). In *Advances in control systems.* 2 (ed. C. T. Leondes), p. 1. Academic Press, New York.

SILJAK, D. D. (1969). *Nonlinear systems.* Wiley, New Yrok.

SILVERMAN, L. M. (1971). *I.E.E.E. Trans. autom. Control,* **16**, 554.

SRIDHAR, B. and LINDORFF, D. P. (1973). *Int. J. Control,* **18**, 993.

TAKAHASHI, Y., RABINS, M. J. and AUSLANDER, D. M. (1970). *Control and dynamic systems.* Addison—Wesley, Reading, Massachusetts.

TRUXAL, J. G. (1972) *Introductory systems engineering.* McGraw—Hill, New York.

WILLEMS, J. L. (1970). *Stability theory of dynamical systems.* Nelson, London.

ZADEH, L. A. and DESOER, C. A. (1963). *Linear system theory.* McGraw—Hill, New York.

Answers to exercises

Chapter 1

1.2.
$$A = \begin{bmatrix} 0 & 0 & 1 & 0 \\ 0 & 0 & 0 & 1 \\ -k_1/m_1 & k_1/m_1 & 0 & 0 \\ k_1/m_2 & -(k_1+k_2)/m_2 & 0 & 0 \end{bmatrix}, \quad B = \begin{bmatrix} 0 \\ 0 \\ 1/m_1 \\ 0 \end{bmatrix}.$$

1.3. $\dot{x}_1 = x_2, \dot{x}_2 = (3g/\ell)\sin x_1 - 3x_2^2 \sin x_1 \cos x_1 - 3\dot{x}_2 \sin^2 x_1 + (3M/m\ell)\dot{x}_4 \cos x_1, \dot{x}_3 = x_4,$
$\dot{x}_4 = -(m/M)(\dot{x}_4 + \ell\dot{x}_2 \cos x_1 - \ell x_2^2 \sin x_1).$

1.6. $g_1 g_2/(1 + g_1 g_2 h - g_1 g_3 h).$

1.7. $x_1(t) = [a_2 x_2(0) - a_4 x_1(0) + e^{dt}(a_1 x_1(0) - a_2 x_2(0))]/d, \ d = a_1 - a_4;$
$x_1(t) = x_1(0), x_2(t) = x_2(0),$ all $t \geqslant 0$, irrespective of d.

1.9. $g_1(1 - g_1 g_3 h)/(1 + g_1 g_2 h - g_1 g_3 h)^2.$

1.10. (a) $Tz/(z-1)^2$ (b) $z/(z - e^a).$

1.13. $F_k = (0.096F_0 + 0.85F_1)(1.063)^k + (0.906F_0 - 0.85F_1)(-0.113)^k.$
$M_k = a_1 (1.063)^k + a_2 (-0.113)^k + a_3 (0.95)^k,$
a_i constants.

Chapter 2

2.26. All finite A; $\sin A = \frac{1}{2} \begin{bmatrix} \sin 5 + \sin 1 & \sin 5 - \sin 1 \\ \sin 5 - \sin 1 & \sin 5 + \sin 1 \end{bmatrix},$

$A^{-1} = \frac{1}{5} \begin{bmatrix} 3 & -2 \\ -2 & 3 \end{bmatrix}, \quad A^{100} = \frac{1}{2} \begin{bmatrix} 5^{100} + 1 & 5^{100} - 1 \\ 5^{100} - 1 & 5^{100} + 1 \end{bmatrix}.$

Chapter 3

3.1. (a) $\begin{bmatrix} x_1(t) \\ x_2(t) \end{bmatrix} = (2x_1(0) - x_2(0))e^{-2t} \begin{bmatrix} 1 \\ 1 \end{bmatrix} + (x_2(0) - x_1(0))e^{-3t} \begin{bmatrix} 1 \\ 2 \end{bmatrix}.$

$$(b) \begin{bmatrix} x_1(t) \\ x_2(t) \\ x_3(t) \end{bmatrix} = (x_2(0) - \tfrac{1}{2}x_3(0))e^t \begin{bmatrix} -1 \\ 1 \\ 0 \end{bmatrix} + (x_1(0) + x_2(0))e^{2t} \begin{bmatrix} 2 \\ -1 \\ -2 \end{bmatrix}$$

$$+ (x_1(0) + x_2(0) + \tfrac{1}{2}x_3(0))e^{3t} \begin{bmatrix} -1 \\ 1 \\ 2 \end{bmatrix}.$$

3.2. $$x(t) = \begin{bmatrix} (-e^{-t} + 2e^{-2t}) & (-e^{-t} + e^{-2t}) \\ 2(e^{-t} - e^{-2t}) & (2e^{-t} - e^{-2t}) \end{bmatrix} x(0); A = \begin{bmatrix} -3 & -1 \\ 2 & 0 \end{bmatrix}.$$

3.6. $$\Phi = \begin{bmatrix} \cos \omega t & \sin \omega t \\ -\sin \omega t & \cos \omega t \end{bmatrix}.$$

3.13. $$x(t) = \begin{bmatrix} (1 + t)e^{-3t} & te^{-3t} \\ -te^{-3t} & (1 - t)e^{-3t} \end{bmatrix} x(0).$$

3.14. $$\begin{bmatrix} e^{2t}(1 + t) & -te^{2t} & te^{2t} \\ -e^t + e^{2t}(1 + t) & e^t - te^{2t} & te^{2t} \\ -e^t + e^{2t} & e^t - e^{2t} & e^{2t} \end{bmatrix}.$$

3.15. $$z(t) - z(0) = t\dot{z}(0) + \tfrac{1}{2}ut^2.$$

3.16. $$\tfrac{1}{3} \begin{bmatrix} 1 + 2e^{-3t} & 2 - 2e^{-3t} \\ 1 - e^{-3t} & 2 + e^{-3t} \end{bmatrix}; T_0 + (2/9)(-1 + 3t + e^{-3t}).$$

3.25. $$\begin{bmatrix} (2^{101} - 3^{100}) & (-2^{100} + 3^{100}) \\ (2^{101} - 2.3^{100}) & (-2^{100} + 2.3^{100}) \end{bmatrix}.$$

3.26 $$\begin{bmatrix} 3(-2)^k - 2(-3)^k & (-2)^k - (-3)^k \\ -6(-2)^k + 6(-3)^k & -2(-2)^k + 3(-3)^k \end{bmatrix}.$$

3.27.
$$(-2)^{k-1} \begin{bmatrix} -2+4k & -4k \\ \\ 4k & -2-4k \end{bmatrix}.$$

3.30.

(a) $T = \frac{1}{2} \begin{bmatrix} -3 & 1 \\ \\ 5 & -1 \end{bmatrix}$, $z^{(2)} + 5z^{(1)} + 6z = u.$

(b) $= \frac{1}{3} \begin{bmatrix} -2 & -5 & 2 \\ -3 & -6 & 3 \\ -3 & -6 & 6 \end{bmatrix}$, $z^{(3)} - 6z^{(2)} + 11z^{(1)} - 6z = u.$

3.31.
$$A = \begin{bmatrix} -\dfrac{1}{k_1} & \dfrac{1}{k_1} - \dfrac{1}{k_2} \\ \\ 0 & -\dfrac{1}{k_2} \end{bmatrix}, \quad b = \begin{bmatrix} \dfrac{1}{k_1} + \dfrac{1}{k_2} \\ \\ \dfrac{1}{k_2} \end{bmatrix}; \quad k_1 \neq k_2;$$

$$T = \frac{1}{8} \begin{bmatrix} 2 & -3 \\ -4 & 8 \end{bmatrix}; \quad C = \begin{bmatrix} 0 & 1 \\ -8 & -6 \end{bmatrix}.$$

3.32.
$$P = \frac{1}{12} \begin{bmatrix} 1 & 1 & 7 \\ 0 & 3 & 0 \\ 0 & 0 & 6 \end{bmatrix}; \quad E = \begin{bmatrix} 0 & 0 & -2 \\ 1 & 0 & 9 \\ 0 & 1 & 0 \end{bmatrix}.$$

Chapter 4
4.2.   c.c. if and only if $k_1 \neq k_2$.

4.4.
$$A = \begin{bmatrix} 0 & 0 & 1 & 0 \\ 0 & 0 & 0 & 1 \\ -k_1/m_1 & k_1/m_1 & -d_1/m_1 & d_1/m_1 \\ k_1/m_2 & -(k_1+k_2)/m_2 & d_1/m_2 & -(d_1+d_2)/m_2 \end{bmatrix}$$

$$B = \begin{bmatrix} 0 \\ 0 \\ 1/m_1 \\ 0 \end{bmatrix},$$

$k_1 \neq \frac{1}{2}.$

4.5. $\dfrac{-20(9e^3 + 5e^2 + 5e + 5)e^t + 120(2e^2 + e + 1)e^{2t}}{e^5 + e^4 - 8e^3 + 8e^2 - e - 1}.$

4.8. $b_1 = \tfrac{1}{2}b_2, b_1 = b_2.$ Cancellations occur.

4.12. $[1, 0, 0]^T, [0, 0, 1]^T.$ 4.14. Yes.   4.15. Yes

4.16. $\dot{x}_1 = (-x_1 + u)/R_1 C, \dot{x}_2 = (-x_2 R_2 + u)/L,$

$$y = (-x_1 + R_1 x_2 + u)/R_1.$$

4.17. $c_1 = -c_2, c_1 = -2c_2.$ Modes vanish.

4.18. No.   4.19. $[3, -1]^T.$ 4.29. $[11, -5].$

4.30. $\tfrac{1}{3}[37, 85, -64].$

4.32.
$$K = \begin{bmatrix} 3 & -4 & 1 \\ 3 & -4 & 1 \end{bmatrix}.$$ 4.33. 1.

4.38. $-[33/2, 14, 6]^T.$

4.43. $A = \mathrm{diag}[s_1, s_2, \ldots, s_p], B = [1, 1, \ldots, 1]^T, C = [k_1, \ldots, k_p].$

4.46.
$$A = \mathrm{diag}[1, -1, -2], B = \begin{bmatrix} 7/6 & 1 \\ -7/2 & -2 \\ 10/3 & 2 \end{bmatrix}, C = \begin{bmatrix} 1 & 1 & 1 \\ -1 & 1 & 2 \end{bmatrix}.$$

4.53. $0{\cdot}11F_0 + 0{\cdot}89F_1$; no change in percentage killed, but steady state, $0{\cdot}05F_0 + 0{\cdot}95F_1$, reached more quickly.

Chapter 5

5.1. $(2, \tfrac{1}{2}). \dot{y}_1 = -2y_2(y_1 + 2), \dot{y}_2 = y_1(y_2 + \tfrac{1}{2}).$

5.3. $kx_1^2 + x_2^2 = c.$ 5.6. (a) Yes (b) No (c) No (d) Yes.

5.7. $[\exp(At)] (x_0 - A^{-1}b) + A^{-1}b.$

5.8.   One inside, three outside.   5.11. $k < 2.$

5.12. Unstable.   5.14. $0 < k < 2; u = \tfrac{1}{3}(-2x_1 - 3x_2 - 2x_3).$

5.18. $(a) -3 \ (b) -1.$

5.19. 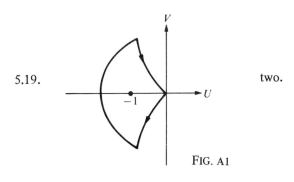 two.

FIG. A1

5.20. 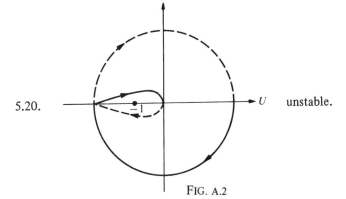 unstable.

FIG. A.2

5.21. 3, 48°. 5.22. $a = b = \frac{1}{2}, c = d = 1$; Asymptotically stable in large.

5.23. $25x_1^2 + 10x_1x_2 + 10x_2^2 - 9 < 0$. 5.24. unstable.

5.25. Unstable; stable. 5.26. $q(0, 0) = 0; q \geqslant -1, x \neq 0$.

5.27. $z_0 < 2$.

5.30.
$$P = \frac{1}{30} \begin{bmatrix} 13 & -1 \\ -1 & 4 \end{bmatrix}$$; asymptotically stable.

5.33. Asymptotically stable; $\frac{1}{4} < k < 4; k > 0$.

5.39. $\det A > 0$, $\operatorname{tr} A < 0$. 5.41. (*a*) unstable (*b*) asymptotically stable.

5.42.

$$\dot{x} = \begin{bmatrix} 0 & 1 & 0 & 0 \\ a_1 & 0 & 0 & 0 \\ 0 & 0 & 0 & 1 \\ a_2 & 0 & 0 & 0 \end{bmatrix} x, a_1 = \frac{3g(M+m)}{\ell(4M+m)}, a_2 = \frac{-3gm}{4M+m}; \text{ unstable.}$$

5.44. $\frac{1}{2}x_1^2 + x_2^2; x_1^2 + 2x_2^2 < 2$.   5.46. stable.   5.47. asymptotically
                                                                                        stable.

5.48.   No.   5.49. $[0, -3/\ell, 0, 4]^T u/(4M+m)$; stabilizable by $u = Kx$.

5.54. $u_i = q_i\omega_i, q_i(\omega) \leqslant 0$.

Chapter 6

6.3. $x_0^T(P - 3P_1 + 2P_2)x_0$.

6.7. $\dfrac{a}{c}\ell n\left(\dfrac{\sec u^* + \tan u^*}{\sec u_0 + \tan u_0}\right)$.

6.8. $2 \cdot 6 + 0 \cdot 04e^t$.   6.12. $u^* = k, 0 \leqslant t \leqslant 100; u^* = k, 0 \leqslant t \leqslant 60;$
                                                               $u^* = 0, 60 < t \leqslant 100.$

6.16. $x_1 = \frac{1}{2}x_2^2 + \frac{1}{2}$, to $(1, -1); x_1 = -\frac{1}{2}x_2^2 - \frac{1}{2}$, to $(-1, 1)$.

6.17. $-1 \cdot 71x_1 - 3 \cdot 16x_2$.

6.18. $u^* = 3(k_1 - k_2)x_1/(k_1 + 3k_2); \ u^* = (3k_1 + k_2)x_1/(k_1 - k_2);$
                                $k_1 = \exp[2(t-1)], \ k_2 = \exp[2(1-t)].$

6.23. $x_1 = 6c/11, x_2 = 3c/11, x_3 = 2c/11$.

6.24. $u^* = -2e^{2(T-t)}x_1/(1 + e^{2(T-t)})$.

Index